Radiologic Science

Workbook and Laboratory Manual

Radiologic Science
Workbook and Laboratory Manual

FIFTH EDITION

STEWART C. BUSHONG, Sc.D.

Professor, Department of Radiology,
Baylor College of Medicine,
Houston, Texas

St. Louis Baltimore Boston Chicago London Philadelphia Sydney Toronto

Mosby
Dedicated to Publishing Excellence

Publisher: Don Ladig
Developmental Editor: Jeanne Rowland
Project Manager: Karen Edwards
Production Editor: Richard Barber
Designer: Julie Taugner

Cover photographs: X-Ray, Osteoporosis of human hip joint: Dr. Vincent Vigorito/Pix∗Elation/Fran Heyl Associates
MRI, human head profile: Pix∗Elation/Fran Heyl Associates
Doppler sonogram of the left adnexa: David A. Nyberg, Lyndon M. Hill, Marcela Bohm-Velez,
Ellen B. Mendelson, from *Transvaginal Ultrasound,* publisher: Mosby–Year Book
Lung X-Ray: Pix∗Elation/Fran Heyl Associates

Printed in the United States of America

Mosby–Year Book, Inc.
11830 Westline Industrial Drive
St. Louis, Missouri 63146

International Standard Book Number 0-8016-6437-3

93 94 95 96 GW/PC 9 8 7 6 5 4 3 2 1

To:

Bettie,
Leslie,
Stephen,
Andrew,
Butterscotch,†
Jemimah,†
Geraldine,†
Casper,†
Ginger,†
Sebastian,†
Buffy,†
Brie,†
Linus†,
Midnight†,
Boef†
Cassie†,
Lucy†,
Toto†,
Choco†,
Molly†
Eboney†,
and Sapphire

†R.I.P.

Preface

This manual is the result of 25 years of supplementary problems, questions, and exercises used in courses of radiologic physics, radiation biology, and radiation protection for radiologic technologists. The workbook and laboratory manual is organized along the lines of the companion textbook of the same title. It contains a total of 111 worksheets and 25 laboratory experiments, each of which deals with a specific subject. Therefore, regardless of the textbook employed for a course, this manual will find application in any school of radiologic technology.

A third section, entitled Math Tutor, was contributed by Quinn Carroll, Director of Education at Midland College, Midland, Texas. Students having difficulty with the mathematics of radiographic technique should find these exercises very helpful. Answers to the Math Tutor can be found in Appendix B.

The manual has been used comfortably in a two-semester course in radiologic science for radiologic technologists totaling 50 classroom hours and 30 laboratory hours. In a moderately paced program, approximately four worksheets each week can be accomodated. Each worksheet is preceded by a brief description of the information covered in the exercises that follow. This introduction is designed as a supplement to the existing material in the companion text. The worksheets will find application as homework assignments, in-class study guides and quiz material. Although all questions are of the single answer type, the range of difficulty is wide. All answers are found in Appendix A. Each worksheet should require from 15 to 45 minutes for completion.

The laboratory exercises are designed for use with conventional x-ray apparatus and inexpensive, easily available radiation protection and measurement equipment. Each laboratory session should require from 1 to 3 hours for completion. The suggested laboratory report has been designed to be brief yet to the point and instructive. Each is designed for easy supplementation and extension at the discretion of the instructor.

Punched and perforated pages are provided so that students can complete the worksheets, submit them to the instructor for evaluation and recording, and retain them in a ring binder for subsequent study and review.

The organization of this edition has been influenced considerably by comments that I have received from students, technologists and educators. The following have been particularly helpful: Pam Alexander, Caldwell Community College, Hudson, NC; Pedro D. Balanag, Mount Sinai Medical Center, Miami Beach, FL; J. Edward Barnes, MTMI, Milwaukee, WI; Judith Baron, College of Lake County, Grayslake, IL; Ronald J. Bohland, St. Charles Hospital, Oregon, OH; Gary S. Brink, Mallinckrodt Institute of Radiology, St. Louis, MO; Karen Brown, Gateway Community College, Phoenix, AZ; Bobbie Burks, Owens Technical College, Toledo, OH; Evelyn Burns, Houston Community College, Houston, TX; Priscilla F. Butler, George Washington University Medical Center, Washington D.C.; Janet Carey, St. Joseph Hospital, Lorain, OH; Quinn B. Carroll, Midland College, Midland, TX; Victor Ciaravino, University of Texas Health Science Center San Antonio, TX; Charles Collins, San Diego Mesa College, San Diego, CA; John E. Cullinan, Eastman Kodak, Rochester, NY; Diane DeVos, Pascack Valley Hospital, Westwood, NJ; Terry R. Eastman, Agfa-Gevaert, Irving, TX; Larry Elder, Hurley Medical Center, Flint, MI; Dan Finley, Santa Fe, NM; Liz Escobido, Laramie County Community College, Cheyenne, WY; Kae Fleming, Columbia State Community College, Columbia, TN; Patricia Franco, Houston Community College, Houston, TX; Michele Gable, The Methodist Hospital, Houston, TX; Mary M. Gerald, Del Mar College, Corpus Christi, TX; Buhrmann D. Gilbert, El Paso Community College, El Paso, TX; Gerald Graddy, Jackson State Community College, Jackson, TN; Simon Growick, Miami-Dade Community Hospital, Miami, FL; Steven Hayes, Midwestern State University, Wichita Falls, TX; Jim Heck, Angelina College, Lufkin, TX; Joleen A. Herrmann, St. Joseph Medical Center, Wichita, KS; Trudi James-Parks, Lorain Community College, Elyria, OH; Manfred Kratzat, Phillips Medical Systems, Shelton, CT; Robert A. Luke, Boise State University, Boise, ID;

Margaret Matczynski, Mount Sinai Medical Center, Miami, FL; Bill Miller, Santa Barbara City College, Santa Barbara, CA; Virginia Mishkin, United Hospital, Port Chester, NY; Mary Moore, Cooper Hospital/University, Camden, NJ; Jeffrey Morgenegg, Avila College, Kansas City, MO; John Myers, Northeast Louisiana State University, Monroe, LA; C. William Mulkey, Midlands Technical College, Columbia, SC; Carolyn Nicholas, Baptist Hospital, Beaumont, TX; Don Nichols, University of Oklahoma Health Science Center, Oklahoma City, OK; Virginia L. Olsen, Lakewood Community College, White Bear Lake, MN; Patricia R. Paris, Del Mar College, Corpus Christi, TX; Linda Parsell, Phillips Medical Systems, Houston, TX; Fred Price, Gerland County Community College, Hot Springs, AK; Ruth Reinhart, Parkview Memorial Hospital, Fort Wayne, IN; Teresa Rice, Houston Community College, Houston, TX; Alan M. Rosich, Lorain Community College, Elyria, OH; Cheryl Ross, Hazel Hawkins Hospital, Hollister, CA; Stanton Sanderson, Carpentersville, IL; Bette A. Schans, Swedish Medical Center, Denver, CO; Diana L. Shatraw, Aims Community College, Greeley, CO; G. Ali Shah, University of Newcastle, Newcastle, England; Linda Shields, El Paso Community College, El Paso, TX; Michele Smith, Northern Ohio Imaging Center, Elyria, OH; Gary D. Stevens, Kaskaskia College, Centralia, IL; Dwayne J. TerMaat, St. Louis Community College, St. Louis, MO; Christi Thompson, El Paso Community College, El Paso, TX; James A. Wasseen, Medical College of Virginia, Richmond, VA; Allen West, University of Alabama at Birmingham, Birmingham, AL; Ezell Westbrook, University of District of Columbia, Washington, D.C.; Randy Whitmore, San Jacinto Junior College, Pasadena, TX; Betty Winslow, Wilker General Hospital, North Wilkerbano, NC; and Diana Zientek, Tomball General Hospital, Tomball, TX.

Kae Fleming, Columbia State Community College, Columbia, TN was particularly helpful with her review, comments, and suggestions of the entire manuscript. The crossword puzzles are her creation. Answers to the crossword puzzles can be found in Appendix C.

I am also deeply indebted to my associates Sharon Glaze and Benjamin Archer who have assisted me with this revision. The illustrations are the product of Kraig Emmert, Spencer Phippen, Ann Sparks, and Angela Dinnean. Their caricatures and cartoons help considerably in easing any pain associated with physics. I am also particularly indebted to Elaine Casey, Judy Faldyn, and Amy Leonard for the many times they had to struggle through my handwritten notes, my slurred dictation, and the unfamiliar symbols and equations. I appreciate their conscientious approach in preparing the final manuscript.

Finally, I would invite users of this fifth edition to let me know if you have additional changes or comments. Our common goal, of course, is to enhance the level of professionalism of radiologic technologists by elevating the educational standards as painlessly as possible.

"Physics is Fun" is the motto of my radiologic science courses, and I believe this manual will help make it enjoyable for the student technologist. Then we can all join together to *legalize physics*.

Stewart C. Bushong

Contents

WORKSHEET SECTION

PART ONE
RADIOLOGIC PHYSICS

Name _____

Date _____

Concepts of Radiation

NATURE OF OUR SURROUNDINGS
·················
SOURCES OF IONIZING RADIATION
·················

An appropriate level of understanding of radiologic science requires a modest knowledge of the nature of radiation and its sources, the levels of radiation experienced in our daily lives, and the biologic effects of those levels. All of these fields also require some understanding of simple mathematics and of the units employed for expressing physical quantities. It is unfortunate that the adoption of the international system of units (SI) complicates this effort, since both classic units and SI units will be employed interchangeably for many years.

Some representative radiation levels are as follows:

In our daily lives

Living next to a nuclear power station	0.5 mrad/yr (5 µGy/yr)
Cross-country jet flight	2 mR (0.52 µC/kg)
Fallout at the height of atomic testing	5 mrad (50 µGy)
Consumer products (e.g., smoke detectors, watch dials, etc.)	3 mrad/yr (50 µGy/yr)

Natural background

Sea level	100 mrad/yr (1 mGy/yr)
Mountains	500 mrad/yr (5 mGy/yr)
Human lethality	350,000 mrad (3.5 Gy)

The healing arts

^{99m}Tc thyroid scan	10 mrad (100 µGy)
Genetically significant dose	20 mrad (200 µGy)
Posteroanterior (PA) chest examination	15 mR (7 µC/kg)
Mean marrow dose	105 mrad (1 mGy)
Panoramic dental x-ray	200 mR (52 µC/kg)
Full mouth dental series	700 mR (0.18 mC/kg)
Lumbar spine examination	1000 mR (0.26 mC/kg)
Abdominal examination	1500 mR (0.39 mC/kg)
Fluoroscopic examination	3000 mR (0.77 mC/kg)

Industry

Maximum permissible dose	5000 mrem/yr (50 mSv/yr)

Table W1-1 summarizes SI and classic radiologic units. Classic units are given in parentheses.

EXERCISES

1 Which of the following items is considered to be matter?
   a. the light from a movie projector
   b. the x rays from an airport surveillance device
   c. heat
   d. a snowball
2 The principal difference between mass and weight is
   a. there is no difference; mass and weight are equal.
   b. mass is measured in pounds (lb), whereas weight is measured in kilograms (kg).
   c. weight does not change with position, but mass does.
   d. mass is the equivalent of energy, and weight is the force exerted by gravity.
3 A good definition of energy in any form is
   a. a force exerted by a body.
   b. anything that occupies space and has shape.
   c. the ability to do work.
   d. the quantity of matter.

TABLE W1-1

Quantity	Name	Symbol	Expression in terms of: Other units	Expression in terms of: SI base units
Activity	becquerel	Bq		1/s
	(curie)	Ci	3.7×10^{10} Bq	
Exposure	coulomb per kilogram	C/kg	C/kg	As/kg
	(roentgen)	R	2.58×10^{-4} C/kg	
Absorbed dose	gray	Gy	J/kg	m^2/s^2
	(rad)	rad	10^{-2} Gy	
Dose equivalent	sievert	Sv	J/kg	m^2/s^2
	(rem)	rem	10^{-2} Sv	

4 Which of the following best represents energy?
 a. a snowman
 b. a snowball gathering speed rolling down a hill
 c. the terminals of a battery
 d. the metal plates in a battery

5 Which of the following is an example of kinetic energy?
 a. an x-ray machine
 b. a portable x-ray machine in motion
 c. light emitted from the filament of an x-ray tube
 d. x rays generated by an x-ray tube

6 In Einstein's famous $E = mc^2$ equation, c stands for
 a. mass-energy equivalence.
 b. the speed of light.
 c. the theory of relativity.
 d. acceleration of mass.

7 Radiation is
 a. energy emitted and transferred through space or matter.
 b. mass with a charge.
 c. stationary particles.
 d. measured in kilograms.

8 The roentgen unit of measurement relates to
 a. ions produced in air.
 b. a radiation absorbed dose.
 c. a dose equivalent.
 d. nonionizing radiation.

9 An example of electromagnetic radiation is
 a. alpha radiation.   c. sound.
 b. light.   d. heat.

10 When ionization occurs, the
 a. positive ion is the resulting atom.
 b. negative ion is the target atom.
 c. negative ion is the ion pair.
 d. negative ion is electromagnetic radiation.

11 X rays are more nearly like
 a. alpha rays.   c. gamma rays.
 b. beta rays.   d. ultrasound.

12 Which of the following is the largest source of human exposure to artificial radiation?
 a. nuclear power generating stations
 b. medical diagnostic x rays
 c. radioactive materials in consumer products
 d. radioactive fallout

13 The approximate annual dose from natural environmental radiation at sea level is
 a. 10 mrad/yr (100 µGy/yr).
 b. 50 mrad/yr (500 µGy/yr).
 c. 100 mrad/yr (1 mGy/yr).
 d. 500 mrad/yr (5 mGy/yr).

14 Which of the following on the average results in the highest annual radiation dose?
 a. cosmic rays
 b. radiation from inside the earth
 c. radionuclides deposited inside the human body
 d. diagnostic x rays

15 Which of the following contributes more than 25 mrad/yr on average to each of us?
 a. fallout radiation
 b. microwave oven radiation
 c. diagnostic x rays
 d. radioisotopes in nuclear medicine

16 The rad is related most closely to
 a. the gray.   c. radiation exposure.
 b. the sievert.   d. dose equivalent.

17 Which of the following would be considered as ionizing electromagnetic radiation?
 a. beta rays   c. ultrasound
 b. microwaves   d. gamma rays

18 Which of the following is a unit of mass?
 a. pound   c. kilogram
 b. volt   d. mrad

19 One collimates the x-ray beam **primarily** to
 a. change x rays to light.
 b. reduce patient dose.
 c. improve image quality.
 d. increase x-ray energy.

Concepts of Radiation

DISCOVERY OF X RAYS
....
DEVELOPMENT OF MODERN RADIOLOGY
....
REPORTS OF RADIATION INJURY
....

It has been almost 100 years since the discovery of x rays. For 20 years, x-ray imaging was very crude. The introduction of the high voltage transformer and the heated filament x-ray tube in 1913 was a major advancement in medical imaging. For the next 30 years, little changed. Shortly after World War II, several improvements in x-ray imaging appeared: the image intensifier tube, multidirectional tomography, xeroradiography, and automatic processing to name a few.

The last 25 years have seen x-ray imaging transformed into **medical imaging.** This period has seen the introduction of totally new imaging devices, some of which do not employ ionizing radiation. Diagnostic ultrasound, radionuclide imaging, computed tomography (CT), and, more recently, magnetic resonance imaging (MRI) have resulted in much greater emphasis being placed on medical imaging for patient care.

What the future holds for the newest developments, such as picture archiving and communication systems and laser stimulatable phosphors is still not clear. It is certain that we are relying more and more on digital imaging techniques.

EXERCISES

1 The device with which Roentgen discovered x rays was a
   a. Coolidge tube.
   b. Crookes tube.
   c. anode tube.
   d. Snook interrupterless transformer.

"There's absolutely no danger. Just relax while I step behind this foot-thick lead barrier."

2 The phosphor that Roentgen employed in his early experiments with x rays was
  a. calcium tungstate.   **c.** barium platinocyanide.
  b. rare earth.   **d.** zinc cadmium sulfide.

3 X-ray tube voltages are measured in
  a. millivolts.   **c.** kilovolts.
  b. volts.   **d.** megavolts.

4 Which of the following early pioneers developed the fluoroscope?
  a. Wilhelm C. Roentgen   **c.** William Crookes
  b. Alexander G. Bell   **d.** Thomas Edison

5 The first application of x-ray beam collimation and filtration was made by
  a. William Crookes.   **c.** William Rollins.
  b. William Coolidge.   **d.** William Longfellow.

6 The type of x-ray tube in use today is a
  a. Leonard tube.   **c.** Snook tube.
  b. Crookes tube.   **d.** Coolidge tube.

7 The Bucky grid introduced in 1921
  a. reduced patient exposure.
  b. increased image contrast.
  c. reduced examination time.
  d. provided x-ray collimation.

8 Regarding x-ray–induced death,
  a. Clarence Dally was the first American death.
  b. the first one did not occur until approximately 1920.
  c. the first one occurred within 1 year of Roentgen's discovery.
  d. radiology has always been considered a completely safe occupation.

9 The Coolidge x-ray tube
  a. was used by Roentgen shortly after he discovered x rays.
  b. has a hot cathode.
  c. is not in use today.
  d. is not as good as the Crookes tube.

10 Roentgen originally identified x rays as
  a. x light.   **c.** cathode rays.
  b. x heat.   **d.** alpha rays.

11 What are the two general types of x-ray procedures?
  a. radiographic and fluoroscopic
  b. roentgenographic and ultrasonic
  c. electromagnetic and ultrasonic
  d. radiographic and tomographic

12 Which of the following provides dynamic x-ray images?
  a. tomography   **c.** fluoroscopy
  b. ultrasound   **d.** xeroradiography

13 The base for a radiograph made in 1910 would have been
  a. cellulose nitrate.
  b. cellulose acetate.
  c. calcium tungstate.
  d. glass.

14 Use of collimation and filtration
  a. degrades image quality.
  b. reduces patient dose.
  c. increases exposure time.
  d. results in patient discomfort.

15 Which of the following imaging modalities is newest?
  a. laser stimulatable phosphors
  b. magnetic resonance
  c. computed tomography
  d. xeroradiography

16 Which of the following radiation responses was not reported before 1910?
  a. anemia   **c.** death
  b. leukemia   **d.** skin damage

Match the following names with the appropriate event:
17 Coolidge _____   **a.** Discovery of x rays
18 Roentgen _____   **b.** Theory of relativity
19 Einstein _____   **c.** Reciprocating grid
20 Bucky _____   **d.** Intensifying screen
21 Pupin _____   **e.** Hot-filament x-ray tube

Match the following events with the appropriate year:
22 Founding of American Society   **a.** 1895
  of Radiologic Technology   **b.** 1905
23 Development of the hot-   **c.** 1913
  filament x-ray tube _____   **d.** 1920
24 Discovery of x rays _____   **e.** 1921
25 Development of reciprocating   **f.** 1973
  grid _____
26 Creation of the theory of relativity _____
27 First magnetic resonance images _____

Concepts of Radiation

BASIC RADIATION PROTECTION
....

Individuals working in diagnostic radiology need to be aware of the principles of radiation control for the protection of patients and themselves. The three cardinal principles of radiation protection are time, distance, and shielding.

A. The dose to an individual is directly related to the duration of the exposure. Therefore keep the time you or your patient is exposed as short as possible.

B. As the distance between the source of radiation increases, the radiation exposure decreases.

C. The radiation exposure to an individual can be reduced by placing shielding material between the radiation source and the exposed person. Lead is the most commonly used material for x-ray shielding.

EXERCISES

1 One of the cardinal principles of radiation protection states that the technologist should minimize
   a. time.
   c. shielding.
   b. distance.
   d. kVp.

2 Which of the following is **not** one of the 10 basic radiation control principles in diagnostic radiology?
   a. Wear protective apparel during fluoroscopy.
   b. Use gonad shields on all patients.
   c. Always wear a radiation monitor while at work.
   d. Collimate the x-ray beam to the smallest appropriate field size.

3 If it is necessary to restrain a patient during a radiographic examination, the most acceptable person to do this is
   a. an 18-year-old brother of the patient.
   b. a 20-year-old female technologist.
   c. a 40-year-old male technologist.
   d. a 50-year-old female friend of the patient.

4 Which of the following is correctly stated for diagnostic radiology?
   a. Gonad shields are equally important for a 70-year-old male as for a 20-year-old female.
   b. Copper is most often used as an x-ray filter.
   c. Use of intensifying screens reduces patient dose.
   d. The radiologic technologist may hold patients for routine examinations.

5 Which of the following will **not** reduce patient dose?
   a. filtration of the x-ray beam
   b. collimation of the x-ray beam
   c. use of protective barriers for technologists
   d. use of gonad shields

6 When conducting an abdominal radiographic examination of a child
   a. the technologist should hold the child if necessary.
   b. the parent should hold the child if necessary, and protective apparel is not necessary.
   c. the parent should hold the child if necessary, but protective apparel is necessary.
   d. gonad shielding is not necessary.

7 All of the following help to reduce patient dose except using
   a. cones.
   c. intensifying screens.
   b. filtration.
   d. fixed protective barriers.

8 Following termination of an x-ray exposure
   a. x rays continue to be emitted for a few seconds.
   b. no more x rays are emitted.
   c. the patient continues to emit scatter radiation for a few seconds.
   d. the patient continues to emit scatter radiation but only for less than 1 second.

9 During fluoroscopy a radiologic technologist should always
   a. remain as close to the patient as possible.
   b. leave the radiation monitor behind the fixed protective barrier.
   c. wear a radiation monitor when examined as a patient.
   d. wear protective apparel.

10 The main reason for using metal filters in x-ray imaging is to
   a. reduce patient dose.
   b. sharpen the image.
   c. absorb penetrating radiation.
   d. absorb heat.
11 Radiologic technologists have a tendency to
   a. become overzealous about radiation protection.
   b. become so familiar with the work environment that they ignore basic radiation protection principles.
   c. become skinny because of radiation exposure.
   d. swap radiation monitors.
12 Which of the following is **not** an example of a collimator?
   a. adjustable light localizers
   b. diaphragms
   c. cones
   d. grids
13 X-ray examination of the pelves of women of reproductive capacity should be limited to the
   a. 10-day interval following the onset of menstruation.
   b. 10-day interval preceding menstruation.
   c. the first 10 days of every month.
   d. the last 10 days of every month.
14 Modern x-ray imaging is based principally on
   a. ultrasound and radiography.
   b. radiography and fluoroscopy.
   c. fluoroscopy and MRI.
   d. MRI and ultrasound.
15 In general, x-ray examinations should be limited to
   a. older patients.
   b. symptomatic patients.
   c. x-ray personnel.
   d. patients who are not pregnant.

16 Gonad shields should be used
   a. for all examinations of all patients.
   b. on all males.
   c. when the gonads are in the useful beam.
   d. when the gonads are in or near the useful beam.
17 The principal reason to avoid repeat examination is that the
   a. patient receives twice the radiation dose.
   b. cost of the procedure is doubled.
   c. patient is inconvenienced.
   d. technologist's workload is doubled.
18 Which of the following is an application of one of the cardinal principles?
   a. reducing the x-ray energy
   b. wearing protective apparel
   c. use of aluminum filtration
   d. halving the exposure time and doubling the mA
19 Which of the following represents use of a radiation protection device?
   a. Abdominal films of expectant mothers should not be taken.
   b. Gonad shielding should be used with all persons of childbearing age.
   c. X-ray examination of asymptomatic patients is not indicated.
   d. A member of the patient's family should be used as a holder.
20 Which of the following represents implementation of a radiation protection procedure?
   a. Avoid repeat examinations.
   b. Remove filtration.
   c. Collimate to the film size not the anatomic part.
   d. Wear protective apparel at the control console.

WORKSHEET 4

Concepts of Radiation

NUMERIC PREFIXES
....

When very large or very small quantities are used, they are often expressed with the aid of numeric prefixes. The numeric prefixes replace the power-of-ten notation in speaking and writing. They are used as a shorthand notation that can be applied to all scientific quantities. For example, we routinely speak of kilovolts instead of thousands of volts and milliamps instead of fractions of amperes. Following are the numeric prefixes now in use; those with an asterisk (*) are most often encountered in radiologic science.

Multiple	Prefix	Symbol
10^{18}	exa-	E
10^{15}	peta-	P
10^{12}	tera-	T
10^{9}	giga-	G
10^{6}	mega-	M
10^{3}	*kilo-	k
10^{2}	hecto-	h
10	deka-	da
10^{-1}	deci-	d
10^{-2}	*centi-	c
10^{-3}	*milli	m
10^{-6}	*micro-	μ
10^{-9}	nano-	n
10^{-12}	pico-	p
10^{-15}	femto-	f
10^{-18}	atto-	a

EXERCISES

1 10 kilometers (km) is equivalent to
  a. 100 m.   **c.** 10,000 m.
  b. 1000 m.   **d.** 100,000 m.

2 A 1/10-second radiographic exposure is equivalent to
  a. 1 ms.   **c.** 100 ms.
  b. 10 ms.   **d.** 1000 ms.

3 A PA chest examination is conducted at 120 kVp. Therefore the peak x-ray tube voltage is
  a. 120 V.   **c.** 12,000 V.
  b. 1200 V.   **d.** 120,000 V.

4 A radiographic exposure made on the 200 mA station is equivalent to
  a. 2 A.   **c.** 200,000 μA.
  b. 20 A.   **d.** 2,000,000 μA.

5 The angstrom (Å) is a unit that was used for many years by optical physicists. 1 Å is equal to 10^{-10} m; therefore
  a. 10 Å = 10^{-11} m.   **c.** 10 Å = 1 nm.
  b. 10 Å = 10 nm.   **d.** 10 Å = 1000 μm.

6 Which of the following is correct?
  a. 1,000,000 eV = 1 keV
  b. 0.001 A = 1 pA
  c. 10^{-9} m = 1 pm
  d. 10 μA = 0.01 mA

7 If your mass is 70 kg, it is also
  a. 7000 g.   **c.** 70 million μg.
  b. 7 million mg.   **d.** 0.07 mg.

8 If your height is 160 cm, you are also
  a. 1.6 m tall.
  b. 16 m tall.
  c. 0.016 km tall.
  d. 1.6×10^{9} μm tall.

9 Scientific prefixes are helpful in expressing power-of-ten notation. Which of the following is correct?
  a. 1 nm is 10^{-9} m.
  b. 1 μCi is 10^{-3} Ci.
  c. 10 kVp is 1000 Vp.
  d. 1 35 keV x-ray has 35×10^{6} eV of energy.

10 A KUB radiograph (radiography of the kidneys, ureters, and bladder) is made at 82 kVp/200 mA/0.25 s. That is equivalent to
  a. 82×10^{3} Vp/2×10^{-1} A/0.25 s.
  b. 8.2×10^{6} mVp/2×10^{2} mA/2.5×10^{2} ms.
  c. 0.82×10^{3} kVp/2×10^{-5} μA/2.5×10^{4} μs.
  d. 8.2×10^{7} μVp/2×10^{5} μA/2.5×10^{6} μs.

LIE VERY QUIETLY AND TRY TO RELAX; EVERYONE IS A LITTLE NERVOUS WITH THEIR FIRST CAT SCAN.

11 The normal source-to-image receptor distance (SID) for an upright chest radiograph is 180 cm. This is equivalent to
a. 18 mm. **c.** 1800 μm.
b. 1800 mm. **d.** 18 m.

12 When a radiographic exposure time is ½ s, it is also
a. 200 ms. **c.** 2000 ms.
b. 500 ms. **d.** 5000 ms.

13 A fluoroscopic examination is conducted at 1.5 A. That is equivalent to
a. 15 mA. **c.** 1500 mA.
b. 150 mA. **d.** 15,000 mA.

14 Normal tube potential for a screen-film mammogram is 28 kVp. This is equivalent to
a. 2800 V. **c.** 2.8×10^2 V.
b. 28,000 V. **d.** 2.8×10^{-3} V.

15 The SID for a portable radiograph is often 80 cm. That is equivalent to
a. 8×10^{-1} m. **c.** 8×10^2 m.
b. 8×10^{-2} m. **d.** 8×10^3 m.

16 A radiographic exposure requires 400 ms. This is also
a. 0.004 s. **c.** 0.4 s.
b. 0.04 s. **d.** 4 s.

17 A radiographic exposure is made at 600 mA, 200 ms. The equivalent mAs is
a. 1.2×5. **c.** 1.2×10^3.
b. 1.2×10^4. **d.** 1.2×10^2.

18 A high-kVp chest radiograph is conducted at 125 kVp. This is equivalent to
a. 1.25×10^2 Vp. **c.** 1.25×10^4 Vp.
b. 1.25×10^3 Vp. **d.** 1.25×10^5 Vp.

19 An average monthly exposure for a radiologic technologist is about 10 mrem. This is equivalent to
a. 1×10^2 rem. **c.** 1×10^{-1} rem.
b. 1×10^0 rem. **d.** 1×10^{-2} rem.

20 A PA chest radiograph will expose a patient to approximately 20 mR. This is equivalent to
a. 2×10^4 μR. **c.** 2×10^0 μR.
b. 2×10^{-2} μR. **d.** 200 μR.

Convert each of the following to either decimal or scientific notation as indicated:

21 1.3×10^{-9} C = **26** 2.54×10^{-4} C/kg =
22 7,000,000 Hz = **27** 5000 mGy =
23 400×10^{-12} A = **28** 8×10^{-2} s =
24 0.001 g = **29** 0.0015 Sv =
25 457,000 V = **30** 3000 eV/μm =

Express as a whole number and in power-of-ten notation (without a prefix):

Whole number		Power of ten
31 1200 mA =		amperes = A
32 10 cm =		meters = m
33 10,000 g =		kilograms = kg
34 1 μl =		liter = l
35 7 mR =		roentgens = R

Convert the following:
36 1.0 g/cm²/s/s to _____ kg/m²/s/s.

Name _____

Date _____

Concepts of Radiation

RADIOLOGIC UNITS
....

The three fundamental units of physical measurement are length, mass, and time. From these all other units are derived, including the five basic radiologic units used to measure radiation and radioactivity.

Incorporating SI units into the classic units results in the following relationships:

EXPOSURE:
$$1\ R = 2.08 \times 10^9 \text{ ion pairs/cm}^3 \text{ of air}$$
$$= 2.58 \times 10^{-4} \text{ C/kg of air}$$
$$1\ C/kg = 3.88 \times 10^3\ R$$
$$= 8.07 \times 10^{12} \text{ ion pairs/cm}^3 \text{ of air}$$

ABSORBED DOSE:
$$1\ rad = 10^2 \text{ ergs/g}$$
$$= 10^{-2} \text{ J/kg}$$
$$= 10^{-2} \text{ Gy}$$
$$1\ gray = 10^2 \text{ rad}$$

DOSE EQUIVALENT:
$$1\ rem = 10^2 \text{ ergs/g}$$
$$= 10^{-2} \text{ Sv}$$
$$1\ Sv = 1 \text{ J/kg}$$
$$= 10^2 \text{ rem}$$

ACTIVITY:
$$1\ Ci = 3.7 \times 10^{10} \text{ atoms disintegrating/s}$$
$$= 3.7 \times 10^{10} \text{ Bq}$$
$$1\ Bq = 1 \text{ atom disintegrating/s}$$

ENERGY:
$$1\ eV = 1.6 \times 19^{-12} \text{ ergs}$$
$$= 1.6 \times 10^{-19} \text{ J}$$

EXERCISES

1 A film badge report would express a technologist's dose equivalent in
   a. roentgens.   c. rem.
   b. rad.   d. curies.

2 A PA chest radiograph delivers a dose of approximately 15 _____ to the patient.
   a. mR   c. rem
   b. mrad   d. eV

3 Some experiments require that mice be irradiated to a total dose of 600 _____ to produce death.
   a. R   c. rem
   b. rad   d. eV

4 The output intensity of an overhead radiographic x-ray tube is 2.5 _____ /mAs at 70 kVp.
   a. mR   c. mrem
   b. mrad   d. mCi

5 ^{99m}Tc is the most often employed radionuclide in diagnostic nuclear medicine. It is used in _____ amounts.
   a. mR   c. mrem
   b. mrad   d. mCi

6 The roentgen is a unit of measure that specifies the
   a. quality of x rays.
   b. character of x rays.
   c. intensity of x rays.
   d. absorption of x rays.

7 Which of the following adequately describes the use of the rad?
   a. the output intensity of an x-ray machine
   b. the dose equivalent received by a technologist
   c. the amount of radioactive material
   d. energy absorbed by a mass of tissue

8 Which of the following is a classical radiologic unit?
   a. sievert   c. rem
   b. ampere   d. coulomb/kilogram

9 If 2 rad is delivered to 2 g of soft tissue, 1 g of this tissue receives
   a. 0.5 rad.   c. 2 g-rad.
   b. 1 rad.   d. 200 ergs.

10 Absorbed dose can be measured by
   a. ergs.
   c. kg-Gy.
   b. J.
   d. Gy.
11 Which of the following is **not** a unit of energy?
   a. becquerel
   c. erg
   b. electron volt
   d. joule
12 Which of the following is equivalent?
   a. a dose of 200 mrad = 2 cGy
   b. a 500 mR exposure = 127 µC/kg
   c. 1 mCi = 37 µC/kg
   d. 1 Sv = 100 erg/g
13 Which of the following is a unit of radioactivity?
   a. R
   c. gray
   b. rad
   d. Ci
14 An absorbed dose can be expressed in
   a. Ci.
   c. ergs.
   b. Bq.
   d. ergs/g.
15 Which of the following is a proper use of the unit roentgen?
   a. The gamma-ray intensity from a cobalt teletherapy unit is 100 R/min.
   b. The total patient treatment dose with a cobalt teletherapy unit is 2000 R.
   c. One-hundred mR of ^{131}I is administered to image the thyroid.
   d. Radiologic technologists should not receive a dose equivalent in excess of 5000 mR/yr.
16 In diagnostic radiology it is acceptable to assume that 1R is equal to
   a. 1 rem.
   c. 1 erg.
   b. 1 Ci.
   d. 1 J.

17 In the SI system
   a. 1 J is approximately equal to 1 MeV.
   b. the dose equivalent is expressed in units of Gy.
   c. a dose of 1000 rad is equivalent to 100 Gy.
   d. a dose of 1000 rad is equivalent to 10 Gy.
18 Rad rate can be expressed in units of
   a. R/min.
   c. J/kg/min.
   b. ergs/g.
   d. kVp/s.
19 Radiation exposure is defined in units of coulombs/kilogram.
   a. Kilogram refers to the patient's mass.
   b. Kilogram refers to the volume of tissue irradiated.
   c. Coulomb refers to electrons released in ionization.
   d. Coulomb refers to energy absored.
20 Which of the following is **not** a unit of energy?
   a. erg
   c. J
   b. C
   d. eV

Match the following:
21 roentgen _____   **a.** joule
22 rad _____   **b.** sievert
23 rem _____   **c.** gray
24 curie _____   **d.** coulombs/kilogram
25 erg _____   **e.** becquerel

Give the SI units for each of the following:
26 energy _____
27 absorbed dose _____
28 radioactivity _____
29 dose equivalent _____
30 exposure _____

Name _____

Date _____

Fundamentals of Physics

REVIEW OF MATHEMATICS
·····················

There are four basic operations in mathematics: addition, subtraction, multiplication, and division. Some useful manipulations derived from these basic operations are as follows:

1. A **ratio** is the comparison of one number to another expressed as a **quotient** or **fraction.**

2. A **proportion** relates the equality of two or more ratios.

EXAMPLE: The mass of a 12 cm pencil is 6 g, and that of a 16 cm pencil is 8 g. Therefore the mass of one is to the mass of the other in the same ratio as their lengths, 6/8 = 12/16; or 6 is to 8 as 12 is to 16.

3. **Rounding off** to significance is the procedure of reducing a complex number to a simpler number. Drop the last digit of a number and raise the next-to-last digit by 1 if the last digit is 5 or greater.

4. **Power-of-ten notation** is a scientific method for writing very large or very small numbers. The method makes these types of numbers easy to manipulate.

The first step in power-of-ten notation is to reduce all numbers to the form $x.y \times 10^z$. This is done by placing the decimal point after the first digit of the number and counting the number of digits the decimal was moved. This number is the superscript of the base 10 or the exponent. If the decimal point was moved to the left, the exponent is positive; if it was moved to the right, it is negative.

EXAMPLE 1: $7621.93 = 7621.93 = 7.6219 \times 10^3$
3 2 1
Left

EXAMPLE 2: $0.000156 = 0.000156 = 1.56 \times 10^{-4}$
1 2 3 4
Right

Numbers in power-of-ten notation can be multiplied, divided, or raised to powers according to the following rules:

$$10^x \times 10^y = 10^{x+y}$$

$$\frac{10^x}{10^y} = 10^{x-y}$$

Numbers in power-of-ten notation are rarely added or subtracted, but when they are, the value of all the exponents must be the same.

EXERCISES

Perform the indicated operations:

ARITHMETIC

1	649	2	38,246
	+ 88		721
			193,405
			5,227
			+ 81,491

3	432.71	4	419.307
	19.878		− 67.227
	+ 1000.092		

5	69.525	6	9413
	− 2.820		× 4

7	6258	8	200
	× .043		× .05

9 $0.31\overline{)421.25}$ 10 $3.1416\overline{)360}$

FRACTIONS

11 $\frac{1}{2} + \frac{2}{8} =$ 12 $\frac{3}{8} + \frac{5}{16} =$

13 $\frac{3}{8} + \frac{19}{16} + \frac{7}{32} =$ 14 $\frac{3}{8} - \frac{3}{16} =$

15 $\frac{3}{5} - \frac{9}{4} =$ 16 $\frac{1}{2} \times \frac{1}{4} =$

17 $\frac{15}{32} \times 1\frac{1}{3} =$

18 $6\frac{7}{8} \times 2\frac{11}{16} =$

19 $\frac{1}{2} \div \frac{1}{3} =$

20 $\frac{12}{9} \div \frac{2}{3} =$

SIGNIFICANT FIGURES

21
$$\begin{array}{r} 70.05 \\ 6.85 \\ 100.003 \\ + 12.1 \\ \hline \end{array}$$

22
$$\begin{array}{r} 6.254 \\ - 1.04 \\ \hline \end{array}$$

23
$$\begin{array}{r} 3.1416 \\ \times 30 \\ \hline \end{array}$$

24
$$\begin{array}{r} 8.05 \\ \times .693 \\ \hline \end{array}$$

25 $2.567)\overline{6.02}$

26 $13a = 126$

27 $168 + b = 42$

28 $c/5 = 3/8$

29 $3 - \frac{3}{8} + \frac{3}{4} = 16$

30 $1\frac{3}{8} + 3x = (1/4)2$

31 What is the ratio of 100 mAs to 400 mAs?

32 $\dfrac{x}{8 \text{ mR}} = \dfrac{300 \text{ mAs}}{400 \text{ mAs}}$

33 $\dfrac{75 \text{ kVp}}{80 \text{ kVp}} = \dfrac{210 \text{ mAs}}{x}$

34 $\frac{3}{4} \times 500$ mAs = ?

35 $\dfrac{150 \text{ mR}}{50 \text{ mR}} = \dfrac{600 \text{ mAs}}{x}$

36 If $12x = 420$ mAs, then x = ? mAs

37 Given $a = bc$, if $a = 189$, $b = 27$, then c = ?

38 A radiographic unit emits 3.7 mR/mAs (95 µC/kg-mAs). If a given technique requires 120 mAs, what will be the exposure?

39 The radiographic output intensity is 4.3 mR/mAs (111 µC/kg-mAs). If a given technique is 200 mA, 1/60 s, what will be the exposure?

Convert each to power-of-ten notation:

40 2741.92

41 9,174,843

42 7713

Convert each to power-of-ten notation and perform the indicated operations:

43
$$\begin{array}{r} 176 \\ + 382 \\ \hline \end{array}$$

44
$$\begin{array}{r} 931.45 \\ - 36.63 \\ \hline \end{array}$$

45
$$\begin{array}{r} 37,000 \\ + 617 \\ \hline \end{array}$$

46 $3.2 \times 48.6 \times 10^{-5} =$

47 $(80,071)(157) =$

48 $\dfrac{921}{3705} =$

49 $(10^5)^4 =$

50 $\dfrac{10 \times 10^3 \times 10^{-2} \times 10^5}{10^2 \times 10^{-4}} =$

51 $\dfrac{(10^{-18})^2 \times (10^7)^3}{10} =$

52 $(2.5 \times 10^{-10}) \times (1.2 \times 10^{18}) =$

Compute the following:

53 An iodine atom has a diameter of about 4×10^{-10} m. A 60 keV x-ray has a wavelength of 2×10^{-11} m. What is the ratio of the atomic diameter to the x-ray wavelength?

54 It is known that there are 6.02×10^{23} atoms in 131 g of ^{131}I. What is the mass of one atom of ^{131}I?

55 The nucleus of a barium atom is approximately 10^{-15} m in diameter. The atom itself is approximately 2×10^{-10} m in diameter. What is the ratio of the diameter of the atom to the diameter of its nucleus?

Name _____

Date _____

Fundamentals of Physics

MILLIAMPERE-SECOND CONVERSIONS

When selecting a radiographic technique, the milli-amperage (mA) and the exposure time(s) are multiplied together to produce the total **milliampere-seconds (mAs).** The total mAs value is very important, because it directly relates to how dark the radiograph will be, something called **optical density.** Neither the exposure time nor the milliamperage can be considered alone in controlling the total optical density of the resulting image.

Milliamperage controls the number of x rays emitted from the x-ray tube each second. To determine the **total number** of x rays exposing the image receptor, this rate must be multiplied by the exposure time, which results in the **total mAs:**

$$mA \times s = mAs$$

Many different combinations of milliamperage and exposure time can be used to achieve the same mAs. Radiologic technologists must become skilled at computing mAs, so they can adapt to different equipment and different situations. For example, suppose you normally use 400 mA and 1/80 s (13 ms) for an ankle examination using fixed equipment, and you are called to do a portable examination. The mobile unit available has a maximum of 300 mA available. It is a timesaving and repeat-avoiding skill to be able to quickly, mentally compute the total mAs value as 5 mAs. To obtain 5 mAs at 300 mA, you should be able to quickly determine that a time of 1/60 s (17 ms) is needed. Such mental math should be second nature to every radiologic technologist.

EXERCISES

Compute the following total mAs values. To benefit from this exercise, **do not figure your calculations on paper—do them mentally,** then write your answer. For additional help with technique math, turn to the "Math Tutor Section" of this workbook.

PART I Decimal/Fraction Conversions

Fraction		Decimal		Decimal		Fraction
1	1/5	=	.2	16	0.05	= 5/100
2	1/20	=	.05	17	0.333	= 333/1000
3	1/8	=	.125	18	0.0125	= 125/10000
4	1/60	=	.0166	19	0.02	= 2/100
5	1/15	=	.03	20	0.4	= 4/10
6	1/40	=	.020	21	0.0167	= 167/10000
7	1/120	=		22	0.025	=
8	2/3	=		23	0.143	=
9	1/30	=		24	0.75	=
10	2/5	=		25	0.0833	=
11	3/20	=	.15	26	0.0667	=
12	2/15	=	.1333	27	0.8	=
13	7/10	=	.7	28	0.00833	=
14	3/5	=	.6			
15	7/20	=	.35			

PART II Decimal Times

	mA	×	time(s)	=	mAs		mA	×	time(s)	=	mAs
29	100	@	0.07	=		49	300	@	0.33	=	
30	100	@	0.013	=		50	300	@	0.033	=	
31	100	@	0.033	=		51	300	@	0.015	=	
32	100	@	0.25	=		52	300	@	0.002	=	
33	100	@	0.009	=		53	400	@	0.08	=	
34	200	@	0.04	=		54	400	@	0.03	=	
35	200	@	0.07	=		55	400	@	0.035	=	
36	200	@	0.025	=		56	400	@	0.2	=	
37	200	@	0.035	=		57	400	@	0.35	=	
38	200	@	0.35	=		58	400	@	0.002	=	
39	200	@	0.12	=		59	500	@	0.07	=	
40	200	@	0.2	=		60	500	@	0.04	=	
41	200	@	0.6	=		61	500	@	0.4	=	
42	200	@	0.005	=		62	500	@	0.004	=	
43	300	@	0.01	=		63	500	@	0.005	=	
44	300	@	0.08	=		64	600	@	0.5	=	
45	300	@	0.05	=		65	600	@	0.02	=	
46	300	@	0.5	=		66	600	@	0.15	=	
47	300	@	0.2	=		67	600	@	0.003	=	
48	300	@	0.16	=		68	600	@	0.125	=	

PART III Fractional Times

	mA	×	time(s)	=	mAs		mA	×	time(s)	=	mAs
69	100	@	1/8	=		89	400	@	1/60	=	
70	100	@	1/120	=		90	500	@	1/12	=	
71	100	@	1/15	=		91	500	@	1/15	=	
72	100	@	1/40	=		92	500	@	1/20	=	
73	100	@	1/6	=		93	600	@	1/40	=	
74	50	@	1/20	=		94	600	@	1/30	=	
75	50	@	1/120	=		95	600	@	1/120	=	
76	50	@	1/80	=		96	600	@	1/25	=	
77	200	@	1/80	=		97	600	@	1/5	=	
78	200	@	1/12	=		98	100	@	2/15	=	
79	200	@	1/15	=		99	100	@	7/20	=	
80	200	@	1/40	=		100	200	@	4/5	=	
81	200	@	1/30	=		101	200	@	3/10	=	
82	200	@	1/6	=		102	300	@	4/5	=	
83	300	@	1/5	=		103	300	@	2/15	=	
84	300	@	1/60	=		104	300	@	3/10	=	
85	300	@	1/15	=		105	400	@	3/5	=	
86	300	@	1/120	=		106	400	@	3/20	=	
87	400	@	1/20	=		107	500	@	3/20	=	
88	400	@	1/80	=		108	600	@	3/20	=	

Name _____

Date _____

Fundamentals of Physics

GRAPHS
······················

A logarithmic scale is often used when data contain a wide range of numbers that cannot be conveniently plotted on a linear graph. For example, consider the points (x = 1, y = 1) and (x = 5, y = 10,000). To plot these on a standard linear graph requires a y axis that would make (y = 10) indistinguishable from (y = 0). To avoid this difficulty, a logarithmic (log) scale containing intervals equal to **one order of magnitude** is used. Equal lengths on a linear scale have equal value. Equal lengths on a log scale have an equal ratio, which is determined by the logarithmic increment involved.

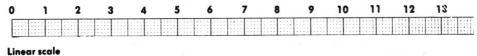

Linear scale

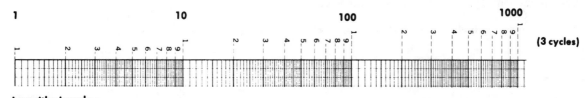

(3 cycles)

Logarithmic scale

EXERCISES

Locate the number indicated at the left on each side of the adjacent scales.

1 0.493

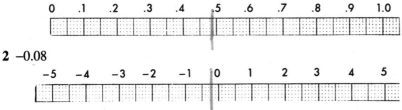

2 −0.08

3 3.6

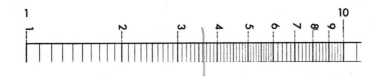

4 0.037

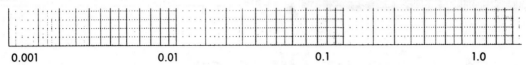

0.001   0.01   0.1   1.0

5 3.7×10^7

10^0 10^1 10^2 10^3 10^4 10^5 10^6 10^7 10^8 10^9 10^{10}

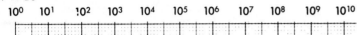

Plot each of the following sets of data on the linear-linear grid and on the linear-log (semilog) graph paper provided:

6 A very small change in filament current results in a very large change in x-ray tube current. A special high-intensity tube design is being tested, and the following data are obtained:

Filament amperes	Tube milliamperes
5.2	25
5.7	50
6.2	100
6.7	200
7.1	300
7.6	500
7.9	700
8.1	900
8.4	1200

7 Measurements of an x-ray beam are taken to determine the necessary shielding for the walls of a radiographic room. The following data are obtained:

Shielding thickness (mm lead)	Radiation intensity (mR)
0	1650
0.1	1236
0.2	995
0.4	661
0.8	343
1.2	174
1.5	129

8 Radioactive ^{131}I has a half-life of 8 days. An unknown quantity is analyzed today (t = 0 days) and results in 9860 counts per minute (c/min). If analysis of this sample continues at 10-day intervals, the data might appear as follows:

Time (d)	Activity (c/min)
0	9860
10	4146
20	1744
30	733
40	308
50	130
60	55
70	23
80	10

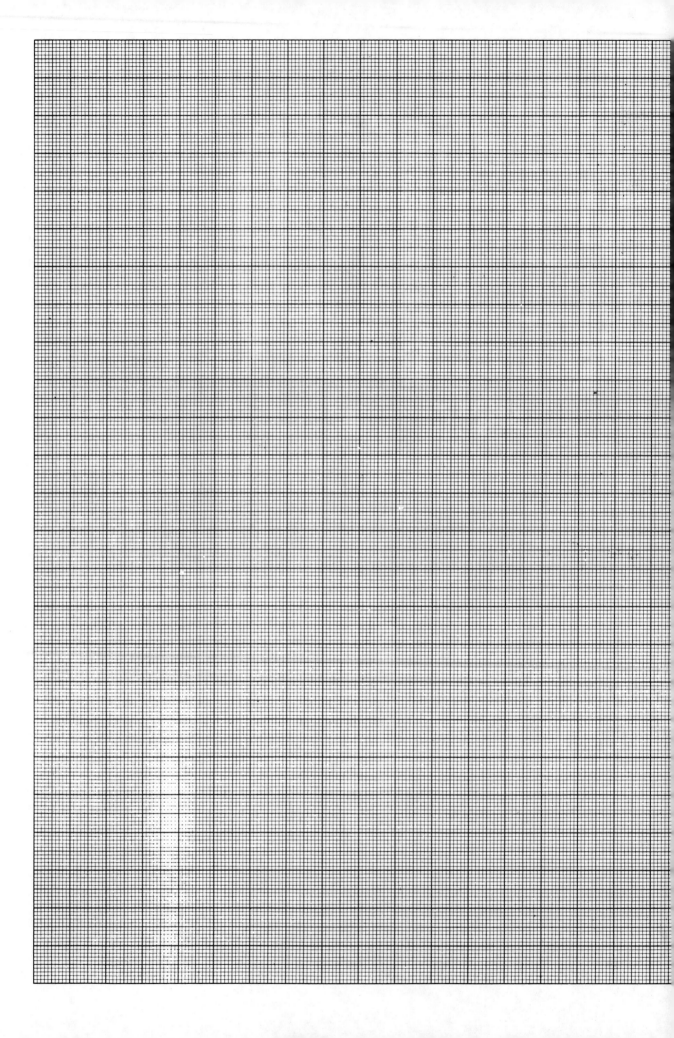

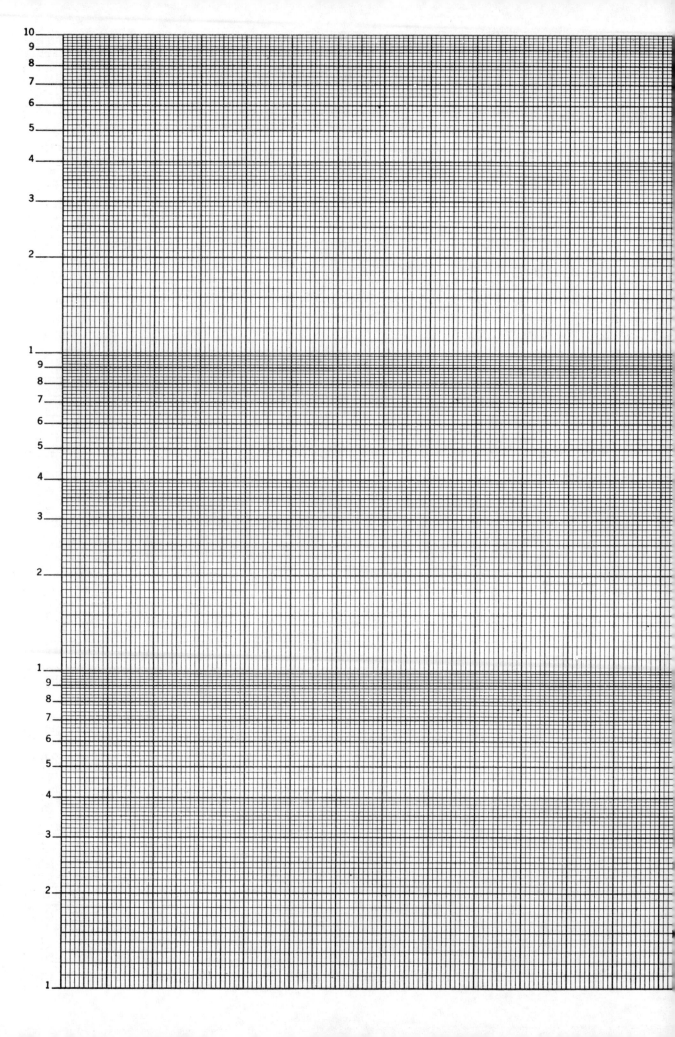

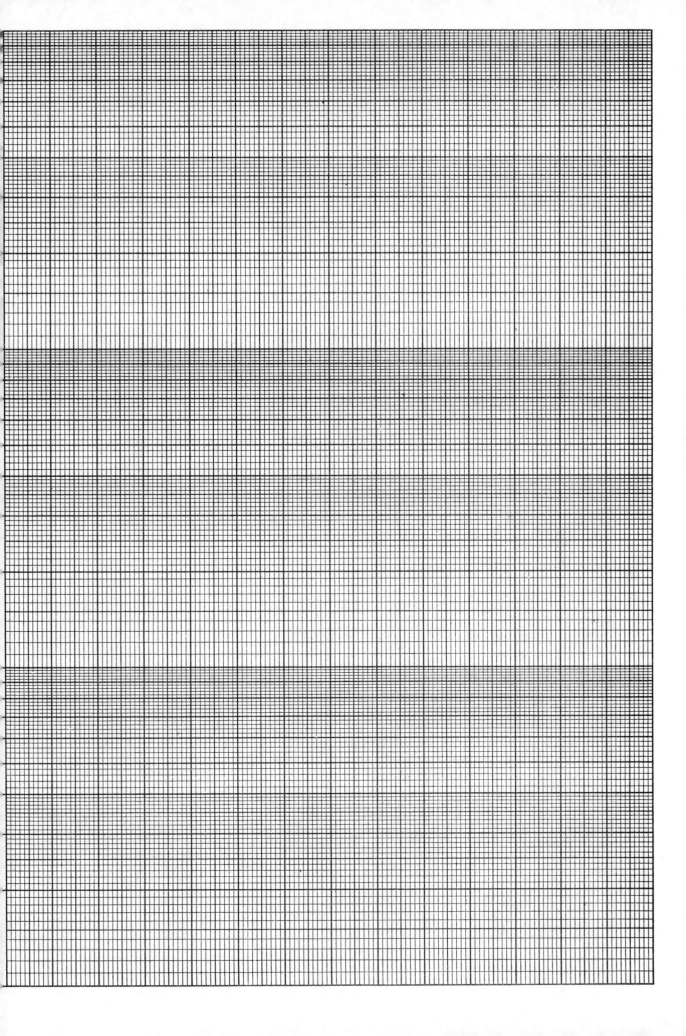

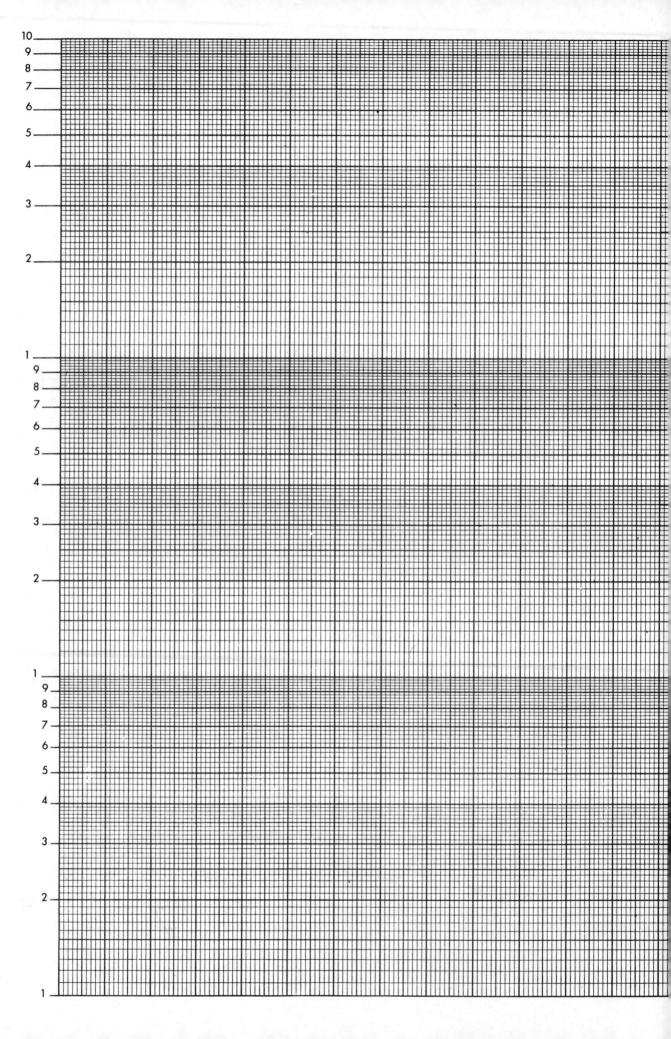

9 This graph shows the amount of each color of light emitted by different types of screens when they are exposed to x rays. Most of the light emitted by the fluorescent screen is of what color?
  a. red
  b. green
  c. blue
  d. ultraviolet

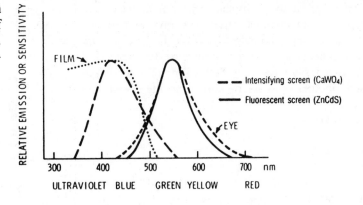

10 This graph shows how increasing exposure to radiation results in shorter periods of time before death occurs. Which type of death occurs at the same time following a large dose range?
  a. nonlethal
  b. hematologic
  c. gastrointestinal
  d. central nervous system

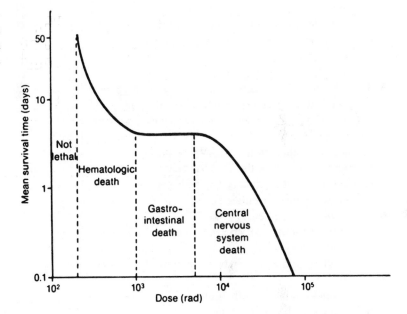

11 This graph shows the relationship between the amount of exposure received by two films and the resulting optical densities. At log relative exposures of less than 1.5, which film will have higher optical density (be darker)?
  a. film A
  b. film B
  c. they are equal
  d. not enough information on graph

12 This graph shows the relationship between the amount of exposure received by two films and the resulting optical densities. In the "straight line" portion of the two curves, which film is getting dark faster?
  a. film A
  b. film B
  c. they are equal
  d. not enough information on graph

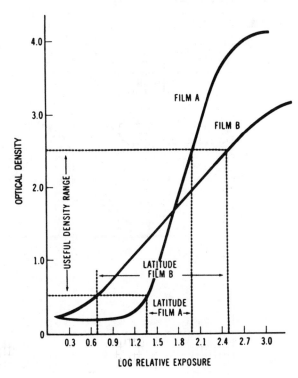

13 The graph at the right shows how frequently two types of interactions between x rays and atoms (Compton and photoelectric) occur in bone and in soft tissue at different x-ray energies. In soft tissue, at what x-ray energy are both Compton interaction and photoelectric interaction occurring about the same?
   a. 10 keV
   b. 20 keV
   c. 60 keV
   d. 90 keV

14 In soft tissue, at 70 keV
   a. photoelectric interaction is more prevalent than Compton.
   b. photoelectric interaction is equal to Compton.
   c. Compton interaction is more prevalent than photoelectric.
   d. Compton interactions no longer occur.

15 The graph below shows how many x rays are produced at each energy when two different peak energies (kVp's) are used. X rays having 70 keV of energy are
   a. more prevalent in the 72 kVp beam.
   b. more prevalent in the 82 kVp beam.
   c. occurring about equally for both beams.
   d. not occurring for either beam.

16 The average x-ray energy (keV)
   a. is higher for the 82 kVp beam than for the 72 kVp beam.
   b. is higher for the 72 kVp beam than for the 82 kVp beam.
   c. is about equal for both beams.
   d. changes with energy range.

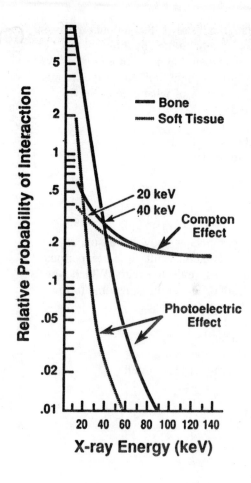

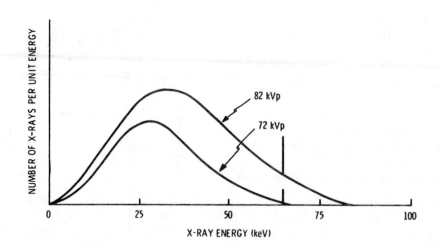

Name _____

Date _____

Fundamentals of Physics

UNITS OF MEASUREMENT

For many years three principal systems of units have been in use in science and engineering. They are most familiarly known as the CGS system (centimeters, grams, and seconds), the MKS system (meters, kilograms, and seconds), and the British system (feet, pounds, and seconds). These three systems of units are often a considerable source of confusion. The base unit quantities employed in each of these systems are the same: length, mass, and time. From these three base quantities are derived many other quantities affecting all the various areas of science and technology.

The International System of Units (SI) has been adopted by nearly all of the technologic societies of the world. It is an expanded version of the MKS system incorporating seven **base units** as its foundation rather than three base units. The base units are then employed to develop so-called **derived units,** some of which are identified by **special names.** The radiologic units are examples of such specially named derived units.

It is important that the units associated with various quantities be properly handled in computations. Two rules must be followed:

1. The same system of units must always be used when working problems or reporting answers:

EXAMPLE:
Incorrect: $3.2 \text{ ft} \times 4.5 \text{ m} \times 0.21 \text{ cm} =$
Correct: $0.98 \text{ m} \times 4.5 \text{ m} \times 0.021 \text{ m} = 0.093 \text{ m}^3$

2. Units should be handled arithmetically in the same way as numbers:

EXAMPLE:
$(3.2 \text{ m/s}^2)(0.5 \text{ s})(11.6 \text{ kg/m}^3)(1.9 \text{ m}^2) =$
$(3.2)(0.5)(11.6)(1.9) \left(\dfrac{\text{m}}{\text{s}^2} \cdot \text{s} \cdot \dfrac{\text{kg}}{\text{m}^3} \cdot \text{m}^2 \right) =$

$(35.3)(\text{kg/s})$

The following tables summarize SI units:

SI BASE UNITS

Quantity	Name	Symbol
Length	meter	m
Mass	kilogram	kg
Time	second	s
Electric current	ampere	A
Thermodynamic temperature	kelvin	K
Amount of substance	mole	mol
Luminous intensity	candela	cd

SI DERIVED UNITS EXPRESSED IN TERMS OF BASE UNITS

Quantity	Name	Symbol
Area	square meter	m^2
Volume	cubic meter	m^3
Speed, velocity	meter per second	m/s
Acceleration	meter per square second	m/s^2
Mass density	kilogram per cubic meter	kg/m^3
Concentration	mole per cubic meter	mol/m^3
Specific volume	cubic meter per kilogram	m^3/kg
Luminance	candela per square meter	cd/m^2

SI DERIVED UNITS WITH SPECIAL NAMES

Quantity	Name	Symbol	Expression in terms of base units
Frequency	hertz	Hz	1/s
Force	newton	N	mkg/s^2
Energy, work	joule	J	m^2kg/s^2
Power	watt	W	m^2kg/s^3
Electric charge	coulomb	C	As
Electric potential	volt	V	m^2kg/s^3A
Capacitance	farad	F	A^2s/kgm^2
Electric resistance	ohm	ω	kg^2/s^3A^2

EXERCISES

1 Which of the following is **not** a base quantity in the SI?
   a. mass
   c. exposure
   b. temperature
   d. electric current

2 Which of the following is a base unit in the SI?
   a. coulomb
   c. kilogram
   b. coulomb/kilogram
   d. gray

3 Which of the following standards of measure is correct?
   a. The meter is related to the visible emission from the sun.
   b. The meter is the length of an engraved platinum-iridium bar.
   c. The second is based on the rotation of the earth around the sun.
   d. The second is based on the vibrations of cesium atoms.

4 Water has a mass density of 1 g/cm^3. Its density can also be expressed as
   a. 1 kg/m^3.
   c. 10^3 kg/m^3.
   b. 10 kg/m^3.
   d. 10^{-3} mg/cm^3.

5 SI stands for
   a. Le Systeme International d'Unites.
   b. incorrect system.
   c. Le Systeme Institutional.
   d. inconsistent system.

6 Which of the following is **not** a system of units?
   a. SI
   c. French
   b. CGS
   d. British

7 Which of the following is an SI name for a base unit?
   a. second
   c. Celsius
   b. newton
   d. milliampere

8 Which of the following is a unit of energy?
   a. rad
   c. gray
   b. erg
   d. newton

9 Which of the following is expressed in the proper units?
   a. exposure: C/kg
   c. dose equivalent: rad
   b. absorbed dose: Sv
   d. activity: rem

10 Which of the following is an SI derived unit?
   a. dyne
   c. horsepower
   b. joule
   d. roentgen

11 Which of the following has units of S^{-1}?
   a. time
   c. dose
   b. frequency
   d. exposure

12 The International Bureau of Weights and Measures is located in
   a. Washington, D.C.
   c. Berlin.
   b. London.
   d. Paris.

13 The one unit of measure that is the same for all systems is the
   a. meter.
   c. second.
   b. kilogram.
   d. pound.

14 The kilogram represents the
   a. mass of 1 lb of water.
   b. temperature rise of 1 lb of water.
   c. energy required to raise 1 lb of water 1°C.
   d. mass of 1000 cm^3 of water.

15 Which of the following employs units of measurement appropriately?
   a. C/kg × kg =
   c. m/s × 1/in =
   b. C/kg × lb =
   d. in × ft × m =

Compute the following:

16 What units result from the following calculation?

m	kgm	s^3	A
s^2	s^2	m^2kg	sA

17 What units result when a coulomb is divided by a second?

18 What common radiologic unit results from the following?

$$\frac{millicoulomb}{second} \times second =$$

19 One dyne is equal to 1 gcm/s^2. How many dynes are in a newton?

20 Compute the number of ergs in a joule (1 erg = 1 gcm^2/s^2).

Name _____

Date _____

Fundamentals of Physics

MECHANICS I

The relationships among mass, weight, and force are governed by Sir Isaac Newton's three laws of motion:

First law: When there is no force acting on an object, it will continue in its present state of motion or rest.

Second law: The force required to change the state of motion of an object is directly proportional to the product of the mass of the object and the acceleration.

Third law: For every force there is an equal but opposite force (reaction).

Mass. Mass is the property of matter that tends to keep a stationary object at rest or that resists a change in the motion of an object already moving (Newton's first law). The unit of mass is the kilogram (kg). The symbol for mass is m. A body with $m = 17.5$ kg measured on the earth would have the same value if measured on the moon or in outer space. The mass of an object **does not** change with location.

Force. Force is simply a push or a pull. Newton's second law, which expresses the concept of force, is his greatest and can be represented by the equation:

$$F = ma$$

Force (newtons [N]) = Mass (kg) × Acceleration (m/s^2)

Note that weight is considered a force and is expressed in newtons. A 70 kg vehicle pushed along a frictionless surface with an acceleration of 4 m/s^2 is being pushed by a force of 280 N. Why?

Weight. The weight of an object is actually the force of gravitational attraction on its mass. In mathematical terms:

$$W = mg$$

Weight (N) = Mass (kg) × Acceleration (m/s^2)

Force and therefore also the newton is the international metric unit of weight, and 1 N is equal to about

4 oz (112 g). The acceleration caused by gravity on the earth is approximately 9.8 m/s^2 (i.e., $g = 9.8$ m/s^2). The weight of an object **does** depend on its location. An object with a mass of 10 kg would weigh 98 N on the earth at sea level but would weigh only about 16 N on the moon. This is because the moon's gravitational field is only one sixth as strong as that of the earth.

Velocity. Velocity is the property of constant motion possessed by moving objects. If the velocity increases, then the object experiences acceleration. We commonly identify velocity as speed and generally express it in units of miles per hour (mph) or kilometers per hour (km/hr). The unit of velocity in the SI system is meters per second (m/s). The unit of acceleration is m/s^2.

EXERCISES

1 Which of the following is **not** correctly stated as an equation of mechanics?
  a. Velocity is equal to distance divided by time.
  b. Force is equal to mass times acceleration.
  c. Momentum is equal to mass times velocity.
  d. Acceleration is equal to the initial velocity plus the final velocity divided by two.

2 Which of the following correctly states Newton's first law of motion?
  a. An object with mass (m) and acceleration (a) is acted on by a force given by $F = ma$.
  b. For every action there is an opposite and equal reaction.
  c. The total momentum before any interaction is equal to the total momentum after the interaction.
  d. An object at rest will remain at rest unless acted on by an external force.

3 Another name for velocity is
  a. mass.   c. time.
  b. speed.   d. distance/time.

4 When you travel 50 mph, you are also doing about
  a. 80 km/hr.   c. 2200 ft/min.
  b. 100 km/hr.   d. 1100 ft/min.

5 Acceleration is also
  a. a time squared.
  b. a rate of change of velocity with time.
  c. a rate of change of time with velocity.
  d. a rate of change of velocity with distance.

6 Which of the following units could be used to express velocity?
  a. m/yr   c. both of the above
  b. nm/ns   d. neither a nor b

7 An automobile travels 30 miles in 30 minutes. Its average velocity is approximately
  a. 88 mpm.   c. 33 mpm.
  b. 60 mpm.   d. 1 mpm.

8 The final speed of a dragster in a quarter mile is 80 mph. The average velocity is
  a. 40 mpht   c. 16 mpht
  b. 32 mpht   d. 8 mpht

9 A dragster requires 8 seconds to reach a speed of 80 mph. What is it's acceleration?
  a. 40 m/hr².   c. 10 m/hr².
  b. 16 m/hr².   d. 8 m/hr².

10 Inertia is
  a. velocity times time.
  b. resistance to a change of motion.
  c. velocity divided by time.
  d. related to Newton's second law of motion.

11 Which of the following statements refers to a vector quantity?
  a. The car was speeding north at 80 mph.
  b. The standard man weighs 70 kg.
  c. The standard man has a mass of 70 kg.
  d. The speed of light is 3×10^8 m/s.

12 A Nolan Ryan fast ball was clocked at 90 mph. How long did it take to travel the 90 feet to the plate?
  a. 1.0 s   c. less than 1 s
  b. 1.5 s   d. more than 2 s

13 How many fundamental laws of motion did Newton formulate?
  a. 1   c. 3
  b. 2   d. 4

14 Should one fall off the edge of the south rim of the Grand Canyon, the force exerted would be measured in
  a. pounds.   c. newtons.
  b. kilograms.   d. m/s.

15 If the acceleration caused by gravity is 9.8 m/s², what is the gravitational force acting on a 50 kg sack pushed off the roof of a 50-story building?
  a. 5.1 N   c. 0.2 N
  b. 490 N   d. 40.2 N

Compute the following:

16 A self-propelled, portable x-ray unit can travel the length of a 90 ft (27 m) corridor in 15 s. Express its average velocity in ft/s and km/hr.

17 An automobile is traveling at a velocity of 60 km/hr. It accelerates uniformly to a velocity of 100 km/hr. What was its average velocity during acceleration?

18 If the time required in problem 17 to speed up from 60 to 100 km/hr was 8 min, what was the rate of acceleration?

19 The mass of an x-ray tube is 2 kg. What is its weight in newtons?

20 What would the same tube weigh on the moon ($g = 1.63$ m/s²)?

21 A force of 60 N and a force of 20 N act on the same object. What is the maximum total force they can exert? What is the minimum force?

22 What force is required to move a 68.4 kg portable x-ray machine with a constant acceleration of 2.31 m/s² along a frictionless surface?

23 Assume in problem 22 that the friction between the machine and the floor produces a 12.6 N force that opposes the motion. What force would be necessary to maintain the 2.31 m/s² acceleration?

24 Any object dropped near the surface of the earth falls with an acceleration of 9.8 m/s². What is its velocity after 2 s if it is released from rest? What is it after 6 s (velocity has units of m/s)?

25 What is the mass of a 4410-N tomographic unit?

26 How may neutrons are in one pound? What is your weight in newtons?

27 If you lift a 5 kg transformer with a force of 60 N, what is the acceleration?

28 What is the acceleration of a rocket ship with a mass of 6.1×10^6 kg that develops a takeoff thrust of 48.1×10^8 N?

29 On the planet Krypton a 7.79×10^3 kg object is found to weigh 4.38×10^4 N. What is the acceleration of gravity on this planet?

Name _____

Date _____

Fundamentals of Physics

MECHANICS II
....

Work. If one exerts a **force** (a push or pull) on a box and moves it across the floor, one does **work** on the box. Following is the formula for work:

$$W = Fd$$

The unit of work is the **joule** (J) if the force is measured in newtons and the distance in meters (1 J = 1 N × 1 m).

Energy. A system capable of doing work is said to have energy. Energy is the ability to do work, and it can take many forms—for example, heat energy, electric energy, nuclear energy, or mechanical energy. Mechanical energy may be potential or kinetic:

1. Potential energy (PE)—energy of an object as a result of its **position.** A brick raised over your head or a coiled spring has potential energy.

2. Kinetic energy (KE)—energy of an object as a result of its motion.

$$KE = 1/2\ mv^2$$

The basic unit of energy is the **joule.** Other units are also used:

1 electron volt (eV) = 1.6×10^{-19} J
1 erg = 10^{-7} J
1 British thermal unit (BTU) = 1.06 J
1 foot-pound (ft-lb) = 1.36 J
1 kilowatt-hour (kW-hr) = 3.6×10^6 J

Power. Power is the rate of doing work. Following is the formula for power:

$$P = W/t$$

The unit of power is the watt (1 watt = 1 J/s). A commonly used unit of power is the **kilowatt,** which is 1000 watts. Another frequently used unit of power is the **horsepower:**

$$1\ hp = 746\ watts$$

EXERCISES

A man lifts a box onto a platform. Choose one or more of the following to complete exercises 1 to 5.

  a. the force used by the man to lift the box
  b. the time required to lift the box
  c. the size of the box
  d. the distance the box is lifted
  e. the velocity of the box
  f. the mass of the box

1 The **work** done depends on ___D, A___
2 The man's **power** output depends on ___A, B, D, E, F___
3 The **KE** of the box depends on ___E, F___
4 The **PE** of the box depends on ___D, F___
5 The total **energy** used depends on ___F, D, E___
6 Concerning work,
  a. the units are the same as energy.
  b. work depends on time.
  c. work is performed when a large weight is held motionless.
  d. it can be measured in watts.
7 A one bedroom apartment might use 1000 kW-hr of electricity. The kilowatt-hour is a unit of
  a. power.   **c.** potential energy.
  b. energy.   **d.** heat.
8 KE is
  a. directly proportional to velocity.
  b. directly proportional to acceleration.
  c. directly proportional to mass.
  d. a vector quantity.
9 Which of the following is the freezing temperature of water?
  a. 0° F   **c.** 0° K
  b. 0° C   **d.** −273° K
10 Which of the following is the primary method of heat dissipation from the anode of an x-ray tube?
  a. heat conduction
  b. power reduction
  c. heat convection
  d. thermal radiation

11 Which of the following statements regarding energy is true?
  a. Energy is the rate of doing work.
  b. Energy is the ability to do work.
  c. Power is a form of energy.
  d. X rays can be described by their potential energy.

12 How much work is done in lifting a 1 kg box of film from the floor to a shelf 2 m high? (HINT: 1 kg = 2.2 lb = 4.5 N)
  a. 1 J   **c.** 4.5 J
  b. 2.2 J   **d.** 20 N

13 A car with a 300-hp engine is very fast. The power of the engine is equivalent to how many kilowatts?
  a. 0.4   **c.** 300
  b. 224   **d.** 2.5

14 Heat is transferred from a glass-enclosed fireplace primarily by
  a. conduction.   **c.** radiation.
  b. convection.   **d.** temperature.

15 A 1° change is equal in thermal energy for which two temperature scales?
  a. Celsius and Fahrenheit
  b. Celsius and Kelvin
  c. Fahrenheit and Kelvin
  d. none of the above

16 The newton is to SI as the _____ is to British.
  a. kilogram   **c.** foot-pound
  b. gram   **d.** pound

Match the following:

17 energy _____
18 power _____
19 work _____
20 force _____
21 KE _____

  a. the product of force and distance
  b. ability to do work
  c. energy of motion
  d. push or pull
  e. rate of doing work

Compute the following:

22 Which of the following has more energy?
  a. a 4.5 kg javelin hurled with a velocity of 58 m/s
  b. a 92.5 kg ape in a tree 8.0 m from the ground

23 If it takes a force of 20 N to push a box a distance of 12 m, which has more energy? What is the difference in energy?

24 If the time required in problem 22 is 6 s, what is the power required?

25 What is the horsepower required?

26 A radiologic technologist exerts a force of 70 N on a heavy portable x-ray machine and pushes it 40 m in 100 s. What is the work done?

27 What is the power used by the technologist in problem 25?

28 The x-ray machine of problem 25 is converted to motor power. The motor exerts a force of 250 N and pushes the cart 40 m in 20 s. What is the work done by the motor?

29 What is the horsepower of the motor in problem 27?

30 What is the KE of a 5600 lb (2546 kg) truck traveling at 60 km/hr? HINT: Change velocity to m/s.

31 The KE of a 20 kg portable x-ray unit is 1000 J. What is the velocity?

32 A dietary calorie is equivalent to about 4186 J of energy. If a cola beverage contains 125 calories, how many joules of energy do you consume when you drink one?

33 If a person uses 3500 calories of food per day in metabolism, how much energy in joules is used? What is the metabolic rate (or power) in watts?

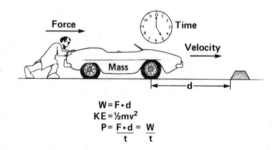

$$W = F \cdot d$$
$$KE = \tfrac{1}{2}mv^2$$
$$P = \frac{F \cdot d}{t} = \frac{W}{t}$$

Name _____

Date _____

The Atom

The periodic table is a systematic grouping of the elements on the basis of similar chemical properties. These groupings result from the fact that certain characteristic properties recur at regular intervals when the elements are arranged in order of increasing atomic numbers.

The vertical columns are called **groups.** The horizontal rows are **periods.** Hydrogen is unique and does not belong to any group. The alkali metals form group I; the halogens form group VII; the inert gases fall into group VIII.

As you proceed from left to right in a period, the number of easily removable or **valence** electrons increases by 1 from one group to the next. Group I metals have one electron that is easily removed, group II metals have two, group III have three, and so on. Group VIII elements hold on tightly to all their electrons and therefore do not readily enter into reactions.

DON'T THEY KNOW A THINKING CAP WHEN THEY SEE ONE?

EXERCISES

1 Which of the following atoms **does not** exist in the history of the theory of the atom?
a. the Greek atom
b. the Dalton atom
c. the Mendeleev atom
d. the Thomson atom

2 In the rendering of the atom by J. J. Thomson,
a. eyes and hooks represented electrons.
b. he called it the cathode ray atom.
c. electrons were concentrated outside the nucleus.
d. uniform positive electrification was theorized.

3 The periodic table presents the elements on the basis of
a. atomic number.   **c.** natural occurrence.
b. number of isotopes.   **d.** atomic charge.

4 There are approximately _____ known elements.
a. 50   **c.** 150
b. 100   **d.** 200

5 The only element that is not placed in any group of the periodic table is
a. helium.   **c.** tungsten.
b. hydrogen.   **d.** uranium.

6 The horizontal rows in the periodic table are called
a. molecules.   **c.** periods.
b. groups.   **d.** compounds.

7 As you move from left to right across the periodic table, the number of outer-shell electrons _____ from one element to the next.
a. decreases by 2   **c.** increases by 1
b. decreases by 1   **d.** increases by 2

8 Which group in the periodic table contains elements having only one electron in the outer shell?
a. holgens   **c.** alkali metals
b. rare earths   **d.** actinide metals

9 Which of the following is a transitional element?
a. carbon dioxide   **c.** cobalt
b. xenon   **d.** barium

10 Atoms with all electron shells filled are
   a. radioactive.
   b. chemically very reactive.
   c. usually found in group I of the periodic table.
   d. chemically stable.
11 Atoms with three electrons in the outer shell are
   a. probably radioactive.
   b. probably inert gases.
   c. considered to have three valence electrons.
   d. compounds.
12 In the periodic table of the elements, the group number identifies the
   a. maximum number of electrons allowable in the outer shell.
   b. principal quantum number of the outermost shell.
   c. total number of electrons in the atom.
   d. valence state of the atom.
13 The period number in the periodic table of the elements is
   a. the maximum number of electrons allowable in the outer shell.
   b. the principal quantum number of the outermost shell.
   c. the number of electrons existing in the outer shell.
   d. the total number of electrons in the atom.
14 All of the following are elements except
   a. oxygen.   c. steel.
   b. carbon.   d. tungsten.
15 How many atoms are there in one molecule of sodium bicarbonate ($NaHCO_3$)?
   a. one   c. four
   b. three   d. six
16 How many elements form a molecule of sodium bicarbonate ($NaHCO_3$)?
   a. one   c. four
   b. three   d. six
17 Which of the following statements is true?
   a. An atomic nucleus has a diameter of approximately 10^{-10} m.
   b. The wavelength of a 100 keV x ray is approximately 10^{-8} m.
   c. A football field is approximately 10^3 m long.
   d. In 1 year light can travel approximately 10^{17} m.
18 Which statement is true?
   a. Atoms combine to form elements.
   b. Molecules combine to form chemical compounds.
   c. An element is a collection of similar molecules.
   d. A molecule is a collection of similar elements.

19 What significant contribution to science was made by Rutherford?
   a. the periodic table of the elements
   b. the description of the nuclear atom
   c. the discovery of artificial radioactivity
   d. the discovery of negatively charged electrons
20 Which of the following is true?
   a. The nucleus is held together by the electrostatic proton-proton attraction.
   b. The atom is mostly empty space.
   c. The number of electrons surrounding the nucleus equals the number of neutrons.
   d. The number of electrons surrounding the nucleus equals the number of protons plus the number of neutrons.
21 Which of the following is true?
   a. Atoms having the same atomic number are atoms of the same element.
   b. Atoms having the same atomic mass interact the same way chemically.
   c. Electrons are more tightly bound in little atoms than in big atoms.
   d. M-shell electrons are more tightly bound than L-shell electrons.
22 In any atom the maximum number of electrons having a principal quantum number of three is
   a. 8.   c. 18.
   b. 16.   d. 32.
23 Who is responsible for our present model of the atom?
   a. Niels Bohr   c. John Dalton
   b. Albert Einstein d. J. J. Thomson
24 The earth is approximately 10^7 m in diameter and the solar system approximately 10^{12}. How many orders of magnitude difference are there?
   a. 5   c. 12
   b. 7   d. 19
25 Which of the following is **not** a major elemental constituent of the body?
   a. oxygen   c. hydrogen
   b. iodine   d. nitrogen
26 Which of the following is **not** an essence of matter as viewed by the ancient Greeks?
   a. air   c. hot
   b. water   d. fire
27 The periodic chart of the elements is attributed to
   a. J. J. Thomson.
   b. Niels Bohr.
   c. John Dalton.
   d. Dimitri Mendeleev.

WORSHEET 13

The Atom

FUNDAMENTAL PARTICLES
....

ATOMIC STRUCTURE
....

The "building blocks" of matter are atoms. All atoms are composed of fundamental particles called **protons, neutrons,** and **electrons.** The positively charged protons and uncharged neutrons make up the **nucleus,** or dense core, of the atom. The negatively charged electrons can be visualized as circling the nucleus in definite orbits, just as the planets orbit the sun.

The atom is held together by the electric charges of its constituent particles. The charge on the proton is $+1.6 \times 10^{-19}$ C. The electron's charge is equal but of the opposite polarity: -1.6×10^{-19} coulombs.

The electron is the lightest of the fundamental particles. The mass of the proton is 1836 times the mass of the electron. The neutron mass is 1839 times larger than that of the electron.

As atoms become larger and more complex, the nucleus will contain more protons and neutrons. The closer electrons are to the nucleus, the more tightly bound they are. The number of electrons in any shell increases to a maximum of $2n^2$, where n is the shell number. No matter how large the atom becomes, however, it will normally have the same number of electrons as protons. This must be the case if the atom is to remain electrically neutral; if this is not the case, the atom is called an **ion.**

EXERCISES

1 Which of the following electrons is farthest from the nucleus?
  a. a K-shell electron **c.** an M-shell electron
  b. a P-shell electron **d.** an L-shell electron
2 When oxygen ($^{16}_8$O) combines with two atoms of hydrogen ($^1_1$H) to form water, the resulting molecule has
  a. a total of 10 nucleons.
  b. a total of 18 protons.
  c. a total of 10 electrons.
  d. a total of 18 electrons.
3 The atomic mass number of an atom is given by the
  a. number of protons.
  b. number of neutrons.
  c. number of electrons.
  d. number of protons plus neutrons.
4 The atomic number
  a. has the symbol A.
  b. is the number of neutrons.
  c. is the number of protons.
  d. is the number of protons plus neutrons.
5 Isotopes are
  a. atoms of the same element.
  b. atoms containing the same number of neutrons plus protons.
  c. atoms that are not ions.
  d. atoms with the same number of nucleons.

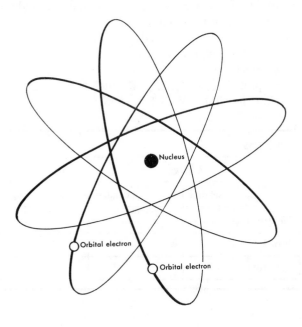

6 Electrons in the M shell will
  a. probably be closer to the nucleus than those in the L shell.
  b. have lower binding energy than those in the N shell.
  c. never exceed 8 in number.
  d. not exist in an atom of carbon ($^{12}_{6}$C).

7 $^{12}_{6}$C and $^{14}_{6}$C have
  a. the same number of nucleons.
  b. the same A number.
  c. the same number of protons.
  d. the same number of neutrons.

8 The binding energy of an electron to a nucleus
  a. increases in value with increasing distance from the nucleus.
  b. is higher for an L shell than for an M shell.
  c. is higher for the K shell of a low Z atom than for the K shell of a high Z atom.
  d. is higher for an N shell than for an M shell.

9 How many nucleons does $^{131}_{53}$I have?
  a. 53   **c.** 131
  b. 78   **d.** 184

10 The number of neutrons in an atomic nucleus is referred to as
  a. atomic charge.   **c.** atomic mass.
  b. atomic number.   **d.** none of the above.

11 A neutron has
  a. a mass of approximately 1 atomic mass unit (amu) and a charge of +1.
  b. a mass of approximately 1/1837 amu and no charge.
  c. a mass of approximately 1 amu and no charge.
  d. a mass of approximately 4 amu and a charge of +2.

12 How many different nucleons are there?
  a. one   **c.** three
  b. two   **d.** four

13 Which of the following is **not** a fundamental particle?
  a. electron   **c.** neutron
  b. alpha particle   **d.** proton

14 What is the maximum number of electrons allowed in the outermost shell of an atom in the third period?
  a. 8   **c.** 32
  b. 18   **d.** 50

15 Tungsten ($^{184}_{74}$W) has how many neutrons?
  a. 74   **c.** 184
  b. 110   **d.** 258

16 What is the maximum number of electrons permitted in the N shell?
  a. 8   **c.** 32
  b. 18   **d.** 50

17 Concerning atomic mass and atomic mass numbers,
  a. atomic mass number is a whole number.
  b. atomic mass is the number of protons.
  c. atomic mass is the number of protons minus neutrons.
  d. atomic mass is the number of neutrons.

18 Which two of the fundamental particles have approximately the same mass?
  a. electron and proton   **c.** neutron and x ray
  b. proton and neutron   **d.** neutron and electron

19 When comparing iodine (Z = 53) with barium (Z = 56),
  a. iodine has more electrons.
  b. iodine K electrons have higher E_b than barium K electrons.
  c. barium L electrons have higher E_b than iodine L electrons.
  d. they are both in the same group of the periodic table.

20 Which of the following has a negative charge?
  a. neutron   **c.** electron
  b. proton   **d.** x ray

21 Tungsten (Z = 74) and lead (Z = 82) are both used in radiology. Which statement is true?
  a. Both will have at least four filled electron shells.
  b. Both have outer electron shells filled.
  c. Tungsten has more electrons than lead.
  d. Tungsten has more protons than lead.

Compute the following:

22 The following atoms are all stable. Rank them in order of increasing K-shell electron binding energy (one for the lowest energy, two . . .).
  a. _____ $^{32}_{16}$S (sulfur)   **c.** _____ $^{88}_{38}$Sr (strontium)
  b. _____ $^{202}_{80}$Hg (mercury)   **d.** _____ $^{27}_{13}$Al (aluminum)

23 A neutral atom has 74 electrons orbiting the nucleus. How many protons are in the nucleus?

24 Water is composed of two atoms of $^{1}_{1}$H and one atom of $^{16}_{8}$O. How many protons are in one molecule of water? How may neutrons?

25 $^{129}_{53}$I is a stable, electrically neutral atom. How many of each of the following are there in such an atom?
  a. electrons _____   **c.** neutrons _____
  b. protons _____   **d.** nucleons _____

26 Complete Table W13-1.

TABLE W13-1

	Charge		Mass		
	Relative	C	Relative	amu	kg
Neutrons					
Protons					
Electrons			1		

WORSHEET 14

The Atom

ATOMIC NOMENCLATURE
....
RADIOACTIVITY
....

Certain atoms, both naturally occurring and artificially produced, emit radiation spontaneously. Such atoms are said to be **radioactive.** Radioactivity is the result of instability in the nucleus. There are three types of radiation that come from a radioactive source: **alpha (α) particles, beta (β) particles,** and **gamma (γ) rays.**

Alpha particles are similar to the nucleus of the helium atom and consist of two protons and two neutrons. They have a positive charge and a large mass but very low penetrating power. Only large, complex atoms can be alpha emitters.

Beta particles are actually electrons that are emitted from the nucleus with high velocity. Since they are electrons, beta particles have a negative charge, have a small mass, and are moderately penetrating. Most radioactive atoms emit beta particles.

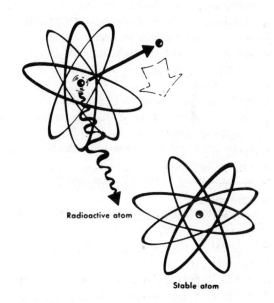

Radioactive atom

Stable atom

Gamma rays are uncharged electromagnetic rays of high energy and high penetrability (much like x rays). They are usually emitted along with alpha and beta particles.

EXERCISES

Match the following:

1 alpha particle _____
2 gamma ray _____
3 beta particle _____
4 radioactivity _____
5 uranium _____
6 radioactive material _____
7 cyclotron _____
8 isotope _____
9 radioisotope _____
10 gold _____

a. a substance composed of atoms with unstable nuclei
b. cannot penetrate a sheet of paper
c. an example of a nonradioactive element that can be made into a radioisotope
d. an example of an element that is naturally radioactive
e. a particle accelerator commonly used to produce artificial radioisotopes
f. any spontaneous emission of energy or particles from unstable nuclei
g. has a charge of -1.602×10^{-19} C
h. usually produced by atomic accelerators from common elements
i. uncharged radiation, highly penetrating
j. atoms with the same number of protons but different numbers of neutrons

11 Which of the following is a radioisotope of barium?
  a. ^{130}Ba **c.** ^{132}Ba
  b. ^{131}Ba **d.** ^{134}Ba

12 When a radionuclide undergoes beta emission,
  a. a gamma ray is always released.
  b. an x ray is always released.
  c. a neutron undergoes conversion to a proton.
  d. a proton undergoes conversion to a neutron.

13 Which of the following atoms are isobars?
  a. ^{129}I and ^{131}I
  b. ^{131}I and ^{198}Hg
  c. ^{2}H and ^{3}H
  d. ^{3}He and ^{3}H

14 Potassium 40 ($^{40}_{19}K$) is a naturally occurring radionuclide that decays by beta emission. Therefore
  a. the daughter nucleus will have 19 protons.
  b. the daughter nucleus will have 19 neutrons.
  c. it has a mass of approximately 20 amu.
  d. the nucleus contains 40 nucleons.

15 Isotopes are
  a. molecules consisting of identical atoms.
  b. atoms having the same atomic number but a different mass number.
  c. atoms having the same mass number but different atomic numbers
  d. atoms having identical mass and atomic numbers.

16 The number of disintegrations per second in 2 mCi of ^{99m}Tc is
  a. 3.7×10^{10}.
  b. 3.7×10^{7}.
  c. 7.4×10^{7}.
  d. 7.4×10^{10}.

17 With regard to the following: $^{90}_{38}Sr^{+2}$,
  a. the symbolism indicates that this is a radioactive nuclide.
  b. there are 90 neutrons in the nucleus of this atom.
  c. the valence is 3.
  d. assuming it is electrically neutral, there is a total of 38 electrons in one such atom.

18 Beta decay
  a. occurs only with light elements.
  b. occurs only with long half-life isotopes.
  c. results in the loss of 1 amu.
  d. results in the gain of a proton.

19 Alpha decay
  a. occurs only with light elements.
  b. occurs only with long half-life isotopes.
  c. results in the loss of 2 amu.
  d. results in the loss of 4 amu.

20 Following radioactive decay through beta emission, the nucleus has
  a. decreased in Z number by 1.
  b. increased in Z number by 1.
  c. decreased in A number by 1.
  d. increased in A number by 1.

21 One curie is equivalent to
  a. 3×10^{10} atoms disintegrating every second.
  b. 3×10^{8} atoms disintegrating every second.
  c. 3.7×10^{8} atoms disintegrating every second.
  d. 2.2×10^{12} atoms disintegrating every minute.

22 Ten microcuries is equivalent to
  a. 3.7×10^{5} Bq.
  b. 10^{-6} Ci.
  c. 3.7×10^{10} atoms disintegrating per second.
  d. 10^{-2} nCi.

23 Which of the following statements is true concerning atoms?
  a. Nucleons are electrons, protons, and neutrons.
  b. An alpha emission contains four units of mass and two units of charge.
  c. $A = Z - N$.
  d. In an atom that has a stable nucleus, the number of protons must equal the number of electrons.

24 Which of the following explains the origin of radionuclides?
  a. They can be naturally occurring.
  b. They can be produced in a nuclear reactor.
  c. They can be produced in a cyclotron.
  d. All of the above are true.

25 Which of the following pairs of atoms are isotones?
  a. $^{1}_{1}H$ and $^{2}_{1}H$ **c.** $^{130}_{53}I$ and $^{131}_{54}Xe$
  b. $^{130}_{56}Ba$ and $^{132}_{56}Ba$ **d.** $^{133}_{54}Xe$ and $^{133}_{55}Cs$

26 Isomers are atoms having
  a. an excess energy state. **c.** different numbers of neutrons.
  b. different numbers of protons. **d.** filled electron shells.

27 Radioisotopes
  a. can be made in an x-ray machine. **c.** are ionized.
  b. have unstable nuclei. **d.** are stable atoms.

28 Which of the following represents decay by alpha emission?
  a. $^{131}_{53}I \rightarrow ^{131}_{54}Xe$ **c.** $^{226}_{88}Ra \rightarrow ^{222}_{86}Rn$
  b. $^{139}_{56}Ba \rightarrow ^{139}_{57}La$ **d.** $^{60}_{28}Ni \rightarrow ^{27}_{54}Co$

29 $^{40}_{19}K$ is a naturally occurring radionuclide deposited in our body tissues.
  a. It contributes to our total radiation exposure.
  b. It can be produced by an x-ray machine.
  c. It can be detected by an x-ray machine.
  d. It has 40 electrons.

30 Complete Table W14-1 with an S if the number is the same and a D if it is different.

TABLE W14-1

	Atomic Number	Atomic Mass Number	Neutron Number
Isomer			
Isotone			
Isobar			
Isotope			

WORSHEET 15

The Atom

RADIOACTIVE HALF-LIFE
·····················

Radioactivity is due to natural or artificially induced instability in the nucleus of an atom. To become stable, the nucleus decays by emitting alpha, beta, or gamma radiation. Some radioactive materials emit more radiation in a given time than others emit. Such sources are said to have different **radioactivities.** The radioactivity of a sample is measured in **curies** or **becquerels.**

$$1 \text{ curie (Ci)} = 3.70 \times 10^{10} \text{ disintegrations/s}$$

$$1 \text{ becquerel (Bq)} = 1 \text{ disintegration/s}$$

The activity of a radioactive sample continually decreases with time. The time required for the activity of a sample to decay to one half its original value is called the **radioactive half-life.** If the half-life of a radionuclide and its present radioactivity are known, its

radioactivity at any other time can be calculated or estimated graphically.

EXERCISES

1 Radioactive half-life is
   a. exactly one half of the quantity of material now present.
   b. the time necessary for one half of the mass to disappear.
   c. the time necessary for one atom to disintegrate.
   d. the time required for the radioactivity to reach one half its original value.

2 How many half-lives must elapse before the remaining activity is less than 0.1% of the original activity?
   a. 4 half-lives   **c.** 8 half-lives
   b. 6 half-lives   **d.** 10 half-lives

3 Given a 50 µCi (0.19 MBq) sample of ^{131}I ($t_{1/2} = 8$ days), the radioactivity will be approximately 3 µCi after how many days?
   a. 24   **c.** 40
   b. 32   **d.** 48

4 A 10 mCi quantity of technetium ^{99m}Tc ($t_{1/2} = 6$ hr) is available at 8:00 AM. At 12:00 noon that same day, the radioactivity will be closer to
   a. 5 mCi than 8 mCi. **c.** 1 mCi than 3 mCi.
   b. 3 mCi than 5 mCi. **d.** 10 mCi than 1 mCi.

5 ^{14}C ($t_{1/2} = 5730$ yr) is used for archeologic dating. Approximately how old is a specimen containing 3 nCi/g (110 Bq/g) if the original concentration of activity is known to be 12 nCi/g (444 Bq/g)?
   a. 5730 yr   **c.** 17,000 yr
   b. 11,000 yr   **d.** 22,000 yr

6 100 mCi (3.7 GBq) of an unknown radionuclide has a half-life of 15 days. Therefore
   a. in 1 month only 75 mCi will remain.
   b. in 15 days only 25 mCi will remain.
   c. in 3½ months the activity will be less than 1 mCi.
   d. 400 mCi should have been available 15 days earlier.

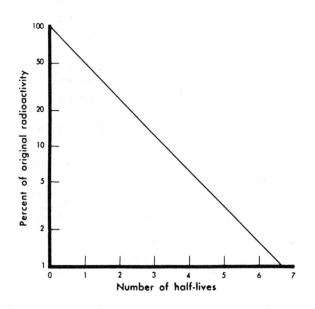

7 How much ^{99m}Tc ($t_{1/2} = 6$ hr) decays in 24 hours?
a. 94%   c. 14%
b. 86%   d. 6%

8 In approximately how many half-lives will the activity of 10 mCi (0.37 GBq) of $^{131}_{53}$I ($t_{1/2} = 8$ d) be reduced to 0.1 mCi (3.7 MBq)?
a. 100   c. 10
b. 12.5   d. 7

9 Which statement is true for a given radionuclide?
a. As the number of atoms decreases, the half-life decreases.
b. The percentage of atoms decaying per unit time is constant.
c. The number of radioactive atoms decreases linearly with time.
d. The half-life increases as the decay constant increases.

10 If the half-life of $^{131}_{53}$I is 8 days, approximately how much $^{131}_{53}$I remains of an original shipment of 50 μCi (1.9 MBq) after 24 days?
a. 50 nCi   c. 6.25 μCi
b. 25 μCi   d. 3.125 μCi

11 10 mCi of ^{99m}Tc is a normal patient dose for imaging. How many becquerels is this?
a. 2.2×10^{11} c. 2.2×10^{8}
b. 3.7×10^{8} d. 3.7×10^{11}

12 ^{123}I has a half-life of 13 hours. If 150 μCi (5.7 MBq) are available at 12 noon on Wednesday, approximately how much will remain at 5 PM on Friday?
a. 10 μCi   c. 20 μCi
b. 15 μCi   d. 30 μCi

13 An unknown radioisotope is assayed to be 40 μCi (15 MBq) at 12 noon on Monday. An assay at 12 AM on Tuesday results in 2.5 μCi (0.1 MBq). What is its half-life?
a. 24 hr   c. 6 hr
b. 12 hr   d. 3 hr

14 Use the graph on the previous page and estimate the percent of activity remaining after 2½ half-lives.
a. 50%   c. 5%
b. 16%   d. 2½%

15 The shape of the radioactive decay curve is
a. a straight line on semilog paper.
b. a straight line on linear paper.
c. a concave-up curve on semilog paper.
d. a concave-down curve on linear paper.

Compute the following:

16 ^{99m}Tc ($t_{1/2} = 6$ hr) is used daily in a number of nuclear medicine procedures. If 200 mCi is present at 8 AM,
a. how many curies is this?
b. how many atoms disintegrating per second is this?
c. how much ^{99m}Tc will remain at 8 AM on the following morning?
d. when was there 800 mCi?

17 ^{133}Xe ($t_{1/2} = 5$ d) is useful in ventilation and perfusion studies. The usual patient dose is 5 mCi (0.19 GBq).
a. How many microcuries is this?
b. If 80 mCi is available, how long will it take to decay to 5 mCi?
c. How many half-lives will elapse in 2 mo (60 days)?
d. How long will it be before less than 1 μCi remains?

18 ^{198}Au (gold) is used for interstitial radiotherapy. It has a half-life of 2.7 days. If 100 mCi is available initially, how much will remain after 13.5 days?

19 ^{67}Ga (gallium), a tumor-localization agent, has a half-life of 78 hr. If 10 mCi (0.37 GBq) is present on Monday at 8 AM, approximately how much will remain on Wednesday at 8 AM? How much will remain the following Monday at 8 AM?

20 250 μCi (9.3 MBq) of ^{75}Se-methionine ($t_{1/2} = 120$ d) is used for a pancreas scan. If 300 μCi (11 MBq) is present, in approximately how many days will this quantity have decayed to 250 μCi?

WORKSHEET 16

The Atom

TYPES OF IONIZING RADIATION
....

Ionizing radiation is any kind of radiation capable of removing an orbital electron from an atom with which it interacts. There are two types of ionizing radiation:
1. Particulate
   a. Alpha particles
   b. Beta particles
   c. Other nuclear particles
2. Electromagnetic
   a. X rays
   b. Gamma rays

Of all ionizing radiation, only beta radiation, x radiation, and gamma radiation are particularly useful in medicine. Alpha and other nuclear particles do not have sufficient range in matter and are relatively difficult to obtain and control. Beta particles are used for radio-therapy and in vitro analysis in the practice of nuclear medicine. Gamma rays are used extensively for in vivo imaging.

X rays, of course, are fundamental to diagnostic radiology. Beta particles and gamma rays are obtained from radionuclides, whereas x rays are produced by a specially designed electrical apparatus.

EXERCISES

1 Specific ionization is
   a. ionization associated with alpha particles.
   b. ionization associated with all particulate radiation.
   c. the range of any ionizing radiation.
   d. the number of ion pairs produced per centimeter of air.

2 In air
   a. an x ray will not normally travel farther than 1 m.
   b. a gamma ray will not normally travel farther than 10 m.
   c. beta particles have a range of 1 to 10 mm.
   d. alpha particles have a range of 1 to 10 cm.
3 When a beta particle has transferred all of its kinetic energy by ionization,
   a. an x ray is released.
   b. a gamma ray is released.
   c. the beta particle comes to rest.
   d. it attracts two electrons.
4 The amount of energy acquired when a beta particle is accelerated by a potential difference of 1 V is
   a. 1 J.   c. 1 Ci.
   b. 1 eV.   d. 1 R.
5 Alpha particles
   a. are like hydrogen nuclei.
   b. have $A = 4$.
   c. are useful in nuclear medicine.
   d. contain two electrons.
6 Of the following radiations, the most penetrating should be a
   a. 4.8 MeV alpha particle.
   b. 2.1 MeV beta particle.
   c. 0.01 MeV x ray.
   d. 100 keV gamma ray.
7 The difference between x rays and gamma rays is
   a. gamma rays always have higher energy than x rays.
   b. their origin.
   c. gamma rays travel faster.
   d. x rays produce bremsstrahlung radiation and gamma rays do not.
8 X-ray photons
   a. have no rest mass and are neutral.
   b. have no rest mass and a charge of +2.
   c. have a negative charge and no rest mass.
   d. have 1 amu and are neutral.

9 Given the general characteristics of ionizing radiation,

    a. the range of a beta particle in tissue can extend to a depth of 10 cm.

    b. the range of gamma rays in air normally will not exceed 1 m.

    c. all photons travel in straight lines even in the presence of a magnetic field.

    d. the neutron is a chargeless particle and therefore is considered to be nonionizing radiation.

10 Which of the following are emitted from outside the nucleus?

    a. alpha particles   **c.** x rays

    b. beta rays   **d.** gamma rays

11 Both x and gamma rays

    a. originate in atoms.

    b. are highly penetrating.

    c. travel with the same velocity.

    d. fulfill all of the above.

12 Electromagnetic radiation _____ than particulate radiation.

    a. is generally heavier

    b. has a higher electrostatic charge

    c. is generally more penetrating

    d. is more densely ionizing

13 Comparing electromagnetic radiation with particulate radiation, it is true that

    a. they are both equally penetrating.

    b. they have equal mass.

    c. both interact by ionization and excitation.

    d. particulate radiation exists only at the speed of light.

14 Particulate ionizing radiation

    a. includes ultrasound.

    b. can include any type of subatomic particle.

    c. travels at the speed of light.

    d. has a range in matter greater than that of electromagnetic radiation.

15 Electromagnetic ionizing radiation

    a. includes alpha and beta particles.

    b. has a lower velocity than light.

    c. has a lower velocity than particulate radiation.

    d. comes from both inside and outside the nucleus.

16 X rays and gamma rays are both examples of electromagnetic radiation. In addition, they both

    a. have little mass.

    b. travel with the velocity of ultrasound.

    c. have the same origin.

    d. have no electric charge.

17 Which of the following are examples of ionizing radiation?

    a. fast moving protons

    b. ultrasound

    c. MRI

    d. microwaves

18 Which one of the following forms of radiation is not deflected in a uniform magnetic field?

    a. electrons   **c.** photons

    b. protons   **d.** heavy ions

19 What are the two principal classes of ionizing radiation?

    a. MRI and ultrasound

    b. MRI and electromagnetic

    c. particulate and ultrasound

    d. particulate and electromagnetic

20 Which one of the following is not ionizing radiation?

    a. x rays

    b. neutrons

    c. diagnostic ultrasound

    d. beta particles

21 Beta particles can differ from alpha particles by

    a. mass and charge.

    b. charge and velocity.

    c. velocity and energy.

    d. all of the above.

22 The principal difference between beta particles and electrons is

    a. origin.   **c.** velocity.

    b. energy.   **d.** all of the above.

23 Specific ionization is measured in units of

    a. electron volts.

    b. joules.

    c. ion pairs per centimeter.

    d. electron volts per ion pair.

WORKSHEET 17

Electromagnetic Radiation

THE WAVE EQUATION

Phenomena such as sound and electromagnetic radiation have energy fields that change in a sinusoidal fashion. Such sine waves have three parameters that are related by the mathematical relationship:

$$v = \lambda \, \nu$$

or

$$\text{Velocity} = \text{Wavelength} \times \text{Frequency}$$

This is the **wave equation.** Photons of electromagnetic radiation always travel at the speed of light (3×10^8 m/s). So $v = c$ and, for electromagnetic radiation, $c = \lambda \, \nu$. From this, one can see that for electromagnetic radiation, wavelength and frequency are inversely proportional. The unit of frequency is the hertz (1 Hz = 1 cycle per second).

EXERCISES

1 Photon wavelength is
 a. inversely proportional to photon velocity.
 b. directly proportional to photon frequency.
 c. inversely proportional to photon frequency.
 d. usually designated by c.
2 As the frequency of sound increases,
 a. low bass notes increase.
 b. velocity increases.
 c. its ability to ionize increases.
 d. its wavelength decreases.
3 Which of the following is true for both a 100 keV x ray and a 10 keV gamma ray?
 a. zero frequency   **c.** zero mass
 b. equal negative charge **d.** equal wavelengths
4 A frequency of 1 MHz is
 a. 1 cycle/s.   **c.** 1000 cycles/s.
 b. 100 cycles/s.   **d.** 10^6 cycles/s.

5 If the photon frequency of electromagnetic radiation is increased tenfold, then the
 a. velocity will increase times 10.
 b. velocity will decrease to 1/10.
 c. wavelength will increase times 10.
 d. wavelength will decrease to 1/10.
6 A good stereo system will reproduce sound faithfully from 20 Hz to 20 kHz. This frequency range is said to cover
 a. a factor of 20.   **c.** a factor of 1800.
 b. a factor of 200.   **d.** three orders of magnitude.
7 Which of the following would apply to 1 kHz sound?
 a. Its frequency is 1,000,000 cycles/s.
 b. $\lambda = v/\nu$.
 c. Its amplitude is independent of frequency.
 d. $\nu = c/\lambda$.
8 A single unit of electromagnetic radiation is also called a
 a. proton.   **c.** strange.
 b. photon.   **d.** quark.
9 Light has a constant velocity of $c = 3 \times 10^8$ m/s. Therefore
 a. if its wavelength increases, its frequency will decrease.
 b. its velocity is also 3×10^{12} cm/s.
 c. its velocity is also 3×10^{12} μm/s.
 d. its mass increases with increasing frequency.
10 The frequency of electromagnetic radiation is
 a. directly proportional to the wavelength.
 b. measured in disintegrations per second.
 c. measured in meters per second.
 d. measured in hertz.
11 When one uses the sine wave as a model, the
 a. distance from one peak to the next is the wavelength.
 b. distance from one valley to the next is the frequency.
 c. amplitude and frequency are directly proportional.
 d. amplitude and wavelength are directly proportional.

12 Given the sine wave model of electromagnetic radiation
  a. amplitude and velocity are inversely related.
  b. frequency and velocity are inversely related.
  c. frequency times velocity is a constant.
  d. frequency times equivalent is a constant.

13 Which of the following is **not** a basic characteristic of the wave equation?
  a. velocity   **c.** wavelength
  b. energy   **d.** frequency

14 Which of the following best represents a continuum?
  a. railroad ties   **c.** traffic flow
  b. railroad track   **d.** telephone ring

15 The velocity of light is
  a. 3×10^8 cm/s.   **c.** 3×10^{12} cm/s.
  b. 3×10^{10} cm/s.   **d.** none of the above.

16 The amplitude of a sine wave is its
  a. vertical distance.
  b. frequency.
  c. wavelength.
  d. velocity.

17 The frequency of a sine wave is the
  a. distance from crest to crest.
  b. distance from crest to valley.
  c. number of valleys that pass per second.
  d. number of seconds that pass per crest.

18 The wave equation is best described by
  a. wavelength is equivalent to velocity divided by frequency.
  b. wavelength is the product of velocity and frequency.
  c. velocity is equivalent to wavelength divided by frequency.
  d. none of the above.

19 The velocity of ultrasound in tissue is 1540 m/s. If a 1 MHz transducer is used, what will be the wavelength of the ultrasound?
  a. 1540 m
  b. 1540 mm
  c. 15.4 cm
  d. 1.54 mm

20 A 1 tesla MRI uses radiofrequency radiation of 42 MHz. What is the wavelength of this radiation?
  a. 42 m
  b. 4.2 mm
  c. 7.1 m
  d. 7.1 mm

If the figure below represents a wave traveling at 25 cm/s, compute the following:

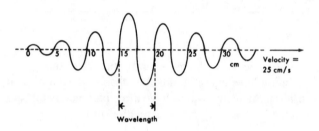

Wavelength

21 How many cycles occur in 1 s (its frequency)?
22 How much time is necessary for two cycles?
23 What is its wavelength?
24 What distance is traveled in 5 s?

Name _____

Date _____

Electromagnetic Radiation

ELECTROMAGNETIC SPECTRUM

The electromagnetic spectrum consists of radiations with frequencies from 10 to 10^{24} Hz. Photons of each of these radiations are similar in that each can be represented as a bundle of energy—a quantum—having sinusoidal electric and magnetic variations and traveling at a constant velocity, the speed of light. Since energy and wavelength are related to frequency, the electromagnetic spectrum can be described by an energy range, 10^{-12} to 10^{10} eV, or a wavelength range, 10^{-16} to 10^6 m.

Sound is not a part of the electromagnetic spectrum.

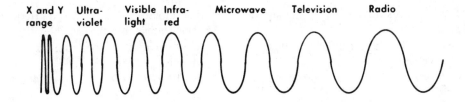

X and Y range   Ultra-violet   Visible light   Infra-red   Microwave   Television   Radio

EXERCISES

1 A photon having energy of approximately 1 eV is most likely
   a. an x ray.   c. a gamma ray.
   b. a radio emission.   d. visible light.

2 On a relative scale, photons of a radio broadcast have
   a. very low energy and very long wavelengths.
   b. very low energy and very short wavelengths.
   c. very high energy and very long wavelengths.
   d. very high energy and very short wavelengths.

3 When white light is refracted through a prism, the following colors are emitted. Which one has the longest wavelength?
   a. yellow light   c. orange light
   b. blue light   d. red light

4 On the long wavelength side of the visible light spectrum are invisible photons that can create a problem in the darkroom. Which of the following are these likely to be?
   a. ultraviolet light   c. laser light
   b. maser light   d. infrared light

5 A principal difference between x rays and gamma rays is their
   a. frequency.
   b. wavelength.
   c. energy.
   d. origin.

6 Radiation emitted from a standard radio broadcast antenna
   a. is sound.
   b. is electromagnetic radiation.
   c. has a higher frequency than gamma rays.
   d. has a higher frequency than microwaves.

7 The energy of a 50 keV gamma-ray photon _____ the energy of a 50 keV x-ray photon.
   a. is greater than   c. is less than
   b. is equal to   d. varies from

8 For any electromagnetic radiation an increase in
   a. velocity results in an increase in energy.
   b. velocity results in an increase in frequency.
   c. frequency results in an increase in energy.
   d. wavelength results in an increase in energy.

9 Electromagnetic radiation
   a. exists at zero velocity.
   b. exists only if its velocity is 3×10^8 m/s.
   c. is usually shown as a square wave.
   d. has mass that increases with increasing velocity.

10 If an x-ray machine is operated at 40 kVp, then
   a. nonionizing x rays are emitted.
   b. zero-energy x rays are emitted.
   c. 20 keV x rays are emitted.
   d. all x rays are emitted at 40 keV.

11 A photon of red light
   a. comes from a nucleus.
   b. has a longer wavelength than a photon of green light.
   c. has the same energy as microwaves.
   d. has a higher frequency than an x ray.

12 Ultraviolet radiation and microwaves have different
   a. energies.   **c.** frequencies.
   b. wavelengths.   **d.** all of the above.

13 Visible light cannot be
   a. absorbed.   **c.** reflected.
   b. refracted.   **d.** weighed.

14 X-ray photons can be
   a. attenuated.   **c.** subdivided.
   b. compacted.   **d.** ionized.

15 The electromagnetic spectrum includes
   a. x rays and radar waves traveling with the speed of light in a vacuum.
   b. radiation described by the formula: wavelength = frequency × velocity.
   c. radiation with physical properties determined by mass.
   d. x rays, gamma rays, electrons, and neutrons that are used in medicine.

16 Which of the following types of radiation would be classified as electromagnetic?
   a. 1000 Hz sound
   b. 30 m radio braodcast
   c. heat from a radiator
   d. beta radiation

17 Which of the following is an example of electromagnetic radiation?
   a. ultraviolet light   **c.** positrons
   b. ultrasound   **d.** alpha rays

18 Examples of electromagnetic radiation would **not** include
   a. light from an exit sign.
   b. 1.5 tesla magnetic field.
   c. phosphorescence from a watch dial.
   d. cellular mobile radio.

19 Which of the following is **not** an example of electromagnetic radiation?
   a. Grenz rays
   b. gamma rays
   c. ultrasonic diathermy
   d. laser radiation

20 The known electromagnetic spectrum extends over a range of approximately
   a. 10^{-12} to 10^2 eV.
   b. 10^2 to 10^{20} eV.
   c. 10^{-7} to 10^{-16} m.
   d. 10 to 10^{24} Hz.

21 Which of the following groups of units of measurement will adequately identify electromagnetic radiation?
   a. m, s, kg   **c.** Hz, eV, kg
   b. m, Hz, eV   **d.** s, kg, Hz

22 The radiofrequency (RF) region of the electromagnetic spectrum is usually identified by
   a. mass.   **c.** charge.
   b. velocity.   **d.** frequency.

23 The range of the visible light region of the electromagnetic spectrum extends from approximately
   a. 10 to 10^2 eV.   **c.** 400 to 700 nm.
   b. 10^2 to 10^3 eV. **d.** 400 to 700 cm.

24 A xeromammogram is conducted at 50 kVp. Which of the following x rays is produced?
   a. 5 keV
   b. 25 keV
   c. 50 keV
   d. all of the above

25 X rays from outside the nucleus are to gamma rays from inside the nucleus as
   a. light is to sound.
   b. electrons are to beta particles.
   c. light is to heat.
   d. mass is to energy.

Electromagnetic Radiation

A widespread belief among early scientists held that light was composed only of waves. This **wave model** satisfactorily explained many of the properties of light. Early in the twentieth century, however, new experimental evidence demonstrated that light sometimes acts like a particle. The experiment that helped to establish this dual nature of light was concerned with the **photoelectric effect.**

To explain the particle-like behavior of light better, a new theory, called the **quantum theory** of light, was developed. According to this theory, light consists of small packets—definite amounts of energy—called photons. A light photon is visualized as a tiny packet of energy traveling through space with a speed of 3.0×10^8 m/s. The energy of each photon is determined by its frequency as expressed in the relationship:

$$E = h\nu$$

where E = energy in joules and $h = 6.63 \times 10^{-34}$ J-s, or where E = energy in electron volts and $h = 4.15 \times 10^{-15}$ eV-s. The symbol ν represents frequency, and h is Planck's constant.

To understand the true nature of photon radiation, both wave and particle concepts must be retained since wavelike properties are exhibited in some experiments and particle-like properties in others.

EXERCISES

1 Which of the following is **not** a characteristic of the wave model of radiation?
   a. reflection   **c.** transmission
   b. refraction   **d.** collision

2 Which of the following most closely represents the term *attenuation?*
   a. partial absorption of x rays
   b. light transmitted through window glass
   c. light reflected from a mirror
   d. light absorbed in black glass

3 Viewing a radiograph, one might properly say that
   a. lung tissue is radiolucent.
   b. bony structures are radiolucent.
   c. soft tissue is radiopaque.
   d. fat is radioreflective.

4 The development of modern quantum theory started with the work of
   a. William Coolidge.   **c.** Neils Bohr.
   b. Max Planck.   **d.** Albert Nobel.

5 According to quantum theory, the energy of an electromagnetic photon is
   a. dependent on its velocity.
   b. directly proportional to its wavelength.
   c. dependent on its origin.
   d. inversely proportional to its wavelength.

6 Planck's constant has a value of 4.15×10^{-15} eV-s. Therefore its value is also
   a. 6.63×10^{-34} J-s.   **c.** 4.15×10^{-34} J-s.
   b. 6.63×10^{-34} erg-s.   **d.** 4.15×10^{-15} J-s.

7 The expression that relates photon energy and wavelength through Planck's constant is
   a. $E = h\nu$.   **c.** $E = hc/\lambda$.
   b. $E = hc$.   **d.** $E = h/c\lambda$.

8 The quantity hc has a value of
   a. 1.24×10^{-7} eV-m.   **c.** 1.99×10^{-7} eV-m.
   b. 1.24×10^{-6} eV-m.   **d.** 1.99×10^{-6} eV-m.

9 Which of the following can be said about visible light?
   a. It sometimes behaves like a wave.
   b. It can travel with any velocity up to 3×10^8 m/s.
   c. Its energy is directly proportional to its wavelength.
   d. The photoelectric effect demonstrates the wave model.

10 Which of the following is true of photons?
  a. "Quantum" means the same as "photon."
  b. A photon of x radiation will have lower frequency than a photon of visible light.
  c. Visible light photons tend to exhibit more particle nature than wave nature.
  d. X-ray photons tend to behave more like waves than particles.

11 Visible light
  a. consists of short-wavelength red radiation and long-wavelength blue radiation.
  b. has higher frequency than ultraviolet light.
  c. has shorter wavelength than microwave photons.
  d. interacts with matter in the same fashion as x rays.

12 Which of the following terms is **not** associated with visible light interaction?
  a. reflection   c. vaporization
  b. absorption   d. transmission

13 Which statement concerning visible light is correct?
  a. If it is transmitted unattenuated, the matter is said to be opaque.
  b. If it is transmitted, but attenuated, the matter is said to be transparent.
  c. If matter attenuates light, it is transparent.
  d. If matter absorbs light, it is opaque.

14 When one takes radiographs of bony structures embedded in soft tissue, the bone
  a. is said to be translucent.
  b. is said to be radiolucent.
  c. is said to be radiopaque.
  d. does not attenuate the x-ray beam.

15 Regarding photon interaction, which of the following statements is true?
  a. Window glass is opaque.
  b. Frosted glass is transparent.
  c. Lead is radiopaque.
  d. Air is transparent and radiopaque.

16 Which electromagnetic radiation is **not** employed for medical imaging?
  a. gamma rays   c. radiofrequency
  b. microwaves   d. visible light

17 When compared with visible light, x rays have greater
  a. mass.   c. wavelength.
  b. velocity.   d. frequency.

18 Which of the following types of electromagnetic radiation interacts with matter like a particle?
  a. microwaves   c. radiofrequencies
  b. gamma rays   d. visible light

19 Visible light should interact most readily at the _____ level.
  a. nucleon   c. molecular
  b. atomic   d. tissue

20 Compared to red light, green light has greater
  a. mass.   c. velocity.
  b. energy.   d. wavelength.

21 Transparent is to transmission as translucent is to
  a. attenuation.   c. absorption.
  b. opaque.   d. reflection.

22 Heat is associated primarily with _____ light.
  a. ultraviolet   c. green
  b. blue   d. infrared

23 A surface painted _____ will reflect the most light.
  a. white   c. green
  b. blue   d. black

24 A surface painted _____ will absorb the most light.
  a. white   c. green
  b. blue   d. black

25 Tissue that absorbs x radiation is called
  a. radiolucent.   c. radiopaque.
  b. radiotransmission. d. radioemission.

Name _____

Date _____

Electromagnetic Radiation

INVERSE SQUARE LAW
....

Radiation intensity decreases rapidly as the distance from the source increases. More specifically, the intensity of radiation is inversely proportional to the square of the distance from the source to the object. This is the **inverse square law,** which may be expressed as follows:

$$\frac{I_1}{I_2} : \frac{d_2^2}{d_1^2} : \left(\frac{d_2}{d_1}\right)^2$$

where I_1 is the intensity at distance d_1 from the source and I_2 is the intensity at distance d_2 from the source.

The rapid decrease in intensity occurs because the total number of photons is distributed over an increasingly large area as the distance from the source is increased. Consequently, the inverse square law is geometric and assumes a point source of radiation. It is independent of absorption and attenuation. A rule of thumb states: **A nonpoint source can be considered a point source at distances from the source exceeding seven times the source size.**

EXERCISES

1 Which of the following is a correct equation for the inverse square law?

a. $I_A = \dfrac{d_B^2 I_B}{d_A^2}$

b. $I_A = I_B \left(\dfrac{d_A}{d_B}\right)$

c. $\dfrac{I_A}{I_B} = \dfrac{d_A^2}{d_B^2}$

d. $\dfrac{d_A}{d_B} = \dfrac{\sqrt{I_A}}{\sqrt{I_B}}$

2 If the exposure rate 1 m from a source is 9 mR/hr (2.3 µC/kg-hr), what will be the exposure rate 3 m from the source?

a. 9 mR/hr
b. 3 mR/hr
c. 1 mR/hr
d. 0.9 mR/hr

3 The inverse square law states that
a. intensity is inversely proportional to the square of the distance.
b. the square of the intensity is inversely proportional to the distance.
c. intensity is directly proportional to the square of the distance.
d. the square of the intensity is directly proportional to the distance.

4 The inverse square law relationship between intensity and distance from a source is a result of
a. attenuation.
b. scatter.
c. absorption.
d. divergence.

5 The inverse square relationship applies to all _____ sources.
a. ultrasound
b. gamma-ray
c. x-ray
d. point

6 Which of the following emissions is likely to obey the inverse square law?
a. visible light from an 8-ft fluorescent bulb
b. infrared radiation from a patient
c. x rays from a portable unit
d. a skylight

7 To apply the inverse square law one must know
a. the frequency or the wavelength of radiation.
b. two distances and one intensity.
c. one distance and one intensity.
d. energy, distance, and intensity.

8 If the distance from a point source is tripled, the intensity will be
a. one third.
b. three times.
c. nine times.
d. one ninth.

9 If an instrument positioned 1 m from a point source is moved 50 cm closer to the source, the radiation intensity will be
a. increased by a factor of 4.
b. increased by a factor of 2.
c. decreased by a factor of 2.
d. decreased by a factor of 4.

10 The distance from the earth to the sun is approximately 150 million km. If the earth were orbiting the sun at 50 million km, the solar intensity on the surface of the earth would be
a. 27 times more intense.
b. 12 times more intense.
c. 9 times more intense.
d. 3 times more intense.

11 A linear source of radium is 15 mm long. Such a source of radiation will obey the inverse square law at which minimum distance from the source?
a. at contact   c. 75 mm
b. 15 mm   d. 105 mm

12 How far from a 4-ft fluorescent bulb must one be before its light obeys the inverse square law?
a. 4 ft   c. 28 ft
b. 20 ft   d. 40 ft

13 A ^{137}Cs source used for instrument calibration has an intensity of 100 mR/hr (25.8 μC/kg-hr) at 20 cm. What would the intensity be 40 cm from the source?
a. 8.25 mR/hr   c. 25 mR/hr
b. 12.5 mR/hr   d. 50 mR/hr

14 The exposure rate from a ^{60}Co source used in radiation therapy is 100 R/min (25.8 mC/kg-min) at 80 cm. What will the exposure rate be 40 cm from the source?
a. 25 R/m   c. 200 R/m
b. 50 R/m   d. 400 R/m

15 A radiographic technique produces a patient dose of 200 mrad (2 mGy) at 80 cm source-to-patient distance. What will be the patient dose at a distance of 160 cm if the technique remains the same?
a. 50 mrad   c. 100 mrad
b. 80 mrad   d. 400 mrad

16 A radiographic technique produces an exposure of 200 mR (52 μC/kg) at a SID of 100 cm. What will the exposure be at 180 cm SID?
a. 31 mR   c. 62 mR
b. 55 mR   d. 111 mR

17 A radiograph produced at a SID of 100 cm results in an exposure of 100 mR (26 μC/kg). What will be the exposure if the SID is reduced to 90 cm?
a. 81 mR
b. 90 mR
c. 111 mR
d. 123 mR

18 The exposure rate 2 ft (61 cm) from a patient during fluoroscopy is 400 mR/hr (0.1 mC/kg-hr). If one assumes that all radiation is scattered from a point within the patient, how far away must a technologist stand to be in a field of only 10 mR/hr (2.6 μC/kg-hr)?
a. 8 ft   c. 40 ft
b. 12.6 ft   d. 80 ft

19 A portable chest unit is to be used for screening and is positioned in the center of a bank lobby. If the exposure at the film plane (SID = 180 cm) is 20 mR (5.2 μC/kg) per view, how far beyond the film plane must the area be controlled to ensure no more than 1 mR (0.26 μC/kg) per view?
a. 360 cm   c. 805 cm
b. 720 cm   d. 36 m

20 A source of ^{99m}Tc produces a radiation intensity of 150 mR/hr (39 μC/kg-hr) at a distance of 10 m. At what distance does the exposure rate equal 1000 mR/hr (2.58 mC/kg-hr)?
a. 3.3 m   c. 5.0 m
b. 3.9 m   d. 6.7 m

Electromagnetic Radiation

_____

X-RAY PHOTONS

....

_____

X rays are one form of electromagnetic radiation. As with other forms of electromagnetic radiation, they may be thought of as an energy disturbance in space. They may also be thought of as bundles of energy called "quanta" or "photons." These x-ray photons travel at the speed of light, have direction, possess no mass or charge, and have electric and magnetic components that vary in a sinusoidal fashion. X rays adhere to the following mathematic relationships:

"We'll start our x-ray examination with your wallet."

$$c = \lambda\nu \qquad E = mc^2$$

$$E = h\nu \qquad \lambda \text{ (nm)} = \frac{1.24}{keV}$$

$$E = \frac{hc}{\lambda}$$

EXERCISES

1 Which of the following type of x rays is **not** associated with radiation therapy?
  a. supervoltage   **c.** superficial
  b. megavoltage   **d.** diffraction

2 Which of the following does **not** apply to an x ray?
  a. reflection   **c.** attenuation
  b. absorption   **d.** penetration

3 Given two x-ray photons, one of 50 keV and the other 70 keV, the 70 keV x ray
  a. most likely came from a nucleus.
  b. will have a longer wavelength.
  c. will have a higher velocity.
  d. will have higher frequency.

4 In the normal representation of an x-ray photon
  a. the mass is indicated by c.
  b. the velocity varies from zero to the speed of light.
  c. the velocity cannot exceed the speed of light.
  d. the wavelength changes from short to long and back to short again.

5 The energy of an x-ray photon is directly proportional to its
  a. wavelength.   **c.** velocity.
  b. frequency.   **d.** velocity squared.

6 In a vacuum, x rays travel with a velocity of
  a. 186,000 km/hr.   **c.** 3×10^{10} m/s.
  b. 186,000 mph.   **d.** 3×10^{10} cm/s.

7 Which of the following will be greater for a 30 keV x ray than for a 60 keV x ray?
  a. wavelength   **c.** mass
  b. frequency   **d.** velocity

8 Which of the following electromagnetic radiations is in the diagnostic x ray region?
  a. 78 eV
  b. 12,000 eV
  c. 65 keV
  d. 36 MeV

9 The photon energy of an x ray of wavelength 10 nm may be obtained most easily from which of the following?
  a. $E = mc^2$
  b. $E = h\nu$
  c. $E = hc/\lambda$
  d. $E = \lambda \nu$

10 When describing x rays it can be said that they
  a. travel in straight lines.
  b. are deflected by a very strong magnet.
  c. can combine with other x rays to form an atom.
  d. have a longer wavelength than radio waves.

11 X-ray photons
  a. are part of the ultrasonic spectrum.
  b. have a higher frequency than visible light.
  c. have the same velocity as ultrasound.
  d. have a longer wavelength than RF.

12 The energy of an x-ray photon
  a. is inversely proportional to its wavelength.
  b. can be computed from its mass.
  c. is a function of Einstein's constant.
  d. increases with increasing wavelength.

13 The model employed to describe an x-ray photon
  a. has an RF field and a visual field.
  b. has an ultrasonic field and a magnetic field.
  c. consists of a sine wave.
  d. consists of a square wave.

14 Planck's constant can have units of
  a. J.
  b. J-eV.
  c. eV-s.
  d. N-s.

15 Which of the following characteristics is true of both x-ray photons and light photons?
  a. Their energy is the same.
  b. Their velocity is the same.
  c. Their wavelength is the same.
  d. Their frequency is the same.

16 Which of the following are used in x-ray therapy of deep-lying tissues?
  a. Grenz rays
  b. superficial x rays
  c. orthovoltage x rays
  d. diagnostic x rays

17 In the model of an x ray
  a. two sine waves are positioned perpendicular to each other.
  b. the amplitude of the sine wave is related to its energy.
  c. the frequency of the sine wave is related to its velocity.
  d. the wavelength of the sine wave is related to its velocity.

18 Diagnostic x rays are
  a. long-wavelength electromagnetic radiation.
  b. high energy electromagnetic radiation.
  c. photons with intermediate mass.
  d. observed with varying velocity.

19 An x ray can also be correctly called a
  a. mass.
  b. quantity.
  c. proton.
  d. photon.

20 Which of the following radiations has energy similar to diagnostic x rays?
  a. Grenz x rays
  b. othovoltage x rays
  c. superficial x rays
  d. megavoltage radiation

21 Which of the following types of x rays have the least energy?
  a. diagnostic
  b. megavoltage
  c. orthovoltage
  d. Grenz

22 In the equation $E = h\nu$ the h
  a. is a variable.
  b. has units of energy.
  c. is called Einstein's constant.
  d. relates photon energy to frequency.

23 The product of hc is equal to
  a. 1.24 keV-nm.
  b. 1.24 eV-mm.
  c. 12.4 keV-nm.
  d. 12.4 eV-m.

24 Longer wavelength x rays have
  a. higher velocity.
  b. lower energy.
  c. higher energy.
  d. higher mass.

25 The numeric value of Planck's constant is 4.15×10^{-15} eV-s. Its value is also
  a. 4.15×10^{-15} J-s.
  b. 4.15×10^{-34} J-s.
  c. 6.62×10^{-34} J-s.
  d. 6.62×10^{-15} J-s.

Electromagnetic Radiation

ENERGY AND MATTER
....

Einstein expressed the equivalence of mass and energy with the following equation:

$$E = mc^2$$

In the equation if E is energy in joules, then c, the speed of light, must be 3×10^8 m/s and m, the mass, must be in kilograms. This relationship indicates that a small mass can be converted into an enormous amount of energy. Such a condition occurs in an atomic bomb. It also implies that energy can be converted into mass. Phrases such as "energy equivalence," "mass equivalence," or "mass energy" are used to express this duality of mass and energy.

EXERCISES

1 Which of the following equations can be used to compute the mass equivalence of an x-ray photon?

a. $E = h\nu$

b. $E = hm$

c. $m = \dfrac{hc}{\lambda}$

d. $m = \dfrac{E}{c^2}$

2 Which of the following equations can be used to compute the mass equivalence of an x-ray photon if its frequency is known?

a. $E = mc^2$

b. $m = \dfrac{hc}{\lambda}$

c. $m = \dfrac{h\nu}{c^2}$

d. $m = \dfrac{h}{\lambda\nu}$

3 In the case of mass-energy conversions,

a. the law of conservation of matter is violated.

b. the law of conservation of energy is violated.

c. nuclear fission is an example of converting energy into mass.

d. nuclear fission is an example of converting mass into energy.

4 In Einstein's relativistic equation, $E = mc^2$,

a. if the mass is in kilograms and the velocity in meters/second, the energy will be measured in joules.

b. if the velocity is 3×10^8 m/s, mass should be in grams.

c. if the velocity is given as 186,000 mi/s, the energy will be in newtons.

d. if the mass is measured in grams, the velocity must be measured in meters/second.

5 When employing Einstein's relativistic equation to compute the energy equivalence of matter, it is usual to express such energy in

a. newtons.

b. coulombs.

c. joules.

d. electron volts.

6 Energy can be

a. created but not destroyed.

b. transformed into matter.

c. destroyed but not created.

d. expressed in newtons.

7 A photon with energy of 1.0 MeV is equivalent to approximately

a. 1.8×10^{-27} kg.

b. 1.8×10^{-29} kg.

c. 1.8×10^{-31} kg.

d. 1.8×10^{-33} kg.

8 The energy equivalence of an electron at rest is 511 keV. It is also

a. 511 eV.

b. 511 MeV.

c. 0.51 eV.

d. 0.51 MeV.

9 When comparing various types of radiation, the mass equivalence of

a. microwaves is greater than x rays.

b. blue light is greater than red light.

c. an FM broadcast is greater than ultraviolet light.

d. a television broadcast is greater than red light.

10 If the entire mass of an electron ($m = 9.1 \times 10^{-31}$ kg) could be converted into an x ray, its energy would be

a. 4.15×10^{-15} eV-s.

b. 4.15×10^{-15} keV-s.

c. 511,000 eV.

d. 511 eV.

11 One amu equals 1.66×10^{-27} kg. Its energy equivalence is
   a. 1.5 mJ
   b. 1.5×10^{-10} J
   c. 1.5 kJ
   d. 1.5×10^{-7} J

12 What is the mass equivalence of a 35 keV x ray?
   a. 6.3×10^{-31} kg
   b. 6.3×10^{-32} kg
   c. 6.3×10^{-33} kg
   d. 6.3×10^{-34} kg

13 The SI unit for energy is the
   a. electron volt.
   b. erg.
   c. joule.
   d. newton.

14 The energy of a 70 keV x ray could also be expressed as
   a. 1.1×10^{-10} J.
   b. 1.1×10^{-12} J.
   c. 1.1×10^{-14} J.
   d. 1.1×10^{-16} J.

15 The equivalence of mass and energy is described by
   a. Planck's theory.
   b. Einstein's theory.
   c. Newton's laws.
   d. Joule's laws.

WORKSHEET 23

Electricity and Magnetism

Electrostatics is the study of fixed electric charges—either positive or negative. A charged object has either an excess of electrons (negative charge) or a deficiency of electrons (positive charge). A fundamental law of electrostatics is **opposite charges attract and like charges repel.** The magnitude of the attraction or repulsion is given by **Coulomb's law.**

$$F = k \frac{Q_a Q_b}{d^2}$$

where F is the force in newtons (attractive or repulsive), Q_a and Q_b are electrostatic charges in coulombs, d is separation distance in meters, and k is a proportionality constant ($k = 9.0 \times 10^9$ N-m^2/C^2).

EXERCISES

1 The principal reservoir for the deposit of excess electric charge is
   a. the atmosphere.   **c.** the earth.
   b. clouds.   **d.** water pipes.

2 Regarding the movement of an electric charge from one atom to another atom,
   a. both positive and negative charges can move.
   b. usually outer-shell electrons move.
   c. usually inner-shell electrons move.
   d. only positive charges are transferred.

3 Coulomb's law states that electrostatic force is
   a. inversely proportional to the square of the distance between charges.
   b. directly proportional to the square of the distance between charges.
   c. inversely proportional to the product of charges.
   d. directly proportional to the square of the product of charges.

4 Which of the following objects should be the easiest to electrify?
   a. a cloud   **c.** a tree
   b. the earth   **d.** a doorknob

5 Which of the following is a method of electrification?
   a. diffraction   **c.** transmission
   b. excitation   **d.** induction

6 Electrification is the addition of
   a. an electric charge to an object.
   b. protons and neutrons.
   c. photons to an atom.
   d. protons to an atom.

7 Electric energy can be converted into
   a. mechanical energy by a battery.
   b. electromagnetic energy by a battery.
   c. chemical energy by an x-ray machine.
   d. thermal energy by a lamp.

8 Electrostatics
   a. governs the movement of electric charges in a conductor.
   b. is the study of photon radiation.
   c. concerns resting electric charges.
   d. concerns the mass-energy conversion of electrons.

9 Static electricity
   a. is the basis for transformer operation.
   b. can result in magnetism.
   c. is the study of electric currents.
   d. can make one's hair stand on end.

10 The principal electrostatic law states that
   a. a proton will repel a neutron.
   b. a neutron will repel a neutron.
   c. an electron will repel a neutron.
   d. an electron will repel an electron.

11 Objects become electrified because of
   a. the transfer of electrons.
   b. the transfer of protons.
   c. an excess of protons.
   d. an excess of neutrons.

12 The phenomenon of lightning occurs when
  a. adjacent clouds have positive electrification.
  b. adjacent clouds have negative electrification.
  c. adjacent clouds are electrically neutral.
  d. one cloud is positively electrified and an adjacent one is negatively electrified.

13 Which of the following would be included in the four most basic electrostatic laws?
  a. Einstein's law
  b. Planck's law
  c. electric-charge concentration
  d. Archimedes' principle

14 An electrostatic force is created when a
  a. proton approaches a proton.
  b. proton approaches a neutron.
  c. neutron approaches an electron.
  d. neutron approaches a neutron.

15 The magnitude of the electrostatic force is
  a. proportional to distance squared.
  b. inversely proportional to distance squared.
  c. inversely proportional to the square of the charges.
  d. proportional to the square of the charges.

16 Electrostatic force can be measured in units of
  a. joules.   **c.** rads.
  b. coulombs.   **d.** newtons.

17 Which of the following are unaffected by charged matter?
  a. electrons   **c.** photons
  b. protons   **d.** beta particles

18 An electrified object
  a. consists of electric charges throughout.
  b. has electric charges on its surface.
  c. has no loose electric charges.
  d. will have an excess of protons.

19 How many electrons are contained in one half of a microcoulomb?
  a. 3.2×10^6 **c.** 6.3×10^{12}
  b. 3.2×10^{12} **d.** 6.3×10^{18}

20 When a solid object such as a copper wire becomes electrified
  a. excess electrons will be uniformly distributed throughout the wire.
  b. a kink in the wire will have higher surface electrification.
  c. the distribution of protons on its surface will be uniform.
  d. the negative charges will concentrate on the surface and positive charges will concentrate throughout the interior.

21 Electrostatic charge is measured in
  a. amperes.   **c.** coulombs.
  b. volts.   **d.** newtons.

22 Electric potential is measured in
  a. amperes.   **c.** coulombs.
  b. volts.   **d.** newtons.

23 Two positive 0.5 C charges are positioned 1.0 m apart. The force acting between them is
  a. attractive.   **c.** neutral.
  b. repulsive.   **d.** variable.

24 A radiographic tube is operated at the 500 mA station. How many electrons per second is this?
  a. 3.2×10^9 **c.** 3.2×10^{18}
  b. 6.3×10^9 **d.** 6.3×10^{18}

25 How many total electrons will pass from cathode to anode of an x-ray tube if the technique is 100 mA, 100 ms?
  a. 6.3×10^{16} **c.** 6.3×10^{12}
  b. 6.3×10^{15} **d.** 6.3×10^9

Name _____

Date _____

Electricity and Magnetism

Ohm's law states that the voltage across the total circuit or any individual circuit element is equal to the electric current times the resistance of the circuit or circuit element. This is expressed in the equation:

$$V = IR$$

or

$$I = V/R$$

or

$$R = V/I$$

where V is the electric potential in volts, I is the electric current in amperes, and R is the electric resistance in ohms (Ω).

There are various types of circuit elements, such as resistors, capacitors, transformers, and meters, each of which can be characterized by its resistance. These circuit elements are connected in series circuits, parallel circuits, or compound circuits—a combination of series and parallel.

Series

Total resistance: $R_T = R_1 + R_2 + R_3 + \ldots$
Total current: $I_T = I_1 = I_2 = I_3 = \ldots$
Total voltage: $V_T = V_1 + V_2 + V_3 + \ldots$

Parallel

Total resistance: $\dfrac{1}{R_T} = \dfrac{1}{R_1} + \dfrac{1}{R_2} + \dfrac{1}{R} + \ldots$
Total current: $I_T = I_1 + I_2 + I_3 + \ldots$
Total voltage: $V_T = V_1 = V_2 = V_3 = \ldots$

EXERCISES

1 Which of the following would you suspect to be the best electric insulator?
  a. copper   **c.** water
  b. aluminum   **d.** wood

2 Which of the following would you expect to be the best electric conductor?
  a. copper   **c.** water
  b. aluminum   **d.** wood

3 The ratio of the electric potential across a circuit element to the current flowing through it is called
  a. voltage.   **c.** resistance.
  b. current.   **d.** power.

4 The flow of 1 C/s in a conductor is
  a. 1 kVp.   **c.** 1 A.
  b. 1 V.   **d.** 1 Ω.

5 The resistance of wire increases as the diameter of the
  a. wire increases.
  b. wire decreases.
  c. insulator decreases.
  d. insulator increases.

6 In a series circuit
  a. the total current is the sum of the individual currents.
  b. the voltage drop across each circuit element is the same.
  c. the total resistance is the sum of the individual resistances.
  d. only three circuit elements are allowed.

7 When an electric current flows through a wire with resistance (R), energy is
  a. liberated as x rays.
  b. liberated as heat.
  c. absorbed as heat.
  d. absorbed as light.

8 When electrons move in a copper wire
 a. the condition is called electrostatics.
 b. ionization occurs.
 c. a resistance to the electron flow exists.
 d. the condition is called electromagnetic force.

9 The number of volts required to cause a current of 40 A to flow in a circuit having a resistance of 5 Ω is
 a. 5 V.   **c.** 45 V.
 b. 8 V.   **d.** 200 V.

10 Electric potential is measured by
 a. coulombs.   **c.** volts.
 b. joules.   **d.** ohms.

11 Ohm's law states that
 a. electric power is equal to voltage times current.
 b. electric power is equal to current squared times voltage.
 c. electric current is equal to voltage divided by resistance.
 d. the electromotive force is equal to current squared times resistance.

12 In electrodynamics, which of the following is a correct expression?
 a. $I = Qt$ **c.** $R = I^2V$
 b. $V = IR$ **d.** $R = IV$

13 Electric insulators
 a. inhibit movement of electric charge.
 b. permit movement of electric charge.
 c. consist of materials like silicon and germanium.
 d. convert electric energy into heat.

14 Which of the following is normally measured in volts?
 a. electromotive force
 b. electromagnetic force
 c. electrostatic force
 d. electromagnetic radiation

15 One ampere is equal to
 a. 1 V/s.
 b. 1 Ω/s.
 c. 1 C/s.
 d. 1 eV/s.

16 Milliampere-seconds (mAs) is a unit of
 a. electromagnetic force.
 b. voltage.
 c. current.
 d. charge.

Match the following circuit elements with their appropriate symbols:
17 resistor _____
18 switch _____
19 transformer _____
20 capacitor _____
21 battery _____

a.
b.
c.
d.
e.

Match the following descriptions of circuit elements with their appropriate symbol:
22 inhibits the flow of electrons _____
23 allows electrons to flow in only one direction _____
24 increases or decreases voltage _____
25 measures electric current _____
26 momentarily stores electric charge _____

a.
b.

c.
d.
e.

With reference to the following circuit,

```
              12 ohms        20 ohms
   0————wwwww————wwwww—————————┐
                                │
220 V         4 ohms        20 ohms
   0————wwwww————wwwww————————————┘
```

27 It has the characteristics of a
 a. parallel circuit.
 b. series circuit.
 c. complex circuit.
 d. powerful circuit.

Calculate:
28 total circuit resistance
29 voltage across the 20 Ω resistor
30 total circuit current

Electricity and Magnetism

ALTERNATING CURRENT AND DIRECT CURRENT
....
ELECTRIC POWER
....

Direct current (DC), usually provided by storage batteries, flows around a circuit in one direction only. Another kind of current that changes direction regularly with time is called an alternating current (AC). It is the current supplied by power companies in the United States, and it has a 60 Hz sinusoidally varying waveform, that is, a 60 Hz frequency.

Electric power is measured in watts (W). Three important equations for calculating electric power follow:

$$P = VI$$
Power (W) = Voltage (V) × Current (A)

and

$$P = I^2R$$
Power (W) = (Current [A])^2 × Resistance (ohms)

and

$$E = Pt$$
Electric energy (J) = Power (w) × time(s)

EXERCISES

Exercises 1 to 6 refer to the following figure:

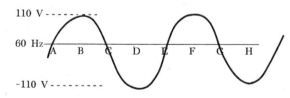

1 The length of time that will elapse between A and E is
  a. ½ s.   **c.** 1/60 s.
  b. 1/30 s.   **d.** 1/120 s.

2 One full cycle extends from
  a. A to C.   **c.** B to F.
  b. C to E.   **d.** D to F.

3 If one considers the voltage waveform from E to G as a positive voltage pulse, how many such pulses would occur each second?
  a. 15   **c.** 60
  b. 30   **d.** 120

4 Given this waveform,
  a. the voltage at C is 60 Hz.
  b. the voltage at D is 60 Hz.
  c. the voltage at E is +110 V.
  d. the voltage at E is zero.

5 When one considers the segment of the figure from A to B compared with that from B to C, then
  a. electrons are speeding up in A to B and slowing down in B to C.
  b. the electromotive force is higher at A than C.
  c. electrons are flowing in opposite directions.
  d. electrons are flowing faster in A to B than in B to C.

6 When one compares the segment from A to C with that from C to E, then
  a. electrons are flowing more slowly between C and E.
  b. electrons have more potential between A and C.
  c. the electromotive force is higher at B than at D.
  d. electrons are flowing in opposite directions at B and at D.

7 The distinct difference between alternating current (AC) and direct current (DC) is that DC cannot attain the high
  a. magnitude of voltage.
  b. magnitude of current that AC can.
  c. electrical resistance that AC can.
  d. electron flow direction.

8 Electricity is purchased on the basis of the number of kilowatt hours one consumes. The unit **kilowatt hours** can also be expressed in
  a. joules.   **c.** volts.
  b. watts per ampere.   **d.** amperes per second.

9 If a 50 W light bulb is operated at 100 V, the current flowing through the bulb is
   a. 0.5 A.   c. 50 A.
   b. 2 A.   d. 5000 A.
10 An x-ray machine is said to have a 30 kW generator. If the maximum tube voltage is 150 kV, what will be the available tube current?
   a. 2 A   c. 5 A
   b. 200 mA   d. 500 mA
11 If a sine curve is employed to represent conventional AC, then
   a. the time from the positive peak to the next negative peak is 1/120 of a second.
   b. the amplitude of the curve is directly related to wavelength.
   c. during the negative half-cycle, there is no electron flow.
   d. the time from zero to maximum amplitude is one cycle.
12 When electricity exists as AC,
   a. electrons flow randomly in both directions.
   b. electrons flow in one direction in alternating bursts.
   c. the velocity of electron flow is proportional to the EMF.
   d. the velocity of electron flow is proportional to the current.
13 During an AC of 1 A,
   a. electrons never come to rest.
   b. the velocity of electron flow is proportional to the current.
   c. in 1 s the net electron flow will be one electron.
   d. twice as many electrons flow compared to an AC of 500 mA.
14 Electric power is measured in
   a. joules.   c. watts.
   b. hertz.   d. newtons.
15 Which of the following equations can be used to calculate electric power consumption?
   a. $P = RI$ c. $P = I^2V$
   b. $P = IV$ d. $P = VR$
16 A hair blower is rated at 1000 W. What current will it consume on normal household voltage?
   a. 9 A   c. 100 A
   b. 10 A   d. 1000 A

17 A fluoroscope is operated at 95 kVp, 2 mA. What is its power consumption?
   a. 47.5 W   c. 190 W
   b. 47.5 kW   d. 190 kW
18 What power is required for a radiographic exposure at 76 kVp, 500 mA?
   a. 19W   c. 19 kW
   b. 38W   d. 38 kW
19 A 110 V heater requires 15A. What is the power consumption?
   a. 15 W   c. 1650 W
   b. 110 W   d. 1800 W
20 How much current will a 60 W light bulb draw from a 120 V receptacle?
   a. 60 mA   c. 1 A
   b. 500 mA   d. 15 A
21 Electric current waveforms are
   a. graphs of current v. time.
   b. graphs of voltage v. resistance.
   c. graphs of voltage v. current.
   d. discontinuous.
22 Electric current flow is in the positive direction, usually to the right, when the waveform is
   a. above zero.
   b. at zero.
   c. below zero.
   d. changing from above to below zero.
23 Theoretically, conduction electrons come to rest momentarily:
   a. at the peak of the waveform.
   b. at the valley of the waveform.
   c. just before either a peak or a valley.
   d. at zero crossing.
24 In the United States normal household current is
   a. 60 V, 110 Hz.
   b. 110 V, 60 Hz.
   c. 50 V, 120 Hz.
   d. 120 V, 50 Hz.
25 Electric ranges, air conditioners, and furnaces require 220 V AC. Therefore, compared with most household appliances, they also require
   a. more semiconductivity.
   b. more conductivity.
   c. a higher electromotive force.
   d. a lower electromotive force.

Electricity and Magnetism

MAGNETISM
....

Most matter is unaffected by magnetic fields and is therefore called nonmagnetic. Strongly magnetized material is called **ferromagnetic,** whereas weakly magnetized material is **paramagnetic.** The molecular theory of magnetism explains the magnetic phenomenon as the result of certain types of atoms or molecules aligning to form **dipoles**—two poles, north and south.

Imaginary lines of the magnetic field exist in the air surrounding a magnet, and these lines are strengthened and consolidated by the presence of ferromagnetic material. This property is called **magnetic permeability** and is used in the transformer.

EXERCISES

1 Which of the following is a physical property that we cannot sense?
   a. mass   **c.** electric current
   b. acceleration   **d.** magnetism

2 Which of the following is capable of creating a magnetic field?
   a. an x ray   **c.** a neutron at rest
   b. a quantum of visible **d.** a proton in motion
        light

3 An example of a magnetic domain is
   a. the earth.   **c.** an atom of iron.
   b. a permanent magnet.   **d.** an electromagnet.

4 If a bar magnet were suspended in space and another bar of nonmagnetic material were brought close to it, what would happen?
   a. Nothing would happen.
   b. The imaginary magnetic field lines would be deviated.
   c. The bar magnet would become demagnetized.
   d. The bar magnet would rotate.

5 If two bar magnets, suspended in space, were brought together, what would happen?
   a. Nothing would happen.
   b. One would rotate.
   c. The north poles would both point in the same direction.
   d. The north pole of one would point to the south pole of the other.

6 A lodestone is an example of
   a. a permanent magnet.
   b. demagnetized matter.
   c. a magnetic domain.
   d. an electromagnet.

7 Alnico is used in
   a. a particular type of electromagnet.
   b. demagnetization.
   c. an artificial permanent magnet.
   d. creating a magnet with only a north pole.

8 Which of the following would likely be classified as ferromagnetic material?
   a. iron   **c.** air
   b. lead   **d.** glass

9 If two magnets are brought together, north to north poles will _____ , whereas north to south poles will _____ .
   a. attract, repel
   b. attract, attract
   c. repel, attract
   d. repel, repel

10 Most magnets
   a. are naturally occurring if used in science and technology.
   b. are affected by another magnetic field.
   c. have north, south, and neutral poles.
   d. have positive, negative, and neutral poles.

11 Most magnetic materials
   a. are radioactive.
   b. are in the shape of a horseshoe.
   c. retain their magnetic property when broken.
   d. are attracted to copper.

12 A navigational compass
   a. is usually made of glass.
   b. has a north pole that will be attracted to the magnetic north pole of the earth.
   c. has a north pole that will be attracted to the equator.
   d. has both a north and a south pole.

13 Which of the following are classifications of magnetism?
   a. coulombic
   b. dipoloic
   c. polar magnetism
   d. paramagnetism

14 The earth's magnetic field is strongest
   a. at the equator.
   b. at the poles.
   c. in the atmosphere above the equator.
   d. in deep space.

15 The laws of magnetism
   a. are similar to the laws of relativity.
   b. are directly related to the laws of electromagnetic radiation.
   c. have a similar formulation as Coulomb's law of electrostatics.
   d. are as yet unknown.

16 The force between the poles of two different magnets
   a. is inversely proportional to the strength of each magnet.
   b. obeys a law similar in form to Planck's law.
   c. depends on the permeability of matter separating the magnets.
   d. varies directly with the distance between them.

17 The physical laws of magnetism
   a. require that there be a south pole for every north pole.
   b. require that there be a south pole for every north pole but only for magnets of certain shapes.
   c. specify a force that increases with increasing distance from the magnet.
   d. include the conservation of magnetism.

18 Magnetism has some properties similar to those of electrostatics;
   a. both refer to iron substances.
   b. both can be sensed by touch.
   c. both involve photon-type radiations.
   d. both obey the inverse square law.

19 Magnetism
   a. requires electricity.
   b. is present in some naturally occurring ores.
   c. is defined as a property that can attract glass, wood, or metal.
   d. depends on monopolar atoms.

20 When a charged particle moves in a straight line, a magnetic field is
   a. erased.
   b. induced perpendicular to the particle motion.
   c. induced along the direction of particle motion.
   d. induced having the same sign as the particle.

21 When iron is fabricated into a magnet, magnetic domains
   a. align.
   b. disappear.
   c. cancel.
   d. magnify.

22 Which of the following has an associated magnetic field?
   a. a neutron
   b. a hydrogen nucleus
   c. a hydrogen molecule
   d. none of the above

23 When iron is brought near a permanent magnet, the lines of the magnetic field are
   a. attracted to the magnet.
   b. repelled by the magnet.
   c. attracted to the iron.
   d. repelled by the iron.

24 Which of the following is **not** a principal classification of magnets?
   a. naturally occurring
   b. electro-
   c. superconducting
   d. artificially induced permanent

25 The physical laws of magnetism are similar to the laws of
   a. the unified field theory.
   b. relativity.
   c. conservation.
   d. gravity.

WORKSHEET 27

Electromagnetism

ELECTROMAGNETIC EFFECT
....
ELECTROMAGNETIC INDUCTION
....

Electromagnetism is magnetism produced with an electric current. A current-carrying coil of wire, called a **solenoid,** will create a weak magnetic field. If an iron core is inserted into the solenoid, the magnetic field is many times more intense because the magnetic permeability of iron is greater than that of air. Such a device is called an **electromagnet.** Electromagnets are used in some x-ray machines as **relays** or **contactors** for switching.

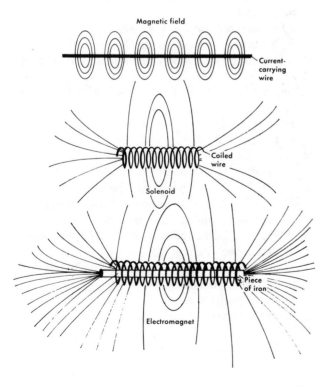

EXERCISES

1 An electron moving in a conductor will
   a. produce light in the conductor.
   b. produce a magnetic field in the conductor.
   c. produce a magnetic field in a plane perpendicular to the conductor.
   d. cause the conductor to behave as a bar magnet.
2 The voltaic pile
   a. was invented by Faraday.
   b. is a modern dry cell battery.
   c. consists of zinc and copper plates sandwiched together.
   d. consists of a magnet and a conductor.
3 EMF
   a. stands for electrical-mechanical force.
   b. is expressed in units of volts.
   c. is expressed in units of joules per kilogram.
   d. was invented by Hans Oersted.
4 The experimental link connecting electric and magnetic forces was discovered by
   a. Oersted.   **c.** Lenz.
   b. Faraday.   **d.** Volta.
5 The device designed to measure electron flow in a conductor is known as a (an)
   a. solenoid.   **c.** ammeter.
   b. electromagnet.   **d.** choke coil.
6 An electric current will flow if the conductor is in a changing magnetic field. This
   a. is known as Faraday's law.
   b. is the statement of the second law of electromagnetics.
   c. was discovered by Lenz.
   d. was discovered by Volta.
7 The term *electromagnetic induction* refers to the production of
   a. electromagnetic radiation.
   b. a magnetic field.
   c. an electric current.
   d. a static charge.

8 The principal difference between self-induction and mutual induction is that
  a. mutual induction is the basis for an electric motor and self-induction is the basis for a transformer.
  b. self-induction requires two coils and mutual induction requires only one.
  c. mutual induction requires two coils and self-induction requires only one.
  d. there is no difference.
9 The magnetic field produced by an electromagnet
  a. has only a north pole
  b. has only a south pole.
  c. has neither a north nor a south pole.
  d. is similar to that produced by a bar magnet.
10 Several electromagnetic laws govern the induction of an electric current by a magnetic field. One states that
  a. an electric current will be induced in a circuit if some part of that circuit is in a magnetic field.
  b. there are two basic types of induction, primary and secondary.
  c. the induced current flows in the opposite direction of the inducing action.
  d. the right-hand rule is used to determine the direction of the induced current.
11 A battery
  a. converts chemical energy into mechanical energy.
  b. is a source of electric resistance.
  c. is a source of electromotive force.
  d. is based on the magnetic property of similar metals.
12 The magnetic field produced
  a. by a solenoid is more intense than that produced by an electromagnet.
  b. in a transformer is based on mutual induction.
  c. in an electromagnet is most intense in the plane perpendicular to its axis.
  d. by an AC source is constant.
13 An electromagnet
  a. produces a magnetic field with or without an electric current.
  b. is a coil of wire wound around an imaginary air core.
  c. produces a monopolar magnetic field.
  d. has a back EMF.
14 Given a closed loop of wire with no electron flow, an electric current can be induced if
  a. no magnetic field is present.
  b. a constant magnetic field is present.
  c. a changing magnetic field is present.
  d. the loop is opened.

15 When an AC source is connected to a coil,
  a. an induced EMF will be generated that opposes the source.
  b. electromagnetic radiation will be produced.
  c. mutual induction occurs.
  d. a front EMF will be produced.
16 If two coils are positioned near each other and a varying source of EMF is passed through the first coil,
  a. electromagnetic radiation will be produced.
  b. self-induction will occur in the second coil.
  c. mutual induction will occur in the second coil.
  d. such an arrangement is a solenoid.
17 Which of the following is an electromechanical device?
  a. solenoid   c. generator
  b. battery   d. transformer
18 Which of the following scientists is **not** associated with the early development of electromagnetism?
  a. Volta   c. Lenz
  b. Planck   d. Faraday
19 A modern dry cell battery is a source of
  a. volts per ohm.   c. coulombs per joule.
  b. ohms per volt.   d. joules per coulomb.
20 When applying the right-hand rule the thumb indicates the direction of the
  a. magnetic field.   c. electric current.
  b. electric field.   d. electromotive force.
21 The principal difference between a solenoid and an electromagnet is magnetic field
  a. polarity.   c. homogeniety.
  b. variability.   d. intensity.
22 Which of the following is based on electromagnetic induction?
  a. radio reception   c. solenoid
  b. battery   d. DC current
23 Which of the following is the symbol for a battery?

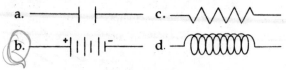

24 A coil of wire will
  a. conduct AC relatively unimpeded.
  b. conduct DC relatively unimpeded.
  c. experience mutual induction from a battery.
  d. experience mutual induction from DC.
25 When an electric current is induced by mutual induction such current flows
  a. according to Oersted's law.
  b. according to Lenz's law.
  c. in the primary coil.
  d. in the secondary coil.

Electromagnetism

ELECTRIC GENERATORS AND MOTORS
....

Electric generators and motors are electromechanical devices. The former converts mechanical energy to electric energy. The latter converts electric energy to mechanical energy.

Both devices require a precisely fashioned magnetic field in order to operate. Electric generators use the mechanical power of water as in a hydroelectric dam or of the atom as in a nuclear power plant to drive turbine blades. The motion of the turbine rotates a coil of wire through a fixed magnetic field inducing an electric current.

Electric motors operate by passing an electric current through a loop of wire while in the presence of a magnetic field. The interaction between the electric current and the fixed magnetic field causes the loop to rotate, thus producing mechanical energy. One type of electric motor, the induction motor, is employed in all rotating anode x-ray tubes.

EXERCISES

1 Which of the following is most important to electromechanical devices?
   a. Lenz's first law of electromagnetics
   b. Oersted's experiment on mutual induction
   c. the voltaic pile
   d. Faraday's experiment
2 In an electric generator,
   a. AC is changed to DC.
   b. a coil of wire is rotated in a magnetic field.
   c. chemical energy is converted to electrical energy.
   d. electrical energy is converted to mechanical energy.

3 In an electric motor,
   a. AC is changed to DC.
   b. a coil of wire is mechanically rotated.
   c. a commutator ring is unnecessary.
   d. electric current is supplied to a coil of wire.
4 Which of the following is **not** required for a DC electric motor?
   a. a magnet   **c.** a commutator ring
   b. an ammeter   **d.** a source of EMF
5 Which of the following statements concerning generators and motors is true?
   a. They convert energy from one form into another.
   b. They have both primary and secondary windings.
   c. They are electromagnets.
   d. They require direct electric contact between primary and secondary.
6 The electric generator is most closely associated with _____ experiments.
   a. Volta's   **c.** Faraday's
   b. Oersted's   **d.** Lenz's
7 The electric motor is most closely associated with _____ experiments.
   a. Volta's   **c.** Faraday's
   b. Oersted's   **d.** Lenz's
8 Which of the following would be classified as electromechanical devices?
   a. transformers and rectifiers
   b. motors and rectifiers
   c. generators and rectifiers
   d. generators and motors
9 Which of the following is **not** required for an electric generator?
   a. a north pole   **c.** magnet
   b. source of EMF   **d.** loop of wire
10 The main difference between an AC and a DC electric generator is the
   a. commutator ring   **c.** magnet.
   b. source of EMF.   **d.** a transformer.

11 Which of the following electric current waveforms is produced by a DC generator?

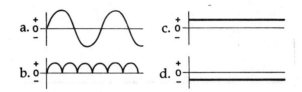

12 The electric current produced by an AC generator has
   a. constant intensity.
   b. pulsating positive intensity.
   c. pulsating negative intensity.
   d. alternating positive and negative intensity.
13 The electric current intensity produced by a DC generator is
   a. constant and in one direction.
   b. pulsating and in one direction.
   c. constant and changing direction.
   d. pulsating and changing direction.
14 One difference between an electric generator and an electric motor is the
   a. types of transformer.   c. source of EMF.
   b. magnetic polarity.   d. loop of wire.
15 An induction motor is used in an x-ray machine to
   a. vary voltage.   c. rotate the anode.
   b. control current.   d. provide rectification.

16 In an induction motor, only the _____ rotates.
   a. rotor
   b. wire loop
   c. stator
   d. electromagnet
17 In an induction motor
   a. only the rotor has windings.
   b. only the stator has windings.
   c. both the rotor and stator may have windings.
   d. neither the rotor nor the stator has windings.
18 In an induction motor an electric current is induced in
   a. only the rotor.
   b. only the stator.
   c. both the rotor and stator.
   d. neither the rotor nor the stator.
19 In an induction motor, an EMF is supplied to
   a. only the rotor.
   b. only the stator.
   c. both the rotor and stator.
   d. neither the rotor nor stator.
20 In electric generators and motors, the commutator ring is a
   a. source of EMF.
   b. converter from DC to AC.
   c. device to vary voltage.
   d. switch.

Electromagnetism

THE TRANSFORMER

A transformer consists basically of two electromagnets that have a common iron core. Therefore a transformer has three principal parts: two coils and a core. A voltage impressed on the **primary** coil will generate a voltage in the **secondary** coil, provided the primary electric power is AC. The transformer law can be written:

$$\frac{V_s}{V_p} = \frac{N_s}{N_p} = \frac{I_p}{I_s}$$

where the subscript s refers to the secondary coil, the subscript p refers to the primary coil, I is current, N is the number of turns of the coil, and V is the voltage. The ration N_s/N_p is known as the **turns ratio.**

In an x-ray machine there are usually three transformers: the variable-voltage autotransformer, the high-voltage step-up transformer, and the step-down filament transformer.

EXERCISES

1 The transformer changes
   a. electric energy to mechanical energy.
   b. electric energy into electromagnetic energy.
   c. electric current into voltage.
   d. the amplitude of electric voltage.
2 A transformer will operate
   a. only on a constant EMF.
   b. on AC but not DC.
   c. on DC but not AC.
   d. on both DC and AC.

3 If a transformer produces a large secondary current from a small primary current
   a. there will be more windings on the secondary side than on the primary side.
   b. the voltage will be larger on the secondary side than on the primary side.
   c. the turns ratio will be less than 1.
   d. the turns ratio will be greater than 1.
4 The turns ratio of a transformer is
   a. the ratio of the number of secondary windings to the number of primary windings.
   b. the ratio of the number of primary windings.
   c. a measure of the power of a transformer.
   d. zero for an autotransformer.
5 The symbol for a transformer is

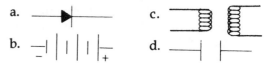

6 The principal application of transformers in an x-ray machine is to
   a. vary frequency.
   b. vary voltage.
   c. provide sufficient electric power.
   d. change DC to AC.
7 The output current in a step-up transformer is
   a. the same as the input current.
   b. higher than the input current.
   c. lower than the input current.
   d. independent of the turns ratio.
8 A transformer with a fixed turns ratio of 10:1 is
   a. an autotransformer.
   b. a step-down transformer.
   c. a step-up transformer.
   d. used to reduce voltage.

9 When one designs and uses a step-up transformer, the

   a. turns ratio will be equal to 1.

   b. primary winding will have more turns than the secondary winding.

   c. secondary voltage will be greater than the primary voltage.

   d. secondary current will be greater than the primary current.

10 When designing a transformer, the change in current across it is

   a. in the same direction as the voltage change.

   b. directly proportional to the voltage change.

   c. proportional to the turns ratio.

   d. inversely proportional to the turns ratio.

11 Which of the following is **not** a type of transformer used in x-ray machines?

   a. autotransformer

   b. rectifier type

   c. step-down type

   d. shell type

12 An autotransformer

   a. is an electromechanical device.

   b. is a shell type of transformer.

   c. contains a single winding to serve as both primary and secondary coils.

   d. is used only to increase voltage.

13 Which of the following is correct regarding transformers?

   a. If there were equal numbers of turns in the primary and secondary coils, the turns ratio would be zero.

   b. Laminated transformer cores are more efficient than unlaminated cores.

   c. In the shell type of transformer, the primary and secondary coils are wound on different cores.

   d. The high-voltage transformer in an x-ray machine is the autotransformer.

14 A transformer "transforms" or changes electric

   a. impedance.   **c.** power.

   b. resistance.   **d.** voltage.

15 Transformers have iron cores in order to intensify the

   a. magnetic field.

   b. EMF.

   c. electric current.

   d. electric potential.

16 Primary to secondary coupling is enhanced by

   a. the iron core.   **c.** AC.

   b. EMF.   **d.** DC.

17 If DC is applied to the primary coil of a transformer

   a. a secondary voltage will result.

   b. a secondary current will result.

   c. a magnetic field will be produced.

   d. nothing will happen.

18 The turns ratio is defined as

   a. primary voltage + secondary voltage.

   b. secondary amperage + primary amperage.

   c. primary windings + secondary windings.

   d. secondary windings + primary windings.

19 Which of the following accurately represents the transformer law?

   a. $I_s/I_p = N_p/N_s$ **c.** $I_s/I_p = V_s/V_p$

   b. $I_s/I_p = N_s/N_p$ **d.** $I_p/I_s = V_p/V_s$

20 The transformer that reminds one of a square donut is called a (an) _____ transformer.

   a. auto   **c.** closed-core

   b. induction   **d.** shell-type

21 A transformer has 10,000 windings on the secondary and 150 on the primary. If the primary voltage is 220 V and the primary current 5 A, what is the turns ratio?

   a. 1.5:1   **c.** 67:1

   b. 15:1   **d.** 100:1

22 A transformer has 10,000 windings on the secondary and 150 on the primary. If the primary voltage is 220 V and the primary current 5 A, what is the secondary voltage?

   a. 110 V   **c.** 14.7 kV

   b. 220 V   **d.** 147 kV

23 A transformer has 10,000 windings on the secondary and 150 on the primary. If the primary voltage is 220 V and the primary current 5 A, what is the secondary current?

   a. 75 mA   **c.** 500 mA

   b. 150 mA   **d.** 5000 mA

24 To produce 99 kVp from a 110 V source would require a turns ratio of about

   a. 99:1.   **c.** 1100:1.

   b. 900:1.   **d.** 9900:1.

25 An x-ray tube filament needs 4.6 A. The primary current is 200 mA. What is the turns ratio?

   a. 0.043:1   **c.** 2.3:1

   b. 0.2:1   **d.** 4.6:1

Electromagnetism

RECTIFICATION
....

Most devices with which we are familiar require an AC power supply for operation. All household electric items and, indeed, nearly everything electric in the hospital operate on AC power. However, in radiology the most important component of an x-ray machine, the x-ray tube, requires a DC source of electromotive force (**EMF**).

As a consequence, to produce x rays, the x-ray tube must be provided with a DC source of EMF even though the x-ray machine is supplied with AC from the hospital. Circuit elements inside the x-ray machine called **rectifiers** transform the AC power source to DC before supplying it to the x-ray tube. The process of conversion from AC to DC is called **rectification.**

Some types of x-ray units, primarily dental and portable systems, are capable of transforming AC into DC themselves, while simultaneously producing x-rays. Such a circuit is said to be **self-rectified. Self-rectification results in half-wave rectification. Full-wave rectification** is most often employed in conventional x-ray machines, and such a circuit requires a minimum of four rectifiers. To full-wave rectify **three-phase power,** a minimum of six rectifiers is required for a six-pulse unit, and 12 are required for a 12-pulse unit.

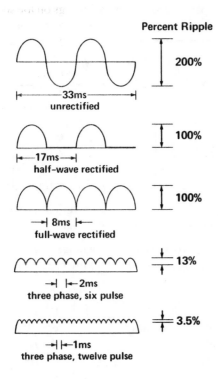

Percent Ripple

200%
—33ms—
unrectified

100%
|—17ms—|
half-wave rectified

100%
→| 8ms |←
full-wave rectified

13%
→| |←2ms
three phase, six pulse

3.5%
→| |←1ms
three phase, twelve pulse

EXERCISES

1 A disadvantage of self-rectification of an x-ray tube is that
   a. four rectifiers are needed.
   b. the exposure time is limited.
   c. only hard x rays can be produced.
   d. there is a possible danger of filament damage.

2 Which of the following types of rectification produces maximum efficiency?
   a. self-rectification
   b. half-wave rectification
   c. two-diode rectification
   d. four-diode rectification

3 To generate three-phase, 12-pulse power, a minimum of how many rectifiers is necessary?
   a. 4
   b. 8
   c. 12
   d. 24

4 A semiconductor rectifier
   a. has a heated cathode.
   b. has a heated anode.
   c. is a solid-state device.
   d. is an electromechanical device.

5 If a single rectifier is inserted into a circuit conducting 60 Hz AC so that it suppresses the positive portion of the waveform, then the output waveform will contain

a. 60 positive pulses per second.
b. 60 negative pulses per second.
c. 120 positive pulses per second.
d. 120 negative pulses per second.

6 The voltage ripple associated with various x-ray generators is
a. 100% for self-rectification.
b. 70.7% for single-phase, full-wave rectification.
c. higher for self-rectification than for half-wave rectification.
d. less for single-phase than for three-phase power.

7 A rectifier
a. refers to a type of electromechanical device.
b. refers to a type of electromagnetic device.
c. converts DC to AC.
d. converts AC to DC.

8 Which of the following is a component of a tube type of rectifier?
a. filament
b. magnetic core
c. primary windings
d. secondary windings

9 In a valve tube rectifier the electron flow is from
a. anode to cathode only when the anode is positive with respect to the cathode.
b. cathode to anode only when the anode is negative with respect to the cathode.
c. anode to cathode ony when the anode is negative with respect to the cathode.
d. cathode to anode only when the anode is positive with respect to the cathode.

10 Under normal conditions of operation a valve tube rectifier will not allow electrons to flow from anode to cathode because
a. all electromagnetic radiation flows in this direction.
b. protons flow in this direction.
c. the cathode is not heated.
d. the anode is not heated.

11 Near the p-n junction of a semiconductor diode one will find
a. p type of material containing excess electrons.
b. n type of material containing excess electrons.
c. a heated cathode.
d. a heated anode.

12 A semiconductor diode
a. is also called an electromechanical rectifier.
b. contains holes that are also called proton traps.
c. allows current to flow only from p type of material to n type.
d. allows current to flow only from n type of material to p type.

13 In a circuit containing a single rectifier,
a. electron flow will be pulsed but uninterrupted.
b. electrons will be permitted to flow in one direction but not the other.
c. the result will be constant potential DC.
d. twice as many electrons will flow in the output coil as in the input coil.

14 If 60 Hz AC power is full-wave rectified, output will consist of
a. 20 pulses per second.
b. 90 pulses per second.
c. 120 pulses per second.
d. zero ripple.

15 The current from a common household wall receptacle is
a. 50 Hz AC.
b. 50 Hz DC.
c. 60 Hz AC.
d. 60 Hz DC.

16 Thermionic emission refers to
a. heat conduction.
b. heat radiation.
c. electron emission from a heated source.
d. heat emission from an electric conductor.

17 Which of the following is the symbol for a diode?

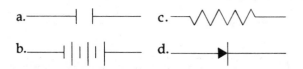

18 The main advantage of full-wave rectification over half-wave rectification is
a. more x rays per cycle.
b. higher kVp.
c. higher mA.
d. less voltage ripple.

19 For rectified three-phase, six-pulse power, how many overlapping pulses are generated in 1 s?
a. 60
b. 120
c. 360
d. 720

20 Inspect the following circuit, and identify which diodes pass current at the same time:

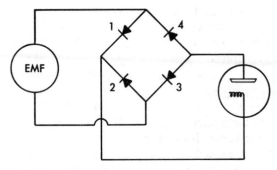

a. 1 and 2
b. 3 and 4
c. 1 and 3
d. 1 and 4

Match the approximate percent voltage ripple with each of the following. Some answers may be used more than once.

21 self-rectified _____
22 full-wave rectified _____
23 three-phase, six-pulse _____
24 three-phase, 12-pulse _____
25 half-wave rectified _____

a. 2
b. 4
c. 13
d. 71
e. 100

Name _____

Date _____

The X-ray Machine

X-RAY TUBE CATHODE

....

The cathode is the negative side of the x-ray tube. Its major components are the **filament** and the **focusing cup.** The filament is a small coil of wire, usually thoriated tungsten, that provides electrons for the production of x rays. The focusing cup directs the beam of electrons to the proper place on the anode. The x-ray tube current is adjusted by controlling the filament current. X-ray tube currents are measured in milliamperes, whereas the filament current is several amperes. A small change in filament current results in a large change in tube current. Normally the console of the x-ray machine contains individual adjustable millamperage settings.

EXERCISES

1 The three principal parts of an x-ray machine are the
   a. anode, cathode, and focusing cup.
   b. anode, cathode, and high voltage generator.
   c. x ray tube, protective housing, and high voltage generator.
   d. x ray tube, control console, and high voltage generator.

2 The primary purpose of the glass envelope is to
   a. control leakage radiation.
   b. ensure against electric shock.
   c. cool the tube.
   d. provide a vacuum.

3 A properly designed x-ray tube has a protective housing to
   a. limit operation to 100 kVp or less.
   b. reduce the hazard of falling.
   c. reduce the hazard of leakage radiation.
   d. control isotropic x-ray emission.

4 A diagnostic x-ray tube is an example of
   a. a cathode.   c. a diode.
   b. an anode.   d. an electrode.

5 The large filament is used during radiography when the heat load is
   a. high and visibility of detail is important.
   b. high and visibility of detail is less important.
   c. low and visibility of detail is important.
   d. low and visibility of detail is less important.

6 In some x-ray tubes there are two filaments to
   a. reduce space-charge effects.
   b. ensure saturation current.
   c. provide two focal spots.
   d. provide two electrodes.

7 The focusing cup is
   a. the grid in a grid-controlled x-ray tube.
   b. usually made of thoriated tungsten.
   c. on the positive side of the x-ray tube.
   d. slightly positive with respect to the filament.

8 Once adequate filament temperature has been achieved, a further small rise in filament temperature will produce a _____ in tube current.
   a. large increase   c. large decrease
   b. small increase   d. small decrease

9 The cathode beam of an x-ray tube is the
   a. primary x-ray beam.
   b. focused electron beam within the tube.
   c. current heating the filament.
   d. secondary radiation.

10 The x-ray tube current
 a. is the current flowing through the filament.
 b. flows through both filaments at the same time.
 c. is controlled by the filament current.
 d. is usually variable from 50 to 1000 A.
11 Most modern x-ray tubes used for radiography
 a. are dual-focus tubes.
 b. operate in the space-charge–limited mode.
 c. employ tungsten filaments that do not vaporize.
 d. do not emit leakage radiation.
12 The cathode is
 a. a diode.
 b. one of two parts of a diode.
 c. designed to supply heat.
 d. positively charged.
13 If a filament burns out, the
 a. filament current is zero.
 b. filament current is maximum.
 c. tube current is maximum.
 d. x-ray intensity is maximum.
14 The space-charge effect
 a. occurs in the vicinity of the cathode.
 b. occurs in the vicinity of the anode.
 c. is more pronounced at low mA.
 d. is more pronounced at high kVp.
15 The x-ray tube filament
 a. conducts current only when an exposure is made.
 b. conducts about 5 A of current.
 c. is the space charge.
 d. is a diode.
16 If saturation is achieved and the filament current is fixed, tube current will
 a. rise with increasing kVp.
 b. fall with increasing kVp.
 c. rise with increasing exposure time.
 d. remain fixed.
17 X-ray tube current
 a. increases when the kVp is decreased.
 b. is measured in amperes rather than milliamperes.
 c. is always zero at filament currents below thermionic emission.
 d. depends on exposure time.
18 The addition of thorium to the tungsten filament
 a. increases filament life.
 b. decreases space-charge effects.
 c. allows higher mA operation.
 d. allows higher kVp operation.

19 Increasing the temperature of the x-ray tube filament
 a. decreases anode heat loading.
 b. increases mA.
 c. increases x-ray energy.
 d. lengthens exposure time.
20 The amount of space charge produced
 a. is called thermionic emission.
 b. tends to limit emission of x rays from the filament.
 c. depends on anode temperature.
 d. depends on the kVp.

Examine the filament-emission chart below and answer exercises 21 to 25.

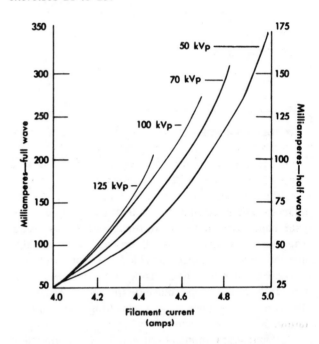

21 What is the full-wave tube current when the filament current is 4.6 A and the tube voltage is 70 kVp?
22 To obtain 125 mA half-wave tube current at 100 kVp, what must the filament current be?
23 At a filament current of 4.3 A, how much higher is tube current under full-wave operation than under half-wave operation?
24 At 70 kVp a change from 4.5 to 4.7 A (a 4% change) in full-wave operation results in what percentage change in tube current?
25 Plot the relationship between full wave tube current and kVp at 4.5 A filament current. What is the saturation current under full-wave and half-wave rectification?

WORKSHEET 32

The X-ray Machine

X-RAY TUBE ANODE

....

The x-ray tube anode is the positive side of the x-ray tube. The anode serves four principal functions: **electrical conduction** of the x-ray tube current, **mechanical support** for the target, **thermal conduction** of heat, and **x-ray production.** Copper is a common anode stem material and is chosen because of its ability to dissipate heat. The active portion of the anode, where x rays are produced, is called the **target.** All targets are made of tungsten (usually alloyed with rhenium). However, some employed exclusively for mammography have molybdenum targets. Two types of anodes are used in diagnostic x-ray tubes—stationary and rotating:

1. **Stationary anodes**—consist of a tungsten target embedded in the copper anode. These are employed principally in dental and portable machines.

2. **Rotating anodes**—consist of a disk of target material connected by a molybdenum shaft to a massive copper rotor.

The advantage of the rotating anode is higher heat capacity. The area of the anode on which the electron beam interacts is called the focal spot. Most rotating anodes revolve at 3400 rpm; however, some high-capacity, three-phase tubes have anodes that rotate at 10,000 rpm. All diagnostic tubes have targets with inclined faces to take advantage of the **line-focus principle.**

EXERCISES

1 A stationary-anode x-ray tube
   a. is used to produce very short exposures.
   b. provides for greater heat dissipation.
   c. incorporates the line-focus principle.
   d. usually has a smaller focal spot.

2 The heel effect occurs because of
   a. reduced tube current.
   b. the space-charge effect.
   c. photon absorption.
   d. the shape of the filament.

3 The main reason for employing the line-focus principle is to
   a. increase heat capacity.
   b. decrease exposure time.
   c. decrease heel effect.
   d. decrease effective focal spot size.

4 Most rotating-anode x-ray tubes
   a. have a tungsten target embedded in a copper anode.
   b. have a copper target embedded in a tungsten anode.
   c. incorporate the line-focus principle.
   d. have target angles less than 10 degrees.

5 X-ray intensity is higher on the cathode side than on the anode side because of
   a. the space-charge effect.
   b. the line-focus principle.
   c. x-ray absorption in the heel of the anode.
   d. x-ray deflection from the heel of the anode.

6 Which of the following target angles is characteristic of a modern rotating-anode x-ray tube?
   a. 1 degree
   b. 15 degrees
   c. 50 degrees
   d. 100 degrees

7 Small target angles result in
   a. small space charge.
   b. small effective focal spot size.
   c. increased heat capacity.
   d. less heel effect.

8 Copper is used for anode stem material because it
   a. has a high atomic number.
   b. has a shiny surface and reflects electrons well.
   c. has longer life.
   d. is a good electric conductor.

9 The target can be damaged by
   a. extensive warm-up of the machine.
   b. using too short an exposure time.
   c. having the tube in the wrong orientation.
   d. anode-bearing failure.

10 The effective focal spot is
   a. smaller than the actual focal spot.
   b. larger than the actual focal spot.
   c. smallest on the cathode side of the central axis.
   d. smallest on the central axis.

11 The heel effect
   a. suggests that in PA chest radiography the cathode should be up.
   b. suggests that the cathode should be toward the thicker anatomy.
   c. is more pronounced when large target angles are used.
   d. occurs only with rotating-anode x-ray tubes.

12 A prominent difficulty in the manufacture of high-speed rotating anodes is
   a. control of space-charge effects.
   b. balance of the rotor.
   c. proper target angle.
   d. target-face polish.

13 Which of the following are components of an electromagnetic induction motor?
   a. filament   **c.** target disk
   b. cathode   **d.** stator

14 Necessary properties of x-ray target material include
   a. high rotation speed.
   b. low atomic number.
   c. high melting point.
   d. low coefficient of friction.

15 An advantage of the rotating-anode tube over the stationary-anode tube is
   a. its ability to employ the line-focus principle.
   b. reduced heel effect.
   c. higher kVp capacity.
   d. shorter exposure time allowed.

16 The anode of an x-ray tube is angled to give
   a. proper reflection.
   b. a smaller actual focal spot.
   c. a smaller effective focal spot.
   d. proper focusing of the electron beam.

17 Which of the following components of a diagnostic x-ray tube are on the positive side of the tube?
   a. the stator
   b. the focusing cup
   c. the grid
   d. the cathode

18 As the anode target angle increases, the
   a. effective focal spot size increases.
   b. heel effect becomes more pronounced.
   c. radiation intensity on the central ray increases.
   d. target rotating speed increases.

19 A stationary anode will most likely be used in
   a. general radiography.   **c.** dentistry.
   b. mammography.   **d.** special procedures.

20 Which of the following is **not** a function of the anode?
   a. conduction of electricity
   b. thermionic emission
   c. thermal conduction
   d. mechanical support

21 In order to design an x-ray anode for high capacity radiologic techniques, the principal hurdle is
   a. radiation quantity.   **c.** rotating speed.
   b. radiation quality.   **d.** heat dissipation.

22 The principal enemy of long x-ray tube life is
   a. x radiation.   **c.** rough handling.
   b. electric surges.   **d.** heat.

23 Tungsten is the choice material for x-ray anodes because of
   a. low atomic number.
   b. high atomic number.
   c. low rpm.
   d. high rpm.

24 The main reason we use rotating anode tubes is to increase
   a. radiation quantity.   **c.** rpm.
   b. radiation quality.   **d.** heat capacity.

25 An induction motor is best described as _____ device.
   a. an electromechanical
   b. an electrophysical
   c. a hydrophysical
   d. a hydromechanical

WORKSHEET 33

The X-ray Machine

Adjustment of kilovolts peak (kVp) is controlled by a series of electric taps on the autotransformer. The autotransformer works on the principle of electromagnetic induction, but it is different from a conventional transformer in that it has only one winding. A number of electric taps along the autotransformer winding allow for selection of the secondary voltage needed as input to the high-voltage step-up transformer. Although primary and secondary taps can be identified, all taps, in fact, are on the single winding. The autotransformer can function in either the step-up or step-down mode, and the transformer law can be used to calculate the secondary voltage:

$$\frac{V_s}{V_p} = \frac{N_s}{N_p}$$

where

V_p = primary voltage
V_s = secondary voltage
N_p = number of windings enclosed by primary taps
N_s = number of windings enclosed by secondary
  taps

When the radiologic technologist uses the major kVp control on the operating console, the voltage is usually tapped in 10 kVp increments, whereas the minor kVp control is usually adjusted in 1 or 2 kVp increments.

EXERCISES

1 Power to the primary side of the high voltage transformer comes from
  a. the primary side of the autotransformer.
  b. the secondary side of the autotransformer.
  c. the line-voltage compensator.
  d. the filament transformer.

2 The output voltage from the autotransformer is
  a. proportional to the turns ratio.
  b. inversely proportional to the turns ratio.
  c. always less than the input voltage.
  d. always more than the input voltage.
3 The autotransformer converts
  a. mechanical energy to electric energy.
  b. chemical energy to electric energy.
  c. electric energy to electric energy.
  d. electric energy to chemical energy.
4 The autotransformer operates on the principle of
  a. Newton's law.   **c.** Coulomb's law.
  b. Oersted's law.   **d.** Faraday's law.
5 The autotransformer is most often physically located in the
  a. x-ray tube housing.   **c.** high voltage tank.
  b. operating console.   **d.** false ceiling.

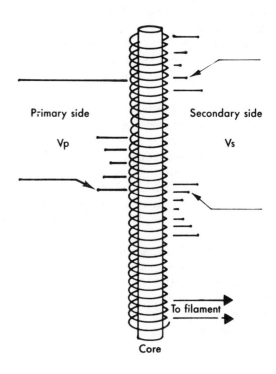

6 The voltage supplied to an x-ray machine is 220 V. The voltage used in radiography is produced by which of the following?
  a. rheostat
  b. autotransformer
  c. filament transformer
  d. high voltage transformer

7 The kVp meter is
  a. on the secondary side of the autotransformer.
  b. on the secondary side of the filament transformer.
  c. on the secondary side of the step-up transformer.
  d. physically located in the high voltage tank.

8 The autotransformer has only one
  a. coil.   **c.** meter.
  b. turns ratio.   **d.** switch.

9 The prereading voltmeter
  a. is on the secondary side of the step-up transformer.
  b. is on the primary side of the autotransformer.
  c. is on the secondary side of the autotransformer.
  d. controls kVp automatically.

10 The autotransformer
  a. is usually oil immersed for heat dissipation.
  b. generates the high voltage.
  c. controls the high voltage.
  d. is physically located in the high voltage generator.

11 The autotransformer is used to select
  a. the voltage to the primary side of the step-up transformer.
  b. the voltage to the secondary side of the step-up transformer.
  c. current to the filament transformer.
  d. the mA station desired.

12 Which of the following is directly connected to the autotransformer?
  a. the x-ray tube   **c.** the kVp meter
  b. the mA meter   **d.** the filament

13 Electric taps on the winding of an autotransformer are used
  a. for focal spot selection.
  b. to set exposure time.
  c. for mA selection.
  d. for line compensation.

14 Line compensation
  a. is necessary to convert AC to DC.
  b. is necessary for proper exposure timing.
  c. is required because of variations in supplied voltage.
  d. adjusts the line frequency to 60 Hz.

15 The autotransformer can be used to
  a. convert AC to DC.
  b. convert DC to AC.
  c. increase kVp.
  d. increase mA.

16 If V stands for electromotive force (EMF) and T for the number of turns enclosed between the taps of an autotransformer, then the autotransformer law is
  a. $V_p/V_s = T_p/T_s$.   **c.** $V_pV_s = T_pT_s$.
  b. $V_pT_p = T_sT_s$.   **d.** $V_s/V_p = T_p/T_s$.

17 In the design of an autotransformer
  a. the major kVp adjustment is on the primary side and the minor kVp adjustment is on the secondary side.
  b. the major kVp adjustment and the line-voltage compensator are on the secondary side.
  c. a single coil serves as primary and secondary coils.
  d. there are separate primary and secondary coils.

18 Selection of kVp
  a. requires a constant input voltage to the autotransformer.
  b. involves two series of autotransformers.
  c. uses meters and switches that are at high kVp.
  d. uses the step-up transformer.

19 To adjust kVp, which controls are manipulated?
  a. primary and secondary
  b. anode and cathode
  c. prereading and postreading
  d. major and minor

20 To know the voltage before exposure, one uses
  a. an autotransformer.
  b. a step-up transformer.
  c. a prereading voltmeter.
  d. a postreading voltmeter.

21 The principal purpose of the autotransformer is to
  a. increase voltage.
  b. reduce voltage.
  c. adjust voltage.
  d. stabilize voltage.

22 The principal purpose of the high voltage transformer is to
  a. increase voltage.   **c.** adjust voltage.
  b. reduce voltage.   **d.** stabilize voltage.

23 220 V is supplied to 500 primary turns of an autotransformer. What will be the output voltage across 4000 turns?
  a. 27.5 V   **c.** 880 V
  b. 55 V   **d.** 1760 V

24 220 V is supplied to 800 primary turns of an autotransformer. What will be the output voltage across 200 turns?
  a. 27.5 V   **c.** 880 V
  b. 55 V   **d.** 1760 V

25 440 V is supplied to 1000 primary turns of an autotransformer. If the desired output voltage is 100 V, how many secondary turns must be tapped?
  a. 100   **c.** 4400
  b. 227   **d.** 10,000

Name _____

Date _____

The X-ray Machine

CONTROL OF MILLIAMPERAGE (mA)
....

The x-ray tube current is controlled by an electric filament circuit separate from that of the high voltage circuit. The circuit elements of importance in supplying and controlling the tube mA are the autotransformer, precision resistors, filament transformer, and filament. On most x-ray consoles, a different precision resistor is selected for each of the various mA stations. This action delivers a specific current to the primary turns of the filament transformer. That current is increased across the filament transformer and conducted to the filament. The precision resistor selected obeys Ohm's law, whereas the filament transformer obeys the transformer law.

The mA meter, although physically located on the operating console, is electrically connected to the secondary side of the high-voltage transformer through a center tap. This allows direct measurement of the tube current with electric safety.

EXERCISES

1 One coulomb per second (C/s) is equivalent to 1 A, and 1 C is equal to 6.3×10^{18} electrons. Therefore operation at the 100 mA station would result in the production of
   a. 6.3×10^{18} electrons.
   b. 6.3×10^{18} electrons/s.
   c. 6.3×10^{17} electrons.
   d. 6.3×10^{17} electrons/s.

2 Operation at 100 mA for 1 s will result in
   a. 6.3×10^{18} electrons.
   b. 6.3×10^{18} electrons/s.
   c. 6.3×10^{17} electrons.
   d. 6.3×10^{17} electrons/s.

3 A filament current of 5 A is necessary for thermionic emission. What electron flow is this?
   a. 3.2×10^{19} electrons/s.
   b. 3.2×10^{18} electrons/s.
   c. 3.2×10^{17} electrons/s.
   d. 3.2×10^{16} electrons/s.

4 A PA chest exposure requires a technique of 125 kVp at 4 mAs. The total number of electrons used to make the exposure is
   a. 6.3×10^{17}.
   b. 6.3×10^{16}.
   c. 2.5×10^{17}.
   d. 2.5×10^{16}.

5 The filament circuit
   a. is located entirely in the operating console.
   b. begins at the autotransformer and ends at the filament transformer.
   c. begins at the filament transformer and ends at the filament.
   d. is located in all three major components of an x-ray machine: the console, the high voltage generator, and the x-ray tube.

6 If a filament transformer has a turns ratio of 0.05 and 200 mA is supplied to the primary side of the transformer, what will be the secondary current?
   a. 100 mA   c. 1 A
   b. 400 mA   d. 4 A

7 The filament transformer in the previous question is supplied with 150 V to the primary side. What is the secondary voltage?
   a. 30 V
   b. 3000 mV
   c. 7.5 V
   d. 750 mV

8 The mAs unit
   a. is directly related to total electron number.
   b. is a unit of electric current.
   c. is a unit of electromotive force (EMF).
   d. could be expressed in coulombs/second.

9 An exposure technique of 100 mA at 100 ms compared with 50 mA at 50 ms will result in
  a. fewer electrons.
  b. twice the total number of electrons.
  c. three times the total number of electrons.
  d. four times the total number of electrons.

10 The control of the focal spot size
  a. is always determined by the mA station selected.
  b. depends on the secondary taps of the autotransformer.
  c. depends on the turns ratio of the filament transformer.
  d. depends on the filament that is energized.

11 The meter that monitors x-ray tube current is
  a. physically located on the control console.
  b. the same as the filament current monitor.
  c. grounded to the primary center tap of the step-up transformer.
  d. connected to the secondary side of the step-down transformer.

12 X-ray tube current is usually measured in
  a. amperes.   **c.** microamperes.
  b. milliamperes.   **d.** mAs.

13 The filament transformer is usually
  a. located in the operating console.
  b. located with the high voltage generator.
  c. a step-up transformer.
  d. an autotransformer.

14 The filament transformer is designed
  a. with a turns ratio less than 1.
  b. with a turns ratio greater than 1.
  c. as a step-up transformer.
  d. with an mA meter grounded to the center tap.

15 Which of the following would be correct units for x-ray tube current?
  a. electron volts
  b. kilovoltage peak
  c. coulombs
  d. coulombs/second

16 Designing fixed mA stations requires the use of
  a. major and minor taps.
  b. primary and secondary windings.
  c. precision resistors.
  d. a center-tapped meter.

17 To provide for two filaments
  a. two filament transformers are required.
  b. a switch is required on the primary windings of the filament transformer.
  c. a switch is required on the secondary windings of the filament transformer.
  d. precision resistors are required.

18 The filament transformer
  a. has four windings.
  b. increases voltage.
  c. increases current.
  d. must have precision resistors.

19 A filament transformer has 800 primary windings and is supplied with 200 mA. If the secondary has 100 windings, what will be the secondary current?
  a. 25 mA   **c.** 400 mA
  b. 100 mA   **d.** 1600 mA

20 A filament transformer has a turns ratio of 1:20. What current must be supplied to the primary windings if 5 A is required by the filament?
  a. 200 mA   **c.** 50 A
  b. 250 mA   **d.** 100 A

The X-ray Machine

EXPOSURE TIMERS
. . . .

Exposure timers are mechanical or electronic devices used to "make" and "break" the high voltage across the x-ray tube. The timing circuit is usually located on the primary side of the high-voltage step-up transformer. Because the current through the primary circuit can be in excess of 100 A, a simple switch will not do. Many timing circuits activate **contactors**—heavy-duty electromagnetic devices.

There are five basic types of exposure timers:

1. **Mechanical timers**—operate by spring action much like a hand-wound alarm clock. These timers are not very accurate, nor are they used on modern equipment.

2. **Synchronous timers**—employ a synchronous motor operating at 60 rps. The shortest possible exposure time is 1/60 s.

3. **Electronic timers**—operate, as their name implies, on an electronic resistive-capacitive circuit based on the time required to charge a capacitor. They are accurate, allow a wide range of time increments including exposures as short as 1 millisecond (ms), and can be used for serial radiography.

4. **mAs timers**—are electronic timers that monitor the product of mA and time and terminate the exposure when the proper mAs is reached. They are often located on the secondary side of the high voltage section.

5. **Phototimers**—are radiation-measuring devices that terminate the exposure when sufficient radiation to produce the desired density reaches the film.

Until recently, timing stations on the x-ray console indicated exposure times shorter than 1 s by a fraction, that is, ½ s, 1/10 s, etc. With more sophisticated timers capable of shorter and more varied exposure times, specification of exposure time in milliseconds is necessary (1000 ms = 1 s).

EXERCISES

1 A radiographic technique calls for a 50 ms exposure, but the exposure control has only fractional notation. Which should be selected?
   a. ¼ s   **c.** 1/20 s
   b. 1/10 s   **d.** 1/40 s

2 A radiographic technique calls for 400 mA, 1/20 s exposure. What is the mAs needed?
   a. 80   **c.** 20
   b. 40   **d.** 10

3 If a unit is operated at 600 mA, 50 ms, the total mAs will be
   a. 6.   **c.** 60.
   b. 30.   **d.** 300.

4 A radiographic technique of 100 mA at ¼ has been used. If one changes to the 500 mA station, the appropriate exposure time for the same mAs is
   a. 1/10 s.
   b. 2/10 s.
   c. 1/20 s.
   d. 3/20 s.

5 Operation at 300 mA for 1/20 s is equivalent to operation at 900 mA for
   a. 8 ms.
   b. 17 ms.
   c. 60 ms.
   d. 200 ms.

6 The control of exposure time is nearly always
   a. on the primary side of the high voltage transformer.
   b. on the primary side of the autotransformer.
   c. on the secondary side of the filament circuit.
   d. automatically set.

7 The exposure timer on a modern three-phase radiographic unit
   a. will usually be automatic.
   b. will usually be electronic.
   c. will usually be synchronous.
   d. will limit exposures to 1/60 s or longer.

8 A phototimer

   a. cannot control exposures of less than 1/120 s.

   b. that employs an ionization chamber may have it positioned between the patient and the image receptor.

   c. does not require a manual timer.

   d. can employ a photomultiplier tube on the entrance side of the patient.

9 To check the exposure timer of a three-phase system,

   a. use a conventional spinning top.

   b. use a synchronous spinning top at 1 rpm.

   c. use a synchronous spinning top at 1 rps.

   d. pulsed radiation must be present.

10 If a 50 ms exposure is being checked, then at single-phase

   a. half-wave rectification, three dashes would be expected.

   b. full-wave rectification, three dashes would be expected.

   c. half-wave rectification, 12 dashes would be expected.

   d. full-wave rectification, 12 dashes would be expected.

11 A timer is checked with a conventional spinning top on the 100 ms station. Which of the following will be true?

   a. If the generator is full-wave rectified, three dashes should appear.

   b. If the generator is full-wave rectified, six dashes should appear.

   c. The top will spin with constant velocity.

   d. If the top spins too fast, dash superimposition may occur, making analysis difficult.

12 A phototimer

   a. requires no attention at all by the technologist.

   b. still requires the technologist to select mAs.

   c. still requires the technologist to select kVp.

   d. terminates the exposure when the patient receives sufficient radiation.

13 If a phototimer is used,

   a. exposures of less than 100 ms are not possible.

   b. it is not necessary to depress the exposure control.

   c. the exposure will start and stop automatically.

   d. a manual timer should be used as a backup.

14 A manual spinning top should not be used to evaluate a three-phase exposure timer because the

   a. x-ray beam quality is too high.

   b. x-ray output is not pulsed.

   c. frequency of operation is too high.

   d. exposure times are too short.

15 If a synchronous spinning top operating at 1 rps is exposed for 100 ms, a three-phase image will cover a

   a. 10-degree arc.   **c.** 72-degree arc.

   b. 36-degree arc.   **d.** 90-degree arc.

16 The shortest exposure possible with single-phase equipment is 1/120 s. How many milliseconds is that?

   a. 8   **c.** 50

   b. 17   **d.** 120

17 Xeromammography sometimes requires exposures as long as 1.5 seconds. This is equivalent to

   a. 100 ms.   **c.** 1000 ms.

   b. 150 ms.   **d.** 1500 ms.

18 The shortest exposure possible with three-phase equipment is 1 ms. What fraction of a second is that?

   a. 1/100   **c.** 1/500

   b. 1/120   **d.** 1/1000

19 The timer of a self-rectified dental x-ray unit is checked with a spinning top at 1/20 s. How should the image appear?

   a. one dash   **c.** three dashes

   b. two dashes   **d.** five dashes

20 A synchronous spinning top is exposed for 20 ms. The resulting image will measure what angle?

   a. 7.2 degrees   **c.** 36 degrees

   b. 20 degrees   **d.** 50 degrees

Name _____

Date _____

The X-ray Machine

HIGH VOLTAGE GENERATION AND RECTIFICATION
....

The high voltage section of the x-ray machine contains the following:

1. The **high voltage transformer,** or step-up transformer (that is, $N_s/N_p > 1$), which converts low voltage from the autotransformer to the required kilovolt level.

2. The **filament transformer,** or step-down transformer (that is, $N_s/N_p < 1$), which reduces the voltage from the autotransformer to about 10 V for heating the filament. At the same time, the filament current is regulated to the 4 to 10 A range.

3 A **rectifier** that converts the alternating voltage into a direct pulsating voltage before use by the x-ray tube.

The accompanying figure shows the change in voltage waveform at each stage of generation.

Voltage waveform	Pulses per second	Percent ripple
Half wave	60	100
Full wave	120	100
Three phase, six pulse	360	13
Three phase, 12 pulse	720	4
High frequency	up to 1000	1

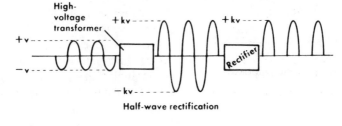

Half-wave rectification

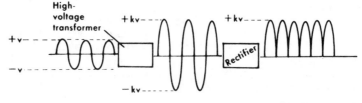

Full-wave rectification

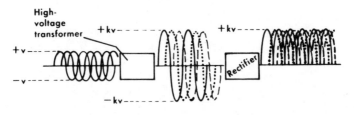

Three-phase rectification

EXERCISES

1 Which of the following is **not** contained in a typical high voltage generator tank?
   a. the mA meter
   b. diodes
   c. the filament transformer
   d. oil

2 A change in the voltage waveform from the primary side to the secondary side of the high voltage transformer produces a change in
   a. frequency.
   b. wavelength.
   c. phase.
   d. amplitude.

3 In a half-wave rectified system, each inverse half cycle in the primary circuit corresponds to _____ voltage pulse(s) across the x-ray tube.
   a. no
   b. one
   c. two
   d. four

4 Which of the following is higher for single-phase equipment than for three-phase?
   a. x-ray quality
   b. usual rotor speed
   c. purchase price
   d. voltage fluctuation

5 Which of the following is a disadvantage of three-phase equipment compared to single-phase equipment?
   a. longer minimum exposure time
   b. higher electrical operating costs
   c. higher capital costs
   d. softer radiation

6 The disadvantage of self-rectified circuits is
   a. cost.
   b. complexity.
   c. that they cannot have a very short exposure time.
   d. that they are limited to dental machines.

7 The high voltage transformer is center tapped
   a. on the primary side.
   b. to produce higher kV.
   c. requiring larger, more insulated cables.
   d. through the mA meter to ground.

8 An exposure of 1/10 s
   a. is 120 ms long.
   b. will produce six pulses in full-wave rectification.
   c. will produce twice as much radiation if full-wave rectified than if half-wave rectified.
   d. cannot be checked with a synchronous timer.

9 Full-wave rectification
   a. requires at least four rectifiers.
   b. reduces ripple when compared with half-wave rectification.
   c. is one example of self-rectification.
   d. produces higher kVp than half-wave rectification.

10 A rectifier
   a. increases voltage.
   b. increases current.
   c. can be a semiconductor.
   d. converts DC to AC.

11 Concerning the transformers employed in the generation of x rays,
   a. a high voltage transformer is a step-up device.
   b. the filament transformer is usually located in the console.
   c. the filament transformer is also an autotransformer.
   d. they operate only on DC.

12 Which of the following is an advantage of three-phase power over single-phase power?
   a. lower capital cost
   b. longer exposure times
   c. increased x-ray intensity per mAs
   d. increased kVp

13 Oil is employed in the high voltage section of an x-ray machine for
   a. thermal conduction.
   b. electric insulation.
   c. reduction of rotor friction.
   d. reduction of voltage ripple.

14 X-ray quality improves with reduced voltage ripple; therefore _____ should provide the highest quality x-ray beam.
   a. self-rectified
   b. full-wave rectified
   c. three-phase
   d. high frequency or constant potential

15 Match the following power supplies with the appropriate voltage ripple:
   a. three-phase, 12-pulse power ____
   b. high frequency power ____
   c. full-wave rectified power ____
   d. three-phase, six-pulse power ____

   1 1%
   2 3%
   3 15%
   4 100%

WORSHEET 37

The X-ray Machine

X-RAY TUBE RATING CHARTS

·····················

Three types of tube rating charts exist: the radiographic rating chart, the anode cooling chart, and the housing cooling chart. Perhaps the most important to the technologist is the radiographic rating chart.

The **radiographic rating chart** shows which techniques are within the safe limits of operation for a particular tube. Any combination of kVp and time that lies above the curve representing the desired mA is unsafe.

The **anode cooling chart** displays the thermal capacity of the anode and the time required for the heated anode to cool. Thermal energy absorbed by the anode is measured in **heat units (HU).**

HU = kVp × mA × seconds for single-phase

HU = 1.35 kVp × mA × seconds for three-phase, six-pulse

HU = 1.41 kVp × mA × seconds for three-phase, twelve-pulse

The housing cooling chart gives the maximum heat capacity of the unit as well as the time required for the x-ray tube housing to cool down.

EXERCISES

Use the charts on p. 89 for exercises 1 to 21.

1 The high speed rotor (10,000 rpm) permits longer exposure times than the low speed rotor single-phase operation (3400 rpm). (T F)

2 If the intersection of time and kVp falls on an mA curve, that mA is safe. (T F)

3 Most of the troublesome heat generated in an x-ray tube occurs at the filament. (T F)

4 Generally, a small focal spot station will allow longer exposure times than a large focal spot station. (T F)

5 The radiographic rating chart reports the time that should elapse between exposures. (T F)

6 It is not possible to exceed the heat capacity of the housing without first exceeding that of the anode. (T F)

7 A tube can become "gassy" because of anode overheating and the release of gas. (T F)

8 The radiographic rating chart is designed primarily to protect the filament. (T F)

9 Rotor speed does not influence heat capacity. (T F)

10 Heat units (HU) can be expressed as exposure rate in R/m (C/kg-m). (T F)

Which of the following conditions of exposure are safe and which are unsafe (S or U)?

11 100 kVp, 150 mA, 500 ms; 3400 rpm, 0.6 mm focal spot U

12 100 kVp, 150 mA, 500 ms; 3400 rpm, 1.2 mm focal spot S

13 100 kVp, 150 mA, 500 ms; 10,000 rpm, 0.6 mm focal spot S

14 100 kVp, 150 mA, 500 ms; 10,000 rpm, 1.2 mm focal spot S

15 100 kVp, 700 mA, 1000 ms; 10,000 rpm, 1.2 mm focal spot U

16 60 kVp, 200 mA, 100 ms; 3400 rpm, 0.6 mm focal spot S

17 120 kVp, 200 mA, 700 ms; 10,000 rpm, 0.6 mm focal spot S

18 80 kVp, 300 mA, 2000 ms; 3400 rpm, 0.6 mm focal spot U

19 120 kVp, 150 mA, 10 ms; 3400 rpm, 0.6 mm focal spot U

20 105 kVp, 700 mA, 100 ms; 10,000 rpm, 1.2 mm focal spot S

21 A certain radiograph requires technique factors of 120 kVp and 25 mAs using a tube with a 0.6 mm focal spot and 10,000 rpm anode rotation. Find the combination of mA and the shortest possible time that will result in a safe exposure.

Use the charts on p. 90 for exercises 22 to 27.

22 How many heat units are produced by each of the techniques in exercises 11 to 20?

23 Would the total heat units of exercise 22 be within the limits of the housing capacity?

24 What is the maximum number of heat units the anode can absorb?

25 How long would it take the tube to cool down completely from this maximum heat of question 24?

26 If an anode absorbs 200,000 HU, how long will it take to cool completely?

27 If an anode absorbs 180,000 HU, how long must one wait before another 180,000 HU can be absorbed?

*Select the **one** correct answer in the following:*

28 To determine whether any set of charts is applicable for a given x-ray tube, one should
   a. make an exposure at a radiographic technique that exceeds the maximum permitted by the charts and check to see if the interlock circuit prevents the exposure.
   b. determine if the operating console allows all of the mA settings indicated for the radiographic rating chart.
   c. determine the type of tube, anode rotation, focal spot size, and the type of generator to make certain that all of these match the specifications on the chart.
   d. check to see that the operating console will allow operation at 150 kVp, since this is the maximum indicated on all radiographic rating charts.

29 Which of the following would be allowed according to the 1.2 mm/10,000 rpm radiographic rating chart on p. 89?
   a. 108 kVp/600 mA/1000 ms
   b. 88 kV/1000 mA/50 ms
   c. 90 kVp/800 mA/500 ms
   d. 82 kV/1000 mA/200 ms

30 If a single exposure were made with factors **slightly** exceeding those permitted by the appropriate radiographic rating chart, which of the following would be the **most** probable result?
   a. The tube filament would burn out.
   b. The anode would pit or crack.
   c. The rotor would freeze and stop.
   d. The useful life of the tube would be reduced.

31 If a single exposure were made with factors **greatly** exceeding those permitted by the appropriate radiographic rating chart, which of the following would be the **most** probable result?
   a. The tube filament would burn out.
   b. The anode would pit or crack.
   c. The rotor would freeze and stop.
   d. The glass envelope would be shattered.

32 Which of the following conditions will **not** damage an x-ray tube?
   a. exceeding the heat storage capacity of the tube housing
   b. exceeding the anode heat storage capacity
   c. exceeding the instantaneous filament emission rate
   d. exceeding the prescribed SID

33 In the design of a conventional rotating-anode x-ray tube
   a. the disk can be made thicker so that the rpm can be increased.
   b. most anodes rotate at either 3400 or 10,000 rpm.
   c. dual-focus tubes require two high voltage, step-up transformers.
   d. dual-focus tubes require two separate anodes.

34 Regarding the tube rating charts on p. 90,
   a. the maximum radiographic exposure time is shown on the anode cooling chart.
   b. the curves on the anode thermal characteristics chart labeled heat units per second refer to the fluoroscopic use of the tube.
   c. the housing cooling chart can be applied only to fluoroscopy.
   d. the anode thermal characteristics chart is for fluoroscopic use only.

35 A fluoroscopic examination at 85 kVp and 4 mA, single-phase requires 4 minutes. The number of anode heat units produced would be approximately
   a. 1360.
   b. 1836.
   c. 40,800.
   d. 81,600.

36 According to the anode thermal characteristics chart on p. 90,
   a. the maximum fluoroscopy time at 80 kVp and 2 mA is unlimited.
   b. the maximum fluoroscopy time at 80 kVp and 2 mA is approximately 6.5 minutes.
   c. maximum capacity is 180,000 HU.
   d. if 180,000 HU is generated, the time required for complete cooling is approximately 4 minutes.

37 The formula for heat units in a single-phase system is
   a. $kVp \times mA \times t$.
   b. $kVp \times mA \times t^2$.
   c. $kVp \times mAs \times t$.
   d. $kVp \times mAs \times t^2$.

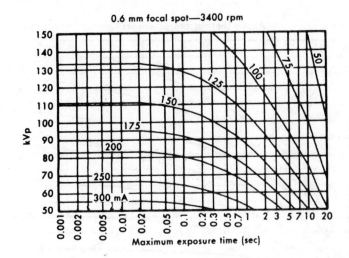

0.6 mm focal spot—3400 rpm

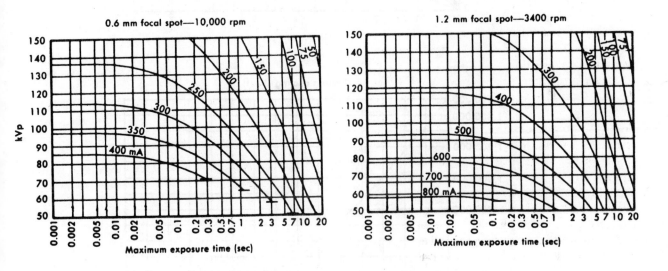

0.6 mm focal spot—10,000 rpm

1.2 mm focal spot—3400 rpm

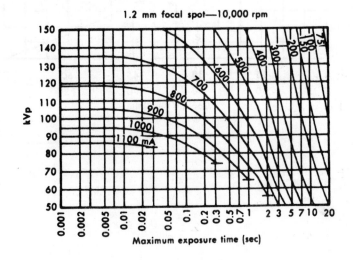

1.2 mm focal spot—10,000 rpm

Anode thermal characteristics

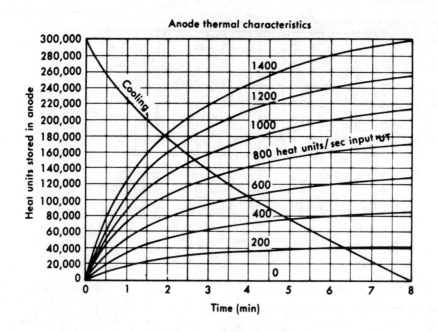

Housing cooling chart

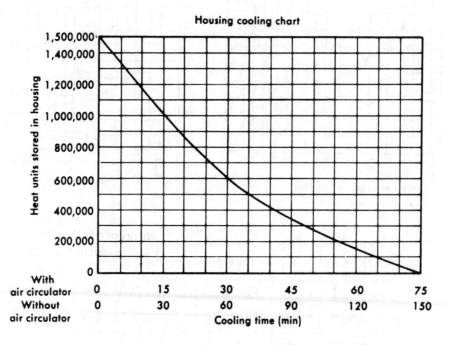

WORSHEET 38

X-ray Production

CHARACTERISTIC RADIATION
······················

In characteristic x-ray production, the projectile electron ionizes a target atom by the removal of a tightly bound inner-shell electron. The hole created in the inner electron shell of the target atom is filled by an outer-shell electron or a free electron falling into the hole. This transition of an electron from an outer shell to an inner shell is accompanied by the emission of an x-ray photon of energy equal to the difference in the binding energies of the two electron shells involved.

Energy of characteristic x ray =

$$BE_{K\text{-shell electron}} - BE_{L\text{-shell electron}}$$

Binding energy of ejected electron — Binding energy of replacement electron

Approximate binding energy (keV)

Shell	Molybdenum (Mo)	Tungsten (W)
K	20.0	69.0
L	3.0	12.0
M	0.5	2.0
N	—	1.0
O	—	0.1

EXERCISES

1 The kinetic energy of an
   a. electron is proportional to its mass squared.
   b. electron is inversely proportional to its mass squared.
   c. x ray is zero.
   d. x ray is proportional to its velocity squared.

2 If mass is expressed in kilograms and velocity in meters per second, kinetic energy will be expressed in
   a. joules.   c. ergs.
   b. coulombs.   d. electron volts.

3 The kinetic energy of the projectile electron
   a. causes ionization in the vacuum of the x-ray tube.
   b. causes excitation in the vacuum of the x-ray tube.
   c. is about 1% efficient in the production of x rays.
   d. is converted to mass.

4 The shift of the characteristic x-ray spectrum to the right will occur because of which of the following?
   a. an increase in kVp
   b. a decrease in kVp
   c. an increase in atomic number
   d. a decrease in atomic number

5 Useful characteristic x rays are produced in tungsten
   a. when the projectile electron interacts with an outer-shell electron.
   b. when a valence electron is removed.
   c. by excitation of a K-shell electron.
   d. by ionization of a K-shell electron.

6 An L-shell electron (binding energy 26 keV) is removed from an atom that has M-shell binding energy of 4 keV and N-shell binding energy of 1 keV. If a free electron fills the vacancy in the L shell, the characteristic x ray produced will have energy of
   a. 4 keV.   c. 25 keV.
   b. 22 keV.   d. 26 keV.

7 In a tungsten-targeted x-ray tube, which of the following characteristic x rays are useful in making a radiograph?
   a. K shell   c. M shell
   b. L shell   d. N shell

8 The energy of characteristic x rays increases with
   a. increasing kVp.
   b. increasing atomic mass of target material.
   c. increasing atomic number of target material.
   d. increasing added filtration.

9 X rays are produced when
   a. current flows through the x-ray tube filament.
   b. the x-ray tube filament is heated to thermionic emission.
   c. projectile electrons interact with target atoms.
   d. projectile electrons bounce off the cathode.

10 Characteristic x rays
   a. vary in energy as kVp is varied.
   b. have velocity varying from zero to the speed of light.
   c. are electromagnetic radiation.
   d. are characteristic of the filter material.
11 When a tungsten-targeted x-ray machine is operated at 68 kVp,
   a. some projectile electrons may have 68 keV of energy.
   b. some projectile electrons may have 75 keV of energy.
   c. one possible K-shell characteristic x ray will have 12 keV of energy.
   d. L-shell x rays cannot be produced.
12 According to the table at the beginning of this worksheet,
   a. tungsten obviously has a lower atomic number than molybdenum.
   b. tungsten obviously has more electrons than molybdenum.
   c. the L-shell characteristic x rays from molybdenum are higher energy than L-shell characteristic x rays from tungsten.
   d. the K-shell characteristic x rays of molybdenum are lower in energy than the L-shell characteristic x rays of tungsten.
13 When x rays are produced in a target material, the electron binding energies of that material are characteristic of the
   a. type of x rays.
   b. filtration of the x rays.
   c. orientation of the target.
   d. atomic number of the target.
14 The target of an x-ray tube consists of atoms of the following electron binding energies: K shell—84 keV; L shell—14 keV; M shell—4 keV. If the x-ray machine is operated at 70 kVp, which of the following characteristic x rays will be produced?
   a. 10 keV   c. 80 keV
   b. 70 keV   d. 84 keV

15 Gold is sometimes used as target material in special types of radiation-producing machines. Its electron binding energies are as follows: K shell—81 keV; L shell—14 keV; M shell—3 keV; N shell—1 keV. Which of the following characteristic x rays will be produced with operation at 90 kVp?
   a. 90 keV
   b. 87 keV
   c. 76 keV
   d. 67 keV
16 The kinetic energy of a projectile electron can be measured in
   a. rads.
   b. joules.
   c. coulombs.
   d. amperes.
17 The efficiency of diagnostic x-ray production is
   a. in excess of 5%.
   b. greater than therapy x-ray production.
   c. independent of tube voltage.
   d. independent of tube current.
18 When the projectile electron excites an outer shell electron _____ is/are produced.
   a. characteristic x rays
   b. bremsstrahlung x rays
   c. heat
   d. energy
19 Which of the following electron transitions in tungsten will result in the highest energy x ray?
   a. K to M   c. O to K
   b. K to O   d. M to K
20 An M to K electron transition in tungsten will result in what energy x ray?
   a. 2 keV   c. 67 keV
   b. 12 keV   d. 69 keV
21 The energy of an
   a. electron is proportional to its mass squared.
   b. electron is inversely proportional to its mass squared.
   c. x ray is proportional to frequency.
   d. x ray is proportional to its velocity squared.

Name _____

Date _____

X-ray Production

BREMSSTRAHLUNG RADIATION
....

Bremsstrahlung x rays are produced when a projectile electron from the cathode does not interact with an orbital electron of a target atom but passes close enough to the nucleus to come under its influence. As the projectile electron passes by the nucleus, it is slowed down and its direction is changed. Therefore it leaves the atom with reduced kinetic energy. The loss in kinetic energy reappears as an x-ray photon. These are bremsstrahlung x rays. They can have energy ranging from zero to a maximum equal to the projectile electron energy. The most frequent bremsstrahlung x-ray energy is about one third the maximum energy of the projectile electron.

EXERCISES

1 In a tungsten-targeted x-ray tube operated at 90 kVp the most abundant x-ray would be
  a. a 10 keV bremsstrahlung x ray.
  b. a 30 keV bremsstrahlung x ray.
  c. a 12 keV characteristic x ray.
  d. a 69 keV characteristic x ray.
2 Which of the following electron transitions results in the most useful bremsstrahlung x ray?
  a. L to K
  b. M to K
  c. M to L
  d. none of the above
3 Bremsstrahlung radiation is produced by
  a. projectile electron–target electron interaction.
  b. conversion of the kinetic energy of the projectile electron to electromagnetic energy.
  c. target electron–nuclear interaction.
  d. conversion of the kinetic energy of the target electron to electromagnetic energy.

4 When a bremsstrahlung x ray is produced,
  a. a target electron will be displaced.
  b. a target electron will be excited.
  c. a projectile electron will lose energy.
  d. a projectile electron will be absorbed.
5 In bremsstrahlung x-ray production
  a. the projectile electron originates in the cathode.
  b. the projectile electron is bound to an atom of tungsten.
  c. the target electron originates in the cathode.
  d. the target electron exists as a free electron.
6 If an average radiographic technique is used,
  a. most x rays are characteristic.
  b. most x rays are bremsstrahlung.
  c. ionization of the target will be almost complete.
  d. the maximum-energy x ray is equal to the K-electron binding energy.
7 When a radiographic technique calls for 74 kVp/80 mAs, which of the following bremsstrahlung x rays will appear?
  a. 12 keV
  b. 69 keV
  c. 74 keV
  d. all of the above
8 If x rays are emitted at 74 kVp/80 mAs,
  a. characteristic x rays will be emitted only at 74 keV.
  b. bremsstrahlung x rays will be emitted at discrete energies.
  c. the energy of characteristic x rays will increase if the voltage is increased to 84 kVp.
  d. the energy of bremsstrahlung x rays will increase if the voltage is increased to 84 kVp.
9 If radiographic operation at 60 kVp/80 mAs is changed to operation at 80 kVp/80 mAs,
  a. characteristic x rays will remain unchanged.
  b. bremsstrahlung x rays will remain unchanged.
  c. the number of projectile electrons will increase.
  d. the number of x rays produced will increase.

10 Bremsstrahlung x rays produced in a tungsten-targeted tube
   a. outnumber characteristic x rays.
   b. are produced in fewer numbers than characteristic x rays.
   c. are all diagnostically useful.
   d. are generally less useful than characteristic x rays.

11 When a bremsstrahlung x ray is emitted,
   a. it results from the conversion of kinetic energy.
   b. the target atom is ionized.
   c. an inner-shell electron is removed from the target atom.
   d. an outer-shell electron is removed from the target atom.

12 The wavelength of a bremsstrahlung x ray
   a. is proportional to its frequency.
   b. is a function of the change in electron kinetic energy.
   c. increases with increasing projectile electron energy.
   d. is longest when the projectile electron loses all its kinetic energy.

13 As projectile electron energy increases
   a. more x rays are produced.
   b. more x rays are produced but only at low energies.
   c. characteristic x-ray energy increases.
   d. characteristic x-ray energy decreases.

14 Bremsstrahlung x-ray production increases with
   a. increasing target atomic number.
   b. decreasing mA.
   c. increasing filtration.
   d. increasing SID.

15 The output intensity of an x-ray tube is
   a. monoenergetic.
   b. limited by the K-shell binding energy.
   c. primarily due to bremsstrahlung x rays.
   d. often measured in curies (Becquerels).

16 Which of the following projectile electron–target electron interactions results in x-ray emission?
   a. excitation of outer-shell electrons
   b. excitation of inner-shell electrons
   c. ionization of outer-shell electrons
   d. ionization of inner-shell electrons

17 When a projectile electron from a filament enters a target atom and interacts with the nuclear force field, it will
   a. increase in velocity.
   b. decrease in velocity.
   c. ionize the atom.
   d. remove an inner-shell electron.

18 If a 50 keV projectile electron undergoes a bremsstrahlung interaction and it emerges from the atom with 20 keV of energy,
   a. an x ray will not be emitted.
   b. a 20 keV x ray will be emitted.
   c. a 30 keV x ray will be emitted.
   d. a 50 keV x ray will be emitted.

19 A 68 keV projectile electron is directed onto a tungsten target. Which of the following bremsstrahlung x rays could be produced?
   a. 12 keV
   b. 57 keV
   c. 68 keV
   d. all of the above

20 During bremsstrahlung interactions
   a. electrostatic attractive forces are present.
   b. electrostatic repulsive forces are present.
   c. attractive and repulsive magnetic forces are present.
   d. gravitational forces are present.

21 When a projectile electron undergoes a bremsstrahlung interaction it
   a. can increase in energy.
   b. transfers energy to the nucleus.
   c. can lose any amount of its kinetic energy.
   d. can lose up to one third of its kinetic energy.

22 Bremsstrahlung x rays are produced only at
   a. discrete energies.
   b. energies above characteristic x rays.
   c. energies below characteristic x rays.
   d. energies up to projectile electron energy.

23 An increase in mAs will
   a. increase the efficiency of bremsstrahlung production.
   b. increase the number of bremsstrahlung x rays.
   c. increase both efficiency and number of bremsstrahlung x rays.
   d. does not affect bremsstrahlung production.

24 An increase in kVp will
   a. increase the energy of bremsstrahlung x rays.
   b. increase the number of bremsstrahlung x rays.
   c. increase both efficiency and number of bremsstrahlung x rays.
   d. does not affect bremsstrahlung production.

25 An increase in which of the following will result in a reduction in bremsstrahlung emission?
   a. filtration
   b. phase
   c. target mass
   d. time

Name _____

Date _____

X-ray Production

X-RAY EMISSION SPECTRUM

....

An x-ray emission spectrum is a graph of the relative number of x-ray photons plotted as a function of the energy of each photon. Two different types of x-ray emission spectra comprise the total x-ray emission spectrum. The characteristic x-ray emission spectrum represents monoenergetic x rays emitted following ionization of the target atom. It consists of vertical lines at fixed energies and is called a **discrete** x-ray emission spectrum.

The bremsstrahlung x-ray emission spectrum, on the other hand, results from photons created by the bremsstrahlung process and has energy ranging from zero to the maximum pojectile electron energy. This spectrum is called the **continuous** emission spectrum, and it has its maximum amplitude at an energy approximately one third the maximum energy. When combined, the discrete and the continuous emission spectra are the total x-ray emission spectrum and appear as shown at the right.

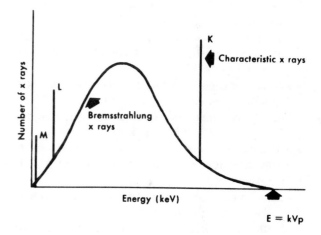

EXERCISES

1 The area under the curve of the x-ray emission spectrum is representative of
   a. the total energy of the x rays.
   b. the average energy of the x rays.
   c. the total number of x rays.
   d. the average number of x rays per unit energy.

2 Normally, the x-ray emission spectrum contains
   a. both characteristic and bremsstrahlung x rays.
   b. only characteristic x rays.
   c. only bremsstrahlung x rays.
   d. only discrete lines.

3 The characteristic x-ray emission spectrum principally depends on
   a. kVp.   **c.** target material.
   b. mAs.   **d.** projectile electron energy.

4 The continuous x-ray emission spectrum principally depends on
   a. exposure time.
   b. mA.
   c. target material.
   d. projectile electron energy.

5 Which of the following factors **does not** explain the low number of x rays produced at low energy?
   a. the low energy of some projectile electrons
   b. the glass envelope enclosing the x-ray tube
   c. the thickness of the filter
   d. the product of tube current and exposure time

6 The x-ray emission spectrum represents
   a. projectile electron energy.
   b. the atomic mass and number of the target atom.
   c. x rays emitted from the tube.
   d. the electron binding energy of target material.

7 Both the shape and position of the characteristic x-ray emission spectrum
   a. are representative of projectile electron energy.
   b. correspond to target electron binding energies.
   c. can be described as continuous.
   d. are described by the number of projectile electrons.

8 Both the shape and position of the bremsstrahlung x-ray emission spectrum
   a. are representative of projectile electron energy.
   b. correspond to target electron binding energies.
   c. can be described as discrete.
   d. decrease with increasing mAs.

9 The x-ray emission spectrum is a plot of
   a. x rays and electrons emitted from cathode atoms.
   b. x rays and electrons emitted from target atoms.
   c. the number of electrons vs. energy.
   d. the number of x rays vs. energy.

10 The shape of the bremsstrahlung x-ray emission spectrum
   a. approaches maximum amplitude at zero energy.
   b. approaches maximum amplitude at an energy equal to the kVp.
   c. has maximum amplitude at an energy equal to the kVp.
   d. has maximum amplitude at an energy approximately one third of the kVp.

11 If the x-ray emission spectrum shown in this worksheet represents operation at 85 kVp with a tungsten target,
   a. at 85 keV the number of electrons emitted would be at a maximum.
   b. the K-characteristic x-ray emission would occur at 69 keV.
   c. x rays representing minimum frequency would occur near 69 keV.
   d. x rays representing minimum wavelength would occur near 0 keV.

12 If the x-ray emission spectrum shown in this worksheet represents operation at 50 kVp with a molybdenum target
   a. K-characteristic x rays would not be produced.
   b. the characteristic radiation would have energy of 20 keV.
   c. the minimum-wavelength x rays would have energy of 20 keV.
   d. the minimum-wavelength x rays would have an energy of approximately 17 keV.

13 Which of the following factors principally accounts for the reduced intensity of x-ray emission at low energy?
   a. the atomic number of the target material
   b. the energy spectrum of the projectile electrons
   c. added filtration
   d. beam collimation

14 Which of the following factors principally accounts for the reduced intensity of x-ray emission at high energy?
   a. the atomic number of the target material
   b. the energy spectrum of the projectile electrons
   c. added filtration
   d. beam collimation

15 Molybdenum has a lower atomic number than tungsten; therefore the molybdenum emission spectrum will
   a. have higher amplitude.
   b. have lower amplitude.
   c. extend to higher energies.
   d. extend to lower energies.

16 In order to construct an x-ray emission spectrum, one must know the
   a. kVp and mAs.
   b. target element and filtration.
   c. projectile electron number and energy.
   d. x ray number and energy.

17 When comparing the emission spectra of molybdenum with tungsten, both at 60 kVp/20 mAs,
   a. molybdenum will be more penetrating.
   b. molybdenum characteristic x rays will have higher energy.
   c. tungsten characteristic x rays will have higher energy.
   d. tungsten will have fewer bremsstrahlung x rays.

18 The area under the x-ray emission spectrum best represents
   a. the total number of x rays.
   b. the total number of projectile electrons.
   c. kVp.
   d. keV.

19 The position of the discrete spectrum along the x axis is best represented by
   a. projectile electron kinetic energy.
   b. target electron binding energy differences.
   c. kVp.
   d. keV.

20 The composite x-ray emission spectrum is composed of _____ separate x-ray emission spectra.
   a. one
   b. two
   c. four
   d. six

Name _____

Date _____

X-ray Production

MINIMUM WAVELENGTH
....

X-ray emission spectra are often expressed as a function of x-ray photon wavelength rather than energy. This is a holdover from early classic physics texts, and, although it is not meaningful today to employ wavelength instead of energy to identify x rays, it is still done and may occur on certain professional examinations. Because photon energy and wavelength are inversely proportional, the highest photon energy corresponds to the shortest photon wavelength, or **minimum wavelength.**

Planck's equation is

$$E = h\nu$$

where

$$\nu = c/\lambda$$

therefore

$$E = \frac{hc}{\lambda}$$

$$E = \frac{(4.14 \times 10^{-15} \text{ eV s})\,(3 \times 10^8 \text{ m/s})}{\lambda}$$

$$E = \frac{12.4 \times 10^{-7} \text{ eV m}}{\lambda} \times \frac{1\text{keV}}{10^3 \text{ eV}}$$

$$E = \frac{12.4 \times 10^{-10} \text{ keV m}}{\lambda}$$

This equation can be rearranged to solve for λ, the wavelength of a photon having energy E in keV:

$$\lambda = \frac{12.4 \times 10^{-10} \text{ keV m}}{E}$$

Minimum wavelength corresponds to the photons with maximum energy, which are of course those produced at the peak tube voltage:

$$\lambda_{min} = \frac{12.4 \times 10^{-10} \text{ keV m}}{kVp}$$

Using the appropriate conversion factor, λ_{min} is usually expressed in nanometers (nm) or Angstroms (Å).

$$\lambda_{min} \text{ (nm)} = \frac{1.24}{kVp}$$

$$\lambda_{min} \text{ (Å)} = \frac{12.4}{kVp}$$

EXERCISES

1 As x-ray photon energy increases, _____ decreases.
   a. photon wavelength   c. target electron energy
   b. photon frequency   d. projectile electron
                                 energy

2 The wavelength of an x-ray photon is
   a. directly proportional to its energy.
   b. inversely proportional to its energy.
   c. determined by the number of projectile electrons.
   d. determined by the number of target electrons.

3 The product of Planck's constant (h) and the velocity of light (c) has units of
   a. eVm.   c. m/keV.
   b. keV/m.   d. m/eV.

4 The product of Planck's constant (h) and the velocity of light (c) equals
   a. 12.4 eVm.   c. 12.4×10^{-5} eVm.
   b. 12.4 keVm.   d. 12.4×10^{-7} eVm.

5 If the minimum wavelength of a given x ray is 10 angstroms (Å), it is also
   a. 1 nm.   c. 100 nm.
   b. 10 nm.   d. 1000 nm.

6 If one knows the minimum wavelength of a given x-ray beam, the kVp of operation can be determined if one also knows
   a. the mA.   c. Planck's constant.
   b. the mAs.   d. that nothing more is
                        needed.

93

7 Indicate which of the following figures represents an x-ray emission spectrum:

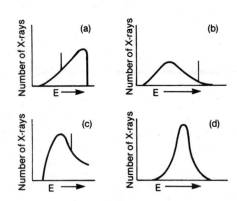

8 The relationship of minimum wavelength of x-ray emission to maximum photon energy expressed in angstroms is sometimes referred to as the
   a. Hurter-Driffield curve.
   b. Dwayne-Hunt law.
   c. Faraday law.
   d. quantum theory of Planck.

9 Minimum wavelength is related to
   a. the kinetic energy of the projectile electron.
   b. the atomic number of the target material.
   c. the total filtration in the x-ray beam.
   d. the degree of collimation of the x-ray beam.

10 In any x-ray emission spectrum, the part of the spectrum associated with the minimum wavelength is
   a. the intersection of the two axes.
   b. the lowest energy characteristic line.
   c. the highest energy characteristic line.
   d. the energy corresponding to maximum x-ray energy.

11 A tungsten-targeted, single-phase x-ray machine is operated at 82 kVp. What is the associated minimum wavelength?
   a. 0.015 nm   **c.** 0.015 Å
   b. 0.15 nm   **d.** 0.0015 Å

12 A molybdenum-targeted x-ray tube is operated at 35 kVp. What is the minimum wavelength?
   a. 0.6 nm   **c.** 0.35 Å
   b. 0.06 nm   **d.** 0.57 Å

13 If one knows the minimum wavelength of an x-ray emission spectrum, one can calculate
   a. mA.   **c.** maximum projectile
   b. mAs.   electron energy.
                        d. maximum filtration.

14 To calculate the minimum wavelength of x-ray operation, the numeric value of _____ must be known.
   a. mAs   **c.** phase
   b. kVp   **d.** filtration

15 What is the wavelength of a ^{99m}Tc gamma ray which has an energy of 140 keV?
   a. 0.0089 nm   **c.** 0.89 Å
   b. 0.089 nm   **d.** 8.9 Å

Name_____

Date_____

X-ray Production

FACTORS AFFECTING THE X-RAY EMISSION SPECTRUM
....

The shape of the emission spectrum and its relative position vary with changes in kVp, mAs, filtration, target material, and the voltage waveform. An understanding of the effect that each of these technique factors has on the emission spectrum will allow more precise technique selection. Higher amplitude in the emission spectrum represents higher x-ray intensity (beam quantity), whereas a shift of the spectrum to the right along the energy axis represents higher penetrability (beam quality).

In general, the following relationships apply:

1. Increasing kVp increases the height of the x-ray emission spectrum and extends it to the right along the energy axis.
2. Increasing mAs increases the height of the x-ray emission spectrum.
3. Increasing filtration decreases the height of the x-ray emission spectrum and shifts the shape to the right along the energy axis.
4. Changing to a higher atomic number x-ray target will increase the x-ray emission spectrum amplitude, shift the spectrum to the right, and result in higher energy characteristic lines.
5. Changing from half-wave to full-wave rectification doubles the height of the spectrum. Changing from single-phase to three-phase power will result in greater amplitude and a shift to the right on the energy axis.

EXERCISES

1 Which of the following statements apply to the x-ray emission spectrum?
 a. Adding filtration affects minimum wavelength (peak energy).
 b. Adding filtration affects the position of the characteristic x-ray emission spectrum.
 c. The target material affects the amplitude of the bremsstrahlung x-ray emission spectrum.
 d. The target material affects the minimum wavelength (peak energy).

2 An increase in mAs results in an increase in the
 a. amplitude of only the characteristic x-ray emission spectrum.
 b. amplitude of only the bremsstrahlung x-ray emission spectrum.
 c. amplitude of both the characteristic and the bremsstrahlung x-ray emission spectra.
 d. minimum wavelength.

3 An increase in kVp results in an increase in
 a. the amplitude of only the characteristic x-ray emission spectrum.
 b. the amplitude of only the bremsstrahlung x-ray emission spectrum.
 c. the minimum wavelength.
 d. radiation quality.

4 The intensity of the total exposure (total mAs) is represented by the
 a. amplitude of the bremsstrahlung x-ray emission spectrum.
 b. amplitude of the characteristic x-ray emission spectrum.
 c. amplitude of highest emission spectrum.
 d. area under the emission spectrum.

Examine the following figure and answer exercises 5 to 8:

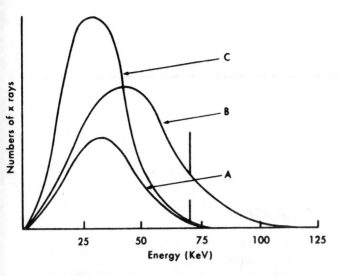

5 In the illustration curves, _____ have equal minimum wavelength and equal maximum energy.
   a. *A* and *B*
   b. *B* and *C*
   c. *A* and *C*
   d. *A, B,* and *C*
6 The three spectra illustrated could have been obtained by operation at the same
   a. kVp.
   b. total mAs.
   c. exposure time.
   d. minimum wavelength.
7 Of the three curves represented
   a. *A* and *C* were probably produced at the same mAs.
   b. *A* and *C* were probably produced at the same kVp.
   c. *A* is probably single phase and *C* three phase.
   d. *A* and *B* probably represent two different targets.
8 Of the three spectra
   a. *C* is more penetrating than *A.*
   b. *A* is more penetrating than *C.*
   c. *C* is more penetrating than *B.*
   d. *B* is more penetrating than *C.*
9 Which of the following factors affects primarily the left or low energy side of the x-ray emission spectrum?
   a. tube current
   b. tube voltage
   c. filtration
   d. voltage waveform
10 In general, when changes are made that affect the x-ray emission spectrum
   a. and the spectrum shifts to the left, a higher quality beam is emitted.
   b. and the spectrum shifts to the right, a more penetrating beam is emitted.
   c. and the spectrum shifts to the left, more filtration was used.
   d. and the amplitude increases, the radiation quantity will decrease.

Answer the remaining exercises about an emission spectrum that represents a diagnostic machine operated at 80 kVp/200 mA/100 ms.

11 How would the bremsstrahlung spectrum change if operation were at 64 kVp/200 mA/100 ms? Its relative position would
   a. shift to the left, and the amplitude would be lower.
   b. shift to the right.
   c. remain the same, but the amplitude would increase.
   d. remain the same, but the amplitude would decrease.
12 How would the characteristic spectrum change if operation were at 64 kVp/200 mA/20 ms? The characteristic x-ray lines would
   a. shift slightly to the left.
   b. shift slightly to the right.
   c. increase in height.
   d. disappear.
13 How would the total emission spectrum be affected by operation at 80 kVp/400 mA/100 ms? The relative position of the spectrum would
   a. shift to the left, and the amplitude would be lower.
   b. shift to the right.
   c. remain the same, but the amplitude would increase.
   d. remain the same, but the amplitude would decrease.
14 How would the emission spectrum be affected by the addition of 2 mm Al filtration? The relative position of the spectrum would
   a. shift to the left, and the amplitude would be lower.
   b. shift to the right, and the amplitude would be lower.
   c. remain the same, but the amplitude would increase.
   d. remain the same, but the amplitude would decrease.
15 How would the emission spectrum be affected if the power supply were changed from single phase to three phase? The relative position of the spectrum would
   a. shift to the left, the amplitude would increase, and the characteristic lines would increase in height.
   b. shift to the right, the amplitude would increase, and the characteristic lines would increase in height.
   c. remain the same, the amplitude would increase, and the characteristic lines would increase in height.
   d. not change, but the energy of the characteristic lines would increase.

WORKSHEET 43

X-ray Emission

X-RAY QUANTITY

....

The intensity of x rays in the useful beam is measured in roentgens (R) (or C/kg) and milliroentgens (mR) and is referred to as x-ray quantity. At 70 kVp the output intensity (or quantity) of a radiographic tube ranges from about 3 to 10 mR/mAs at 100 cm source-to-image receptor distance (SID). This wide range of x-ray emission quantity exists because of differences in tube design, filtration, and voltage generation.

There are three adjustable factors that affect x-ray quantity:

1. mAs—x-ray quantity is directly proportional to milliampere-seconds:

$$\frac{I_1}{I_2} = \frac{mAs_1}{mAs_2}$$

2. kVp—x-ray quantity varies approximately as the square of the change in kVp:

$$\frac{I_1}{I_2} = \left(\frac{kVp_1}{(kVp)_2}\right)^2$$

3. Distance—x-ray quantity varies inversely with the square of the distance from the target (the inverse square law):

$$\frac{I_1}{I_2} = \left(\frac{d_2}{d_1}\right)^2$$

Employing these factors collectively, we can estimate x-ray exposure of a patient to a reasonable approximation by the following equation:

$$\text{Exposure (mR)} = \frac{15\,(mAs)\,(kVp)^2}{(d)^2}$$

where d is the source-to-skin distance in centimeters. The constant 15 is an average value and will vary from about 10 to 30, depending on many factors, such as kVp, voltage phase, filtration, or field size.

EXERCISES

1 When the mAs is increased, x-ray quantity
   a. increases as the square of the mAs.
   b. increases proportionately.
   c. decreases proportionately.
   d. decreases as the square of the mAs.
2 When the kVp is increased, x-ray quantity
   a. increases as the square of the kVp.
   b. increases proportionately.
   c. decreases proportionately.
   d. decreases as the square of the kVp.
3 When distance is increased, x-ray quantity
   a. increases as the square of the distance.
   b. increases proportionately.
   c. decreases proportionately.
   d. decreases as the square of the distance.
4 When tube filtration is increased, x-ray quantity
   a. increases proportionately.
   b. increases exponentially.
   c. decreases in a complex fashion.
   d. decreases proportionately.
5 In general, x-ray quantity will increase with a(an)
   a. decrease in tube current.
   b. decrease in exposure time.
   c. increase in kVp.
   d. increase in distance.
6 The output of an x-ray machine is usually measured as
   a. absorbed dose in roentgens.
   b. exposure in roentgens.
   c. absorbed dose in rad.
   d. exposure in rad.

7 A tungsten-targeted x-ray machine is operated at 63 kVp/150 mAs and has an output intensity of 600 mR (155 µC/kg). Therefore
   a. the most frequent x-ray emission will be in the 20 to 25 keV range.
   b. no useful bremsstrahlung radiation will be produced.
   c. most electron target atom interactions will result in x-ray emission.
   d. if the mAs is increased to 200, the minimum wavelength will be increased.

8 X-ray quantity should be measured in
   a. C/kg.   c. Sv.
   b. Gy.   d. Bq.

9 Another way to express x-ray quantity is x-ray
   a. energy.   c. intensity.
   b. quality.   d. penetrability.

10 Which of the following does **not** affect x-ray quantity?
   a. mA   c. radioactivity
   b. time   d. filtration

11 In order to maintain a constant film density, an increase of _____ in kVp should be accompanied by a reduction of one half in mAs.
   a. 5%   c. 15%
   b. 10%   d. 30%

12 An extremity radiograph requires 5 mAs and results in an exposure of 18 mR. What will be the exposure if the mAs is changed to 7?
   a. 13 mR   c. 25 mR
   b. 15 mR   d. 36 mR

13 An abdominal view is taken at 82 kVp and results in a patient exposure of 132 mR. To improve contrast the kVp is changed to 74. What is the new patient exposure?
   a. 108 mR   c. 146 mR
   b. 119 mR   d. 162 mR

14 A portable chest x ray is taken at 80 cm SID and the patient exposure is 28 mR. What will the exposure be if the distance is increased to 180 cm?
   a. 6 mR   c. 63 mR
   b. 12 mR   d. 142 mR

15 The output intensity for an x-ray unit operated at 70 kVp/400 mA and 50 ms is 70 mR (18 µC/kg). If the mA selector is changed to 600 mA and the exposure time is increased to 80 ms, what will be the output intensity?
   a. 105 mR   c. 168 mR
   b. 112 mR   d. 210 mR

16 An x-ray unit employed for mammography is normally operated at 30 kVp and produces 0.4 mR/mAs (0.1 µC/kg-mAs). If the kVp is increased to 48 with other factors remaining constant, the output will be
   a. 0.64 mR/mAs.
   b. 1.02 mR/mAs.
   c. 1.6 mR/mAs.
   d. 2.56 mR/mAs.

17 A mammogram was taken with factors 28 kVp/400 mA/500 ms at an SID of 60 cm, resulting in an exposure of 800 mR (206 µC/kg). If greater detail is required and the SID is increased to 75 cm, what will be the output intensity, with other factors remaining equal?
   a. 512 mR   c. 800 mR
   b. 640 mR   d. 1000 mR

18 At 70 kVp/100 mAs, the exposure is 250 mR (65 µC/kg). At 80 kVp/50 mAs, the expected exposure will be
   a. 125 mR.   c. 286 mR.
   b. 163 mR.   d. 653 mR.

19 A lumbar spine technique calls for 78 kVp/400 mA/500 ms at 100 cm SID and results in an exposure of 1000 mR (258 µC/kg). If the same machine is used for a lateral skull radiograph at 66 kVp/200 mA/800 ms at 80 cm SID, what will be the new x-ray quantity?
   a. 573 mR   c. 846 mR
   b. 716 mR   d. 895 mR

20 The output of a radiographic unit is 0.35 mR/mAs (0.9 µC/kg-mAs) at 70 kVp. What is the expected exposure at 86 kVp/600 mA/200 ms?
   a. 1.5 mR   c. 181 mR
   b. 63.4 mR   d. 517 mR

Name _____

Date _____

X-ray Emission

X-RAY QUALITY
....

HALF-VALUE LAYER
....

An x-ray beam that easily penetrates soft tissue and bone is said to be of high quality, whereas a beam that is readily absorbed is referred to as low quality. X-ray quality therefore is a measure of the penetrating power of an x-ray beam. A hard x-ray beam is a high quality beam; a soft x-ray beam is a low quality beam.

X-ray quality is influenced by a number of factors. As the kVp of operation is increased, the penetrating power of the x-ray beam increases and therefore quality increases. Similarly, when filtration is added to the beam, it becomes more penetrating, harder, and therefore of higher quality. Tube current (mA), time, and distance do not influence the quality of an x-ray beam.

X-ray beam quality is usually measured by the **half-value layer (HVL).** The HVL is that thickness of an absorber that will reduce the x-ray intensity to one half its original value. Diagnostic beams have HVLs ranging from about 1 to 5 mm Al. The average beam will have a total filtration of 2.5 mm Al, and this will result in an HVL of approximately 2.2 mm Al at 70 kVp.

Usually beam quality cannot be computed. It must be measured experimentally.

EXERCISES

1 Which of the following is the **most** appropriate measure of x-ray beam quality?
 a. kVp   **c.** mAs
 b. HVL   **d.** total filtration
2 The quality of an x-ray beam is chiefly governed by its
 a. mAs.   **c.** SID.
 b. field size.   **d.** kVp.

3 The HVL is affected by a change in the
 a. mAs.
 b. source-to-skin distance.
 c. x-ray intensity.
 d. kVp.
4 When filtration is added to an x-ray tube, _____ increases.
 a. radiation output
 b. radiation quality
 c. radiation quantity
 d. SID
5 Which of the following is the probable HVL of a radiographic beam at 70 kVp?
 a. 0.5 cm soft tissue   **c.** 0.5 cm Al
 b. 5.0 cm soft tissue   **d.** 5.0 cm Al
6 As filtration is added to an x-ray beam
 a. high energy x rays are removed more readily than low energy x rays.
 b. all x rays are removed about equally from the useful beam.
 c. low energy x rays are removed more readily than high energy x rays.
 d. no x rays are removed, but their energy changes.
7 An increase in mAs will increase
 a. x-ray quantity.
 b. x-ray quality.
 c. HVL.
 d. total filtration.
8 It is often stated that mAs controls quantity and kVp controls
 a. output.   **c.** quality.
 b. total filtration.   **d.** SID.
9 However, it should be clear tha mAs controls quantity and kVp controls
 a. output and total filtration.
 b. total filtration and quality.
 c. SID and quality.
 d. quality and quantity.

10 If the mA during fluoroscopy is increased by 25%,
  a. the x-ray output is decreased by 25%.
  b. the scatter exposure to the operator is decreased by 25%.
  c. the scatter exposure to the operator is increased by 25%.
  d. the effective energy of the beam is increased.

11 A minimum HVL is required for diagnostic x-ray beams because
  a. a lower HVL would result in an increased absorbed dose to the patient with no improvement in film quality.
  b. a greater HVL would result in an increased absorbed dose to the patient with no improvement in film quality.
  c. a lower HVL would result in decreased subject contrast.
  d. a greater HVL would mean lower than average x-ray energy.

12 An x-ray beam can be made harder by
  a. increasing mAs.   **c.** adding filtration.
  b. increasing SID.   **d.** removing filtration.

13 From the data below, obtained at 30 kVp, which of the following is closest to the HVL?

mm A1	0	0.5	1.0	1.5	2.0
mR	94	69	52	39	30

  a. 0.75 mm A1   **c.** 1.25 mm A1
  b. 1.0 mm A1   **d.** 1.5 mm A1

14 Which of the following can be employed to improve x-ray beam quality?
  a. mAs   **c.** SID
  b. mA   **d.** total filtration

15 Reducing kVp will
  a. soften the x-ray beam.
  b. harden the x-ray beam.
  c. increase the x-ray quantity.
  d. increase the x-ray quality.

16 Changing the kVp influences the value of
  a. x-ray quantity.
  b. x-ray quality.
  c. both of the above.
  d. none of the above.

17 Adding filtration to an x-ray tube will
  a. increase x-ray quality.
  b. decrease x-ray quality.
  c. increase x-ray quantity.
  d. increase inherent filtration.

18 A radiographic tube has 0.5 mm Al inherent filtration, 1.0 mm A1 added filtration, and 1.0 mm A1 filtration in the light localizing collimator. Therefore the total filtration is
  a. 0.5 mm A1.   **c.** 2.0 mm A1.
  b. 1.0 mm A1.   **d.** 2.5 mm A1.

19 A representative radiographic tube has 0.5 mm A1 inherent filtration and 2.0 mm A1 added filtration. Therefore
  a. the total filtration is 1.5 mm Al.
  b. an additional 1.0 mm Al will increase total filtration to 3.0 mm Al.
  c. 1.0 mm Al additional filtration will harden the x-ray beam.
  d. an additional 1.0 mm Al will increase the x-ray quantity.

20 Which of the following is the softest radiation?
  a. diagnostic x rays   **c.** megavoltage x rays
  b. orthovoltage x rays   **d.** Grenz rays

21 Half-value layer is defined as
  a. twice the required shielding.
  b. half the required shielding.
  c. a thickness of attenuator that will halve x-ray quantity.
  d. a thickness of attenuator that will double x-ray quantity.

22 To measure HVL, which of the following is needed?
  a. a collimator   **c.** a penetrometer
  b. a sensitometer   **d.** aluminum absorbers

23 As the HVL of a beam increases, its penetrability
  a. increases as Z^2.   **c.** decreases.
  b. increases.   **d.** decreases as Z^2.

24 If the HVL is increased by increasing the kVp, x-ray quantity will
  a. increase by kVp^2.   **c.** decrease.
  b. increase.   **d.** decrease by kVp^2.

25 If the HVL is increased by the addition of 1 mm Al, x-ray quantity will
  a. increase by $(mm\ Al)^2$.   **c.** decrease.
  b. increase.   **d.** decrease by $(mm\ Al)^2$.

26 At 70 kVp the x-ray beam is attenuated in soft tissue approximately
  a. 0.05%/cm.   **c.** 5%/cm.
  b. 0.5%/cm.   **d.** 50%/cm.

Examine the following illustration and answer exercises 27 to 28:

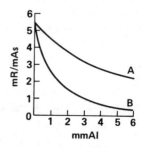

27 The approximate HVL of curve A is closest to
  a. 1 mm Al.   **c.** 3 mm Al.
  b. 2 mm Al.   **d.** 4 mm Al.

28 The approximate HVL of curve B is closest to
  a. 1 mm Al.   **c.** 3 mm Al.
  b. 2 mm Al.   **d.** 4 mm Al.

X-ray Emission

FILTRATION
....

Filters are metal sheets placed in the radiation beam to attenuate low energy radiation before it reaches the patient. In diagnosis the metal filters are either aluminum or molybdenum and are used specifically for reducing patient dose. In diagnostic x-ray tube assemblies two types of filtration may be used:

1. **Inherent filtration**—resulting from the glass envelope of the tube and the window in the tube housing. The inherent filtration of a radiographic tube is usually equivalent to about 0.5 mm Al.
2. **Added filtration**—the result of placing an absorber in the path of the x-ray beam. The absorber, usually 1 or 2 mm Al, is positioned between the collimator and the tube housing. Light-localizing variable-aperture collimators usually contain approximately 1 mm Al added filtration.

During some special x-ray examinations, a different kind of filter, called a compensating filter, may be used. Compensating filters have nothing to do with patient dose; they are employed specifically for shaping the x-ray intensity over the beam area so that the radiation reaching the image receptor is more uniform and results in more uniform optical density. Copper, tin, and plastic may be used for such compensating filters.

EXERCISES

1 The inherent filtration in a general purpose radiographic tube is usually equivalent to
a. 0 mm Al.   **c.** 1.0 mm Al.
b. 0.5 mm Al.   **d.** 2.5 mm Al.

2 The equivalent added filtration provided by a conventional light-localizing, variable-aperture collimator is closest to
a. 0 mm Al.   **c.** 1.0 mm Al.
b. 0.5 mm Al.   **d.** 2.5 mm Al.

3 The purpose of a wedge filter in diagnostic radiology is to
a. harden the beam.
b. soften the beam.
c. produce a uniform intensity across the prepatient beam.
d. produce a nonuniform intensity across the prepatient beam.

4 The primary purpose of adding filtration to a diagnostic x-ray beam is to
a. cause high-energy photons to undergo Compton scattering.
b. protect the film from low-energy x rays.
c. remove low-energy electrons.
d. remove low-energy x rays.

5 A filter has the **greatest** effect on dose reduction to
a. the whole body.
b. selected organs.
c. the skin.
d. the gonads.

6 X rays of higher maximum energy can be obtained by
a. increasing filtration.
b. use of a higher Z target.
c. increasing kVp.
d. reducing inherent filtration.

7 The light-localizing, variable-aperture collimator contributes
a. to inherent filtration.
b. to added filtration.
c. no filtration when its light is on.
d. no filtration when its light is off.

8 If 5 mm Al filtration is added to the x-ray tube,
a. patient dose will increase.
b. radiographic contrast will increase.
c. motion unsharpness will decrease.
d. radiographic density will decrease.

9 An x-ray beam can be made harder by increasing
a. mA.   **c.** SID.
b. mAs.   **d.** filtration.

10 When filtration is added to a normally filtered beam, the x-ray emission spectrum will
a. exhibit higher energy discrete lines.
b. shift to the left.
c. increase in amplitude.
d. decrease in amplitude.

11 Added filtration
a. protects the patient from useless radiation.
b. is usually thinner than inherent filtration.
c. is expensive.
d. increases x-ray quantity.

12 Inherent filtration
a. consists of sheets of aluminum.
b. helps harden the x-ray beam.
c. tends to decrease with tube age.
d. is mainly due to the light localizer.

13 To produce low inherent filtration in an x-ray beam,
a. insulating oil is placed around the tube.
b. a thin section of glass is used.
c. windows made of copper are sometimes used.
d. one should remove the collimator.

14 Wedge filters are
a. widely used in diagnostic radiology.
b. occasionally used to obtain radiographs of uniform density.
c. always better than uniform filters because they attenuate more x rays.
d. employed in all procedures.

15 For mammographic procedures utilizing film as the image receptor,
a. reduced total filtration is desirable.
b. added filtration is removed to increase x ray quality.
c. the total filtration should be between 2 and 3 mm Al.
d. no filtration is required.

16 When added filtration is increased,
a. x-ray quality is increased.
b. x-ray quantity is increased.
c. the effective x-ray energy is decreased.
d. kVp must be decreased.

17 Given the following conditions of operation: 95 kVp/80 mAs/100 cm SID, 0.7 mm Al inherent filtration, 2.0 mm Al added filtration,
a. the HVL will be 2.7 mm Al.
b. the total filtration will be 2.0 mm Al.
c. if the tube potential is changed to 85 kVp, additional filtration is necessary to maintain the same HVL.
d. if the tube current is increased to 150 mAs, additional filtration is necessary to maintain the same HVL.

18 With a radiographic tube having 0.5 mm Al inherent filtration and 2.0 mm Al added filtration,
a. the total filtration is 1.5 mm Al.
b. an additional 1.0 mm Al will increase the total filtration to 2.5 mm Al.
c. an additional 1.0 mm Al will increase the x-ray quantity.
d. an additional 1.0 mm will harden the x-ray beam.

19 Inherent filtration is
a. produced by slowing down electrons.
b. dependent on the kind of aluminum used.
c. increased with tube age.
d. increased with patient thickness.

20 An x-ray tube has a total filtration of 3.0 mm Al, has an HVL of 2.5 mm Al, and emits 180 mR (46 µC/kg). Therefore the
a. addition of 1.0 mm Al filtration will increase the quantity of the beam.
b. addition of 1.0 mm Al will increase the quality of the beam.
c. addition of 2.5 mm Al will reduce the output intensity to 135 mR.
d. addition of 2.5 mm Al will reduce the output intensity to 100 mR.

21 An x-ray tube has the following characteristics: inherent filtration 0.7 mm Al, added filtration 1.5 mm Al, HVL 2.2 mm Al, quantity 120 mR. Which of the following is true?
a. An additional 0.7 mm Al will result in 60 mR.
b. An additional 1.5 mm Al will result in 60 mR.
c. An additional 2.2 mm Al will result in 30 mR.
d. An additional 4.4 mm Al will result in 30 mR.

22 A radiographic tube has a total filtration of 3.0 mm Al and an HVL of 2.5 mm Al. How much additional filtration will be required to reduce the x-ray intensity to approximately 6% of its original value?
a. 7.5 mm Al   c. 10 mm Al
b. 9.0 mm Al   d. 12 mm Al

23 If an x-ray tube emits 6.2 mR/mAs through total filtration of 3.5 mm Al with an HVL of 2.5 mm Al, approximately how much additional filtration will reduce the output to 1.5 mR/mAs?
a. 2.5 mm Al   c. 5 mm Al
b. 3.5 mm Al   d. 7 mm Al

24 A trough filter is usually employed in
a. chest examinations.
b. CT examinations.
c. digital examinations.
d. extremity examinations.

25 What type of compensating filter is most likely to be used with a long-leg film changer?
a. bow tie   c. wedge
b. step wedge   d. conical

X-ray Interaction with Matter

COMPTON EFFECT
....

X-ray interaction with outer shell electrons, known as the **Compton effect,** is responsible for scatter radiation. The incident x-ray photon interacts with an outer-shell electron of a target atom and transfers some of its energy to the orbital electron. Following the interaction—which can be visualized as the collision of two billiard balls—the electron is ejected from its orbit (the atom is ionized) and the x-ray photon is deflected (scattered). Since the incident photon imparts some of its energy to the Compton electron, it loses energy and undergoes an increase in wavelength.

The probability that an x ray will undergo a Compton interaction decreases slowly with increasing x-ray energy. The occurrence of the Compton effect is essentially independent of the atomic number of the absorber. In conventional radiographs of the chest or abdomen more than 70% of the incident x rays undergo Compton interactions, and this is the interaction that contributes to the film fog that reduces contrast.

EXERCISES

1 Which of the following is **not** one of the five basic x-ray interactions with matter?
   a. Compton scattering   **c.** photodisintegration
   b. photoelectric effect   **d.** bremsstrahlung
                                     radiation
2 Which of the following x rays would be most likely to undergo classical scattering?
   a. 5 keV   **c.** 50 keV
   b. 25 keV   **d.** 100 keV
3 Which of the following interactions contributes to film fog?
   a. bremsstrahlung   **c.** Compton scattering
      radiation   **d.** photodisintegration
   b. photoelectric effect

4 Which of the following occurs in a Compton interaction?
   a. The secondary photon has wavelength equal to the primary photon.
   b. The secondary electron has kinetic energy equal to the incident photon.
   c. The secondary electron has kinetic energy equal to the difference between the energy of the incident photon and the electron binding energy.
   d. An atom is ionized.
5 If E_i = incident photon energy, E_s = scattered photon energy, E_b = electron binding energy, and E_{KE} = secondary electron kinetic energy, then
   a. $E_i = E_s + E_b + E_{KE}$.
   b. $E_i = E_s - E_b - E_{KE}$.
   c. $E_i = E_s - E_b + E_{KE}$.
   d. $E_i = E_s + (E_b - E_{KE})$.
6 If E_i = incident photon energy, E_s = scattered photon energy, E_b = electron binding energy, and E_{KE} = secondary electron kinetic energy, then
   a. $E_s = E_b + E_{KE} + E_i$.
   b. $E_s = E_b - (E_{KE} + E_i)$.
   c. $E_s = E_{KE} - (E_b + E_i)$.
   d. $E_s = E_i - (E_b + E_{KE})$.
7 During the Compton effect, most of the incident photon energy is given to
   a. characteristic radiation.
   b. the electron binding energy.
   c. the electron kinetic energy.
   d. the scattered photon.
8 Backscatter radiation
   a. is radiation that is scattered through 0 degrees.
   b. can produce image artifacts.
   c. is of no importance in diagnostic radiology.
   d. results in a photoelectron.
9 Compton interaction affects the making of a radiograph by increasing
   a. resolution.   **c.** contrast.
   b. fog.   **d.** speed.

10 The probability that an x ray will interact with an outer-shell electron is principally influenced by the
   a. atomic number of the absorber.
   b. binding energy of the electron.
   c. kinetic energy of the electron.
   d. energy of the incident photon.
11 The Compton effect is
   a. independent of Z.
   b. proportional to Z.
   c. inversely proportional to Z.
   d. proportional to Z^3.
12 The Compton effect is
   a. the source of static marks on the film.
   b. the source of image fog.
   c. also called classical scattering.
   d. the same as the Thompson effect.
13 If a 45 keV x-ray photon interacts with the K-shell electron in an atom of molybdenum, ejecting it with 8 keV energy, what will be the energy of the scattered photon?
   a. 17 keV   c. 37 keV
   b. 25 keV   d. 45 keV
14 The angle of deflection of the Compton scattered photon
   a. can vary only between 0 and 90 degrees.
   b. can vary only between 90 and 180 degrees.
   c. is 0 degrees when no energy is transferred.
   d. is 0 degrees when there is total energy transfer.
15 The probability that a given photon will undergo Compton interaction
   a. increases the increasing photon energy.
   b. decreases with increasing photon energy.
   c. increases with increasing electron energy.
   d. increases with decreasing electron energy.
16 During the Compton interaction, the incident x-ray energy is
   a. completely absorbed.
   b. partially absorbed.
   c. shared by the scattered x ray and the primary x ray.
   d. absorbed by the orbital electron and nucleus.
17 The Compton interaction involves so-called un-bound electrons because
   a. free, completely unbound electrons are ejected.
   b. ionization occurs.
   c. K-shell electrons are not involved.
   d. they have a very low binding energy.

18 The x-ray interaction within the diagnostic radiographic range that does not cause ionization is
   a. classical scattering.   c. photoelectric effect.
   b. Compton scattering.   d. pair production.
19 When an x-ray photon undergoes Compton interaction,
   a. an electron emerges from the atom.
   b. a photon emerges from the atom.
   c. an electron and a photon emerge from the atom.
   d. nothing emerges from the atom.
20 Compton-scattered photons
   a. are helpful in diagnostic radiology.
   b. produce image artifacts.
   c. result from bremsstrahlung.
   d. have lower energy than the incident photon.
21 Compton-scattered x rays
   a. result in personnel exposures during fluoroscopy.
   b. can be used to determine whether a machine is operating at single-phase or three-phase power.
   c. can be used to determine the kVp of operation.
   d. provide approximately one half of the useful information on the radiograph.
22 Of the following interactions, which occurs with the lowest energy x rays?
   a. Compton scattering
   b. Thompson scattering
   c. pair production
   d. photodisintegration
23 Following Compton scattering, the scattered photon has
   a. higher energy.
   b. longer wavelength.
   c. higher frequency.
   d. lower velocity.
24 During Compton scattering, photon interaction is more likely to occur with
   a. an inner-shell electron.
   b. a loosely bound electron.
   c. a projectile electron.
   d. a secondary electron.
25 The probability that an x ray will undergo Compton scattering decreases with
   a. increasing energy.
   b. decreasing mass density.
   c. decreasing optical density.
   d. increasing optical density.

Name _____

Date _____

X-ray Interaction with Matter

PHOTOELECTRIC EFFECT

....

The photoelectric effect occurs when an incident x ray imparts all its energy to an orbital electron, usually a K-shell electron. The photon disappears, and the orbital electron is ejected from the atom. This electron, called a **photoelectron,** escapes its atom with kinetic energy equal to the difference between the incident photon energy and its own binding energy.

The relative probability that a given x ray will undergo a photoelectric interaction is **inversely** proportional to the third power of the photon energy $(1/E^3)$ and **directly** proportional to the third power of the atomic number (Z^3) of the absorber.

X rays that interact with atoms of the human body are, in a negative way, those that are responsible for the image on radiographic film. X rays that do not interact with the body are transmitted through to the film. The difference between the pattern of incident x rays and transmitted x rays is the image pattern. Compton-scattered x rays do not contribute to the image but only serve to fog the film.

Contrast studies incorporating barium or iodine are successful because the atomic number of these atoms

T = Transmitted x rays
P = X rays absorbed photoelectrically
S = Compton-scattered x rays

is higher than the atoms of surrounding soft tissue. This results in more x-ray absorption in iodine or barium.

EXERCISES

1 If E_i = incident photon energy, E_s = scattered photon energy, E_b = electron binding energy, and E_{KE} = photoelectron kinetic energy, then
   a. $E_i = E_s + E_b + E_{KE}$.
   b. $E_i = E_s - (E_b + E_{KE})$.
   c. $E_i = E_b + E_{KE}$.
   d. $E_i = E_b - E_{KE}$.

2 If E_i = incident photon energy, E_s = scattered photon energy, E_b = electron binding energy, and E_{KE} = photoelectron kinetic energy, then
   a. $E_{KE} = E_1 - E_b$.
   b. $E_{KE} = E_i/E_b$.
   c. $E_s = E_i - (E_b + E_{KE})$.
   d. $E_s = (E_b + E_{KE}) - E_i$.

3 The photoelectric effect is principally associated with
   a. bremsstrahlung production.
   b. characteristic x-ray production.
   c. scattering of the incident photon.
   d. absorption of the incident photon.

4 Photoelectric interaction with an atom is much more likely to occur with
   a. high-energy photons than with low-energy photons.
   b. low-density material than with high-density material.
   c. high atomic number tissue than with low atomic number tissue.
   d. bremsstrahlung radiation than with characteristic radiation.

5 Which of the following has the lowest effective atomic number?
   a. muscle   **c.** lungs
   b. fat   **d.** iodine

6 Photoelectric interaction with soft tissue is most prevalent with which one of the following photon energies?

a. 0.3 keV   **c.** 30 keV

b. 3.0 keV   **d.** 300 keV

7 During photoelectric interaction

a. the material is made radioactive.

b. an electron is emitted.

c. a photon is emitted.

d. the incident photon reappears with reduced energy.

8 During operation at 80 kVp, which of the following photoelectric interactions is most probable?

a. 30 keV x ray and fat

b. 30 keV x ray and bone

c. 70 keV x ray and fat

d. 70 keV x ray and bone

9 The radiographic image is

a. contained in the uniform distribution of incident x rays.

b. principally determined by photoelectric interactions.

c. principally determined by Compton scattering.

d. blurred by Compton scattering.

10 A 35 keV x-ray will most likely undergo K-shell photoelectric interaction with which of the following?

a. calcium ($E_b = 4$ keV)

b. iodine ($E_b = 33$ keV)

c. barium (E = 37 keV0

d. tungsten ($E_b = 69$ keV)

11 The probability of photoelectric effect varies as photon

a. E^2.   **c.** E^3.

b. E^{-2}.   **d.** E^{-3}.

12 As a result of photoelectric interaction

a. an electron leaves the atom.

b. an electron is absorbed.

c. the incident photon leaves the atom with reduced energy.

d. the incident photon is scattered.

13 The photoelectric effect

a. refers to the complete absorption of an electron with the subsequent emission of a photon.

b. refers to the complete absorption of a photon with the subsequent emission of an electron.

c. is a partially ionizing event.

d. is a partially exciting event.

14 Lead has a K-shell electron binding energy of 88 keV. Therefore

a. an 84 keV x ray can undergo photoelectric interaction with the K-shell electron.

b. an 84 keV x ray can undergo photoelectric interaction with the L-shell electron.

c. an 87 keV x ray is more likely to undergo photoelectric interaction with a K-shell electron than a 84 keV x ray.

d. an 87 keV x ray is more likely to undergo photoelectric interaction with an L-shell electron than an 84 keV x ray.

15 A 39 keV photon undergoes a photoelectric interaction with a K-shell electron (binding energy = 37 keV). Therefore

a. the scattered photon will have 2 keV energy.

b. the scattered photon will have 37 keV energy.

c. the photoelectron will have 2 keV energy.

d. the photoelectron will have 37 keV energy.

16 The probability of photoelectric effect varies as the _____ of the target atom.

a. Z^2

b. Z^{-2}

c. Z^3

d. Z^{-3}

17 Which of the following photoelectric interactions is most probable?

a. 30 keV x ray and fat (Z = 6.3)

b. 30 keV x ray and lung (Z = 7.6)

c. 30 keV x ray and muscle (Z = 7.4)

d. 30 keV x ray and bone (Z = 13.8)

18 When a single x ray interacts photoelectrically with a single atom, which is most likely?

a. 30 keV x ray and bone (Z = 13.8)

b. 30 keV x ray and lung (Z = 7.6)

c. 60 keV x ray and fat (Z = 6.3)

d. 60 keV x ray and muscle (Z = 7.4)

19 A 50 keV x ray has a 0.02 chance of photoelectric interaction with muscle. What is its chance of interacting with bone?

a. 0.01   **c.** 0.07

b. 0.04   **d.** 0.13

20 When a single x ray interacts photoelectrically with a single atom, which is most likely?

a. 30 keV x ray and bone (Z = 13.8)

b. 50 keV x ray and lung (Z = 7.6)

c. 90 keV x ray and muscle (Z = 7.4)

d. 120 keV x ray and fat (Z = 6.3)

WORKSHEET 48

X-ray Interaction with Matter

_____

DIFFERENTIAL ABSORPTION

....

_____

Only two interactions of the incident x-ray photon are important in diagnostic radiology—Compton scattering and the photoelectric effect. The photoelectric effect predominates when low energy x rays interact with atoms having a high atomic number. The probability of x-ray photoelectric interaction is directly proportional to Z^3 and inversely proportional to E^3.

Compton scattering predominates at high kVp and accounts for most of the interactions between x rays and tissue. It is relatively independent of the atomic number of the absorber. The absolute probability of this interaction decreases with increasing energy. However, the ratio of Compton effect relative to photoelectric effect increases with increasing x-ray energy.

Other than photoelectric and Compton interactions, the only course open to an x ray incident on a patient is transmission through the patient. The pattern of absorption and scatter of the incident x-ray beam caused by atomic number, density, and thickness of the structure under examination are called **differential absorption.** Because of the photoelectric effect, differential absorption is high at low kVp. But transmission through the patient is low, and this results in increased patient dose. At high kVp, differential absorption is low because most x rays that are not transmitted are Compton scattered. This results in a gray, low contrast radiograph and often requires devices such as grids to reduce the number of scattered x rays reaching the film.

EXERCISES

1 Anatomic structures that readily transmit x rays
   a. are usually very dense
   b. are called radiolucent.
   c. have a high effective atomic number.
   d. have a high probability for photoelectric effect.

2 Differential absorption, although a complicated process, is basically the result of
   a. the Compton effect.
   b. differences between high Z and low Z tissue.
   c. differences between high E and low E photons.
   d. differences between Compton attenuation and transmission.

3 When making a radiograph
   a. with increasing kVp, differential absorption increases.
   b. high kVp is preferred for maximum differential absorption.
   c. low kVp is necessary when imaging soft tissue because it leads to high Compton effect.
   d. low kVp is necessary when imaging soft tissue because it leads to high photoelectric effect.

4 At what approximate photon energy is the probability of a photoelectric interaction in soft tissue equal to the probability of a Compton interaction?
   a. 10 keV   **c.** 40 keV
   b. 20 keV   **d.** 80 keV

5 Which of the following has the highest density?
   a. muscle   **c.** bone
   b. fat   **d.** lungs

6 Differential absorption between lung and soft tissue occurs principally because
   a. the x-ray beam is homogeneous.
   b. the x-ray beam is polyenergetic.
   c. there is a difference in effective atomic numbers (Z).
   d. there is a difference in densities.

7 Air-contrast studies such as a colon examination are successful
   a. because x rays are produced with a continuous-energy spectrum.
   b. principally because of differences in mass density.
   c. principally because of differences in effective atomic number.
   d. only if high kVp technique is employed.

8 In mammography
   a. low kVp is necessary to take advantage of the Compton effect.
   b. the main x-ray interaction is the photoelectric effect.
   c. low kVp is required because the breast is composed of high Z atoms.
   d. high kVp can be used with adequate filtration.

9 Differential absorption between bone and soft tissue in diagnostic radiology occurs because
   a. the x-ray beam is monoenergetic.
   b. the x-ray beam is polyenergetic.
   c. there is a difference in effective atomic number.
   d. there is a difference in reflectance.

10 Cerebral angiography with iodinated compounds
   a. would be impossible with monoenergetic x rays.
   b. relies principally on differences in density.
   c. relies principally on differences in effective atomic number.
   d. results in higher contrast at higher kVp.

11 Differential absorption
   a. is basically the difference between those x rays that are absorbed and those that are reflected.
   b. is basically the difference between those x rays that are absorbed and those that are transmitted.
   c. increases with increasing kVp.
   d. increases with increasing Compton interaction.

12 As kVp is increased, the number of x rays
   a. interacting with tissue increases.
   b. interacting by way of the photoelectric effect increases.
   c. interacting by way of Compton effect increases.
   d. transmitted without interaction increases.

13 Differential absorption in which of the following tissues is most dependent on density differences?
   a. muscle and fat   **c.** lung and bone
   b. muscle and bone   **d.** lung and fat

14 The SI unit of mass density is
   a. g/m^3.   **c.** newton.
   b. kg/m^3.   **d.** joule.

15 The photoelectric interaction of x rays with tissue is _____ to the density of the tissue.
   a. proportional
   b. inversely proportional
   c. proportional to $(density)^3$
   d. inversely proportional to $(density)^3$

16 Lungs are imaged on a chest radiograph principally because of differences in
   a. beam energy.   **c.** subject density.
   b. beam intensity.   **d.** subject atomic number.

17 The colon is imaged during a barium enema examination principally because of differences in
   a. beam energy.   **c.** subject mass density.
   b. beam intensity.   **d.** subject atomic number.

18 The total reduction in the number of x rays remaining after passing through matter is called
   a. exponential.   **c.** attenuation.
   b. absorption.   **d.** scattering.

19 Because x-ray transmission decreases exponentially
   a. the number of x rays is never reduced to zero.
   b. the x ray beam becomes more penetrating.
   c. x ray scattering increases.
   d. there is a definite thickness for 100% absorption.

20 Which of the following plots represents x-ray attenuation in matter?

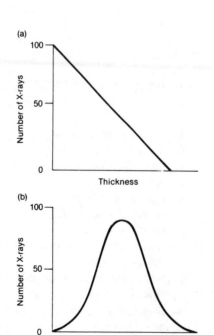

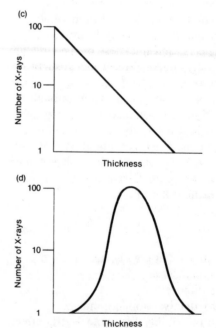

Name _____

Date _____

Radiographic Film

The radiograph is, generally speaking, no better than the characteristics of the weakest link in the imaging apparatus. The physical characteristics of film make it perhaps the strongest link in the radiographic imaging system. Radiographic film consists of two principal parts—the base and the emulsion—the manufacture of each being precisely controlled. The bulk of the film is contained in the base, whereas the image-containing portion of the film is in the emulsion.

EXERCISES

1 An easily **observable** difference between x-ray film and regular photographic film is the
   a. thickness and rigidity of the base.
   b. thickness of the emulsion.
   c. speed of the film.
   d. processing requirements.
2 The principal characteristic of the emulsion that makes it particularly radiation sensitive is its
   a. density.   **c.** atomic mass.
   b. atomic number.   **d.** sensitivity speck.
3 Average silver halide crystal size in radiographic film is approximately
   a. 0.1 µm.   **c.** 10 µm.
   b. 1.0 µm.   **d.** 100 µm.
4 The radiographic film base appears blue
   a. because of added hardeners.
   b. so that viewing the image is more pleasant.
   c. to match the light emitted by intensifying screens.
   d. because of the silver halide crystals.
5 Which of the following has been employed as a film base?
   a. silver halide   **c.** cellulose tritrate
   b. gelatin   **d.** cellulose nitrate

6 The photographic emulsion commonly used in x-ray film consists of
   a. cellulose acetate and silver halide.
   b. gelatin and silver nitrate.
   c. silver nitrate and cellulose acetate.
   d. silver halide and gelatin.
7 A common base of contemporary x-ray film is
   a. polyurethane.
   b. polyester.
   c. silver bromide.
   d. silver nitrate.
8 In the manufacture of radiographic film,
   a. single-emulsion type is most frequently produced.
   b. the emulsion layer is thicker than the base.
   c. direct-exposure film contains a thicker emulsion layer with more silver halide crystals than screen film.
   d. x-ray interaction accounts for approximately one half the latent-image centers in screen film exposure.
9 The adhesive layer of radiographic film
   a. is between 5 and 25 µm thick.
   b. is approximately 200 µm thick.
   c. ensures uniform adhesion of the emulsion to the base.
   d. ensures uniform adhesion of the protective layer to the emulsion.
10 The two basic parts of radiographic film are
   a. phosphor and base.
   b. base and emulsion.
   c. emulsion and phosphor.
   d. emulsion and supercoating.
11 The supercoating usually consists of
   a. cellulose.   **c.** silver halide.
   b. polyester.   **d.** gelatin.
12 Dimensional stability is the property of maintaining the size and shape of the
   a. base.   **c.** image.
   b. emulsion.   **d.** supercoating.

13 When comparing polyester with cellulose triacetate as a base, which of the following **does not** apply to polyester?
   a. less warping with age
   b. better dimensional stability
   c. stronger
   d. thicker

14 The principal purpose of gelatin in the emulsion is to
   a. provide for easier roller transport.
   b. produce film that is lucent.
   c. support the silver halide crystals uniformly.
   d. provide dimensional stability to the film.

15 Which of the following properties of silver halide is most important in the production of a latent image?
   a. mass
   b. dimensional stability
   c. density
   d. atomic number

16 X-ray film is sensitive
   a. only to x rays.
   b. only to x and gamma rays.
   c. only to x and gamma rays and visible light.
   d. to all electromagnetic radiation.

17 Conventional x-ray film used with intensifying screens has
   a. emulsion coated on both sides of the base.
   b. a perfectly clear base.
   c. a base that is often made of cellulose nitrate.
   d. a treatment to make the film especially sensitive to x rays.

18 Which of the following is usually thinner than 5 μm?
   a. supercoating   c. phosphor
   b. emulsion   d. base

19 Which of the following is a principal component of the radiographic emulsion?
   a. cellulose nitrate   c. silver bromide
   b. cellulose triacetate   d. silver nitrate

20 Compared with screen film, film that is manufactured for direct x-ray exposure
   a. has a wider range of silver halide crystal sizes.
   b. has a thicker emulsion.
   c. should not be used without screens.
   d. is more sensitive to longer wavelength radiation.

21 Which of the following ingredients is **not** normally found in the film emulsion?
   a. silver bromide   c. silver halide
   b. silver iodide   d. silver nitrate

22 Conventional radiographic screen film is approximately _____ thick.
   a. 1 μm.   c. 0.25 mm
   b. 25 μm.   d. 25 mm

23 Which of the following has the highest atomic number?
   a. silver   c. iodine
   b. tungsten   d. bromine

24 The special imaging properties of crystals known as the photographic effect are thought to be due to
   a. gelatin.
   b. silver nitrate.
   c. silver sulfide.
   d. potassium impurities.

25 The term *sensitivity speck* refers to
   a. an artifact.
   b. film speed.
   c. an emulsion contaminant.
   d. crystal size.

Radiographic Film

FORMATION OF LATENT IMAGE
....

The process of making a radiograph is similar to that of making a photograph. The radiographic image results from transmitted electromagnetic radiation; the photographic image results from reflected electromagnetic radiation. When nonscreen radiographic film is employed, the electromagnetic radiation is the x ray. When screen films are employed, most x rays interact with the screen, producing visible light. The visible light then interacts with the emulsion.

The interaction of electromagnetic radiation—light or x rays—with the emulsion results in a latent image. The latent image is the invisible alteration occurring in the silver halide crystalline component of the emulsion.

The latent image is made manifest (made visible) by proper processing. There are six necessary steps in processing a radiograph: wetting, development, stop bath, fixation, washing, and drying. All are important, but the two most critical steps are development and fixation. During development, the latent image is made visible. During fixation, that visibility is made permanent.

EXERCISES

1 The latent image is actually formed in the
  a. base.
  b. gelatin.
  c. silver halide crystal.
  d. bromine atom.
2 During the photographic process, metallic silver accumulates at
  a. the bromine atom.
  b. the secondary electron.
  c. the sensitivity speck.
  d. the base.

3 The latent image at the crystal level
  a. is visible under a light microscope.
  b. is present whether that crystal was irradiated or not.
  c. is a collection of bromine atoms.
  d. is a collection of silver atoms.
4 The term *latent image* actually refers to
  a. reciprocity law failure.
  b. film inertia.
  c. image intensification.
  d. an undeveloped radiographic image.
5 The sensitivity speck is usually silver
  a. bromide.   **c.** iodide.
  b. sulfide.   **d.** atoms.
6 In the manufacture of the emulsion, which of the following molecules is particularly light sensitive?
  a. $AgNO_3$ **c.** $AgBr$
  b. KBr **d.** KNO_3
7 With processing, the latent image becomes a(n) _____ image.
  a. induced   **c.** dimensional
  b. crystal   **d.** manifest
8 What do we call the radiation exiting the patient that is responsible for latent image formation?
  a. remnant   **c.** scatter
  b. useful beam   **d.** leakage
9 When x rays interact with film, which of the following atoms may be involved?
  a. silver   **c.** iodine
  b. bromine   **d.** all of the above
10 Given only one atom of each of the following, which is most likely to be involved with x-ray interaction?
  a. silver   **c.** iodine
  b. bromine   **d.** carbon
11 An ion is an atom
  a. that is radioactive.
  b. that is not electrically neutral.
  c. with a sensitivity speck.
  d. with too many nucleons.

12 The interstitial atoms in a crystal of silver halide include
   a. silver, bromine, and iodine.
   b. bromine, iodine, and gelatin.
   c. iodine, gelatin, and silver.
   d. gelatin, silver, and bromine.

13 The result of x-ray interaction with silver halide is the formation of
   a. an ion.
   b. a latent-image center.
   c. a secondary electron.
   d. all of the above.

14 Following irradiation, a secondary electron will most likely interact with a silver ion to form a
   a. silver atom.
   b. silver halide crystal.
   c. sensitivity speck.
   d. positive ion.

15 The formation of a manifest image follows many sequential steps, the first of which is
   a. secondary electron migration.
   b. ionization.
   c. formation of atomic silver.
   d. the loss of crystal surface charge.

16 What happens at the sensitivity speck?
   a. bromine ions collect.
   b. secondary electrons are trapped there.
   c. surface electrification is increased.
   d. silver bromide is formed.

17 The migrating secondary electrons involved in latent-imaging formation come from all but which of the following?
   a. silver
   b. bromine
   c. iodine
   d. gelatin

18 Processing
   a. is required for latent-image formation.
   b. is required for manifest-image formation.
   c. includes neutral silver migration.
   d. includes AgBr formation.

19 The latent-image center
   a. forms on the surface of a crystal.
   b. forms at the sensitivity speck.
   c. consists of silver ions.
   d. consists of halide crystals.

20 The formation of a latent image follows which interaction with the emulsion?
   a. classic scattering
   b. photoelectric
   c. photodisintegration
   d. pair production

21 If one observes a film immediately after exposure, what is seen?
   a. a latent image   c. a manifest image
   b. a visible image   d. nothing

22 Which of the following theories best explains the photographic effect?
   a. Duane-Hunt   c. Gurney-Mott
   b. Hurter-Driffield   d. Planck-Bohr

23 In a silver halide crystal, which of the following is missing an electron?
   a. silver   c. iodine
   b. bromine   d. sulfide

24 A latent-image center becomes a collection of
   a. silver ions.   c. halide ions.
   b. silver atoms.   d. halide atoms.

25 Processing is necessary to convert
   a. silver atoms to ions.
   b. halide atoms to ions.
   c. a latent image to a manifest image.
   d. a manifest image to a latent image.

Radiographic Film

TYPES OF FILM
....

HANDLING AND STORAGE OF FILMS
....

Although it is important that the technologist be familiar with the construction of radiographic film and the mechanisms responsible for forming the latent image, it is more important that the technologist be able to translate this information into proper selection and handling of radiographic film. The technologist cannot influence the manufactured characteristics of radiographic film except by selecting film most suited to the examination. The technologist, however, can influence proper latent-image formation by selection of appropriate radiographic technique. Also, film selection and handling of unexposed and unprocessed film will greatly influence the resulting radiographic image.

Radiologic imaging has advanced so far technologically that it is imperative that the technologist be aware of the various image receptors available and the basis for differences among radiographic films. There are literally hundreds of different films and film-screen combinations available. Only a few are optimum for a given imaging task. **Contrast, speed,** and **spectral characteristics** are three exceedingly important parameters by which a technologist should judge the selection of a film. Because of the various radiographic intensifying screens available, proper matching of film emulsion with screen phosphor is also essential.

Film emulsion characteristics also dictate in large measure how the preprocessed film should be handled. Proper darkroom safelight protection is absolutely essential. Storage in a climate-controlled environment is necessary for the ultimate production of acceptable images. Attention must be paid not only to storage location, but also to storage time, because radiographic films have a finite shelf life. Needless to say, unnecessarily rough handling of radiographic film should be avoided since it will produce artifacts and degrade the final radiographic image.

EXERCISES

1 The most commonly employed radiologic image receptor is
   a. screen film
   b. nonscreen film.
   c. direct-exposure film.
   d. single-emulsion film.

2 Which of the following is **not** a characteristic the technologist should consider when selecting film?
   a. contrast   **c.** light emission
   b. light absorption   **d.** sensitivity

3 The contrast of radiographic film
   a. is directly proportional to its sensitivity.
   b. is inversely proportional to its latitude.
   c. is unimportant to film selection.
   d. all of the above.

4 High contrast films have
   a. less silver halide.
   b. smaller grain size.
   c. a wide range of grain size distribution.
   d. a thinner base.

5 Fast films differ from slow films principally in _____ of the silver halide crystals.
   a. size
   b. shape
   c. concentration
   d. charge

6 The spectral response of an emulsion refers to its
   a. ability to detect x rays.
   b. emission of visible light.
   c. absorption of visible light.
   d. sensitivity to x rays.

7 Calcium tungstate screens emit
   a. blue light.   **c.** yellow light.
   b. green light.   **d.** red light.

8 Most rare earth screens emit
   a. blue light.   c. green light.
   b. violet light.   d. all of the above.
9 Orthochromatic film is sensitive to
   a. the total visible light c. yellow light.
      spectrum.   d. red light.
   b. green light.
10 The principal result of using rare earth screens with green-sensitive film is
   a. increased patient   c. higher contrast.
      dose.   d. reduced patient dose.
   b. darkroom fog.
11 When green emitting rare earth screens are used with properly matched film _____ safelights are required.
   a. no   c. amber
   b. green   d. red
12 Present mammography films
   a. are coarse-grain,   c. have a thick
      double-emulsion films.   emulsion.
   b. are screen films.   d. have a thin base.
13 When comparing 35 mm cine film with 16 mm, the 35 mm film has
   a. better resolution.   c. twice the area.
   b. higher contrast.   d. four times the area.
14 Which of the following will **not** fog film?
   a. radiation from an adjacent nuclear medicine laboratory
   b. radiation from the adjacent x-ray room
   c. fringe magnetic fields
   d. a darkroom light leak
15 If film is stored near steam pipes, the most likely result in the processed radiograph will be
   a. the appearance of   c. loss of contrast.
      radiopaque artifacts. d. loss of latitude.
   b. loss of speed.
16 Which of the following is **not** important to proper storage of radiographic film?
   a. The shelf life is less than 3 months.
   b. Approximately 45 days should be the maximum storage time.
   c. Monthly deliveries are common.
   d. Lengthy storage increases fog.
17 Which of the following is most likely to fog film?
   a. an improper safelight filter
   b. storage of film for longer than 1 month
   c. 0.2 mR
   d. high humidity

18 Which of the following can produce a radiopaque artifact?
   a. extended storage time
   b. improper radiographic technique
   c. dirty processor transport rollers
   d. excessive drying time
19 Which of the following are acceptable storage conditions for film?
   a. 32° C and 50% humidity
   b. 20° C and 90% humidity
   c. 16° C and 10% humidity
   d. 50° C and 50% humidity
20 Which of the following darkroom conditions is not acceptable?
   a. silver halide emulsion, amber safelight
   b. orthochromatic film, red safelight
   c. green-sensitive film, amber safelight
   d. blue-sensitive film, amber safelight
21 The most commonly employed radiographic image receptor is _____ film.
   a. single-emulsion
   b. screen
   c. panchromatic
   d. direct-exposure
22 Which of the following would be considered a film artifact?
   a. a smudge mark on the viewbox diffuser
   b. a pressure mark
   c. an unexposed but processed film
   d. film identification mark
23 Other factors being equal, a _____ emulsion is fastest.
   a. blue-sensitive
   b. green-sensitive
   c. small grain
   d. large grain concentration
24 Which of the following is the **least** important characteristic of screen film?
   a. cost
   b. contrast
   c. sensitivity
   d. light absorption
25 A high contrast emulsion is characterized by
   a. exceptional thickness.
   b. high crystal concentration.
   c. small, uniform grain size.
   d. large, nonuniform grain size.

Name _____

Date _____

Processing the Latent Image

PROCESSING CHEMISTRY
....

There are essentially two steps in producing a quality radiograph: exposing the radiographic film and processing the exposed film. Both require careful attention by the radiologic technologist.

Very few radiographs are processed manually. Automatic processing uses three principal chemistries, each contained in a separate tank of the processor. The **developer** contains developing agents, activators, hardeners, preservatives, and water. The **fixer** contains clearing agents, activators, preservatives, and hardeners. The third chemistry is **water,** which is used in copious amounts at high flow rates to wash the film clear of unused chemistries. In the automatic processor the exposed film is fed from the developing tank into a fixing tank and then into a wash, through a drying chamber, and finally to the receiving bin as a finished radiograph.

The latent image is made visible during development. The developing process is immediately stopped when the film enters the fixer. The fixer also removes all unexposed silver from the emulsion. All that remains of the emulsion when it enters the wash tank is the reduced silver, gelatin, and any residual chemistry. Removal of the residual chemistry during washing is necessary to ensure good archival quality.

EXERCISES

1 At what stage in automatic processing is the latent image made visible?
  a. wetting   **c.** stop bath
  b. developing   **d.** fixing

2 The component of the developer that helps to keep unexposed crystals from the developing agent is
  a. hydroquinone.   **c.** potassium bromide.
  b. phenidone.   **d.** sodium carbonate.

3 Which of the following automatic processing chemistries best controls the image on a radiograph in the density range that is most important?
  a. hydroquinone   **c.** Metol
  b. phenidone   **d.** none of the above

4 Aerial oxidation is controlled by the
  a. fixer.   **c.** preservative.
  b. restrainer.   **d.** activator.

5 The hardeners in a fixer
  a. remove excess hypo from the emulsion.
  b. cause the emulsion to swell.
  c. cause the emulsion to shrink.
  d. clean the rollers of the transport system.

6 The most common result of inadequate washing is
  a. incomplete development.
  b. incomplete fixing.
  c. excess hypo retention.
  d. a damp film.

7 Conversion of the latent image to a visible image occurs
  a. in the fixing tank.
  b. when silver bromide is converted to silver.
  c. in less than 10 seconds.
  d. in the gelatin portion of the emulsion.

8 Which of the following ingredients of the developer is responsible for producing the blackest parts of a radiograph?
  a. potassium bromide
  b. glutaraldehyde
  c. hydroquinone
  d. phenidone

9 Hydroquinone and phenidone interact synergistically. Which of the following examples best describes a synergistic interaction?
  a. taking a bomb on board a plane since the probability of two bombs on a plane is lower than that for one bomb
  b. doubling the dose of a drug to treat disease
  c. drinking and driving
  d. pushing one car with another

10 The archival quality of a radiograph is principally
  a. established during development.
  b. established during fixing.
  c. controlled by the activator.
  d. controlled by the developing agent.
11 Which of the following terms does not belong?
  a. clearing agent   c. hypo
  b. stop bath   d. thiosulfate
12 Which of the following is **not** a separate stage in automatic processing?
  a. wetting   c. washing
  b. development   d. drying
13 The preservative normally used in both the developer and the fixer is
  a. glutaraldehyde.   c. potassium alum.
  b. sodium carbonate.   d. sodium sulfite.
14 Which of the following is a reducing agent?
  a. Metol   c. sodium sulfite
  b. glutaraldehyde   d. none of the above
15 Which of the following ingredients in the fixer functions as a stop bath?
  a. the preservative   c. the clearing agent
  b. the hardener   d. the activator
16 Hypo retention refers to
  a. replenishment of a clearing agent.
  b. the formation of silver sulfide.
  c. the formation of sodium sulfite.
  d. thiosulfate left in the emulsion.
17 Development fog will increase when which of the following is abnormally low in the developer?
  a. potassium bromide   c. sodium sulfite
  b. glutaraldehyde   d. hydroquinone
18 The component of the developer that is most responsible for archival quality is
  a. hydroquinone.   c. glutaraldehyde.
  b. sodium sulfite.   d. sodium carbonate.
19 The wetting agent used in automatic processors is usually
  a. acetic acid.   c. silver halide.
  b. silver sulfite.   d. water.
20 The temperature of the wash water should be approximately
  a. 5° C below the developer.
  b. 5° F below the developer.
  c. 5° C below the fixer.
  d. 5° F below the fixer.

21 Which of the following is sometimes used as a developing agent?
  a. water   c. sodium sulfite
  b. glutaraldehyde   d. phenidone
22 A developer ingredient that controls pH is
  a. silver sulfide.
  b. sodium sulfite.
  c. sodium carbonate.
  d. potassium bromide.
23 Which of the following will **not** be found in the developer?
  a. clearing agent   c. activator
  b. preservative   d. hardener
24 Which of the following will **not** be found in the fixer?
  a. glutaraldehyde   c. ammonium thiosulfate
  b. acetic acid   d. water
25 One hardener is
  a. glutaraldehyde.   c. ammonium thiosulfate.
  b. acetic acid.   d. water.
26 The first step in processing is designed to
  a. fix the image.
  b. soften the emulsion.
  c. preserve the developer.
  d. harden the base.
27 The purpose of a stop bath is to
  a. make the latent image manifest.
  b. reduce silver ions to atomic silver.
  c. stop the fixation process.
  d. remove excess developer from the emulsion.
28 During development, silver
  a. atoms are changed to ions.
  b. ions are changed to atoms.
  c. atoms are ionized.
  d. ions are oxidized.
29 What stage of processing involves a synergistic reaction?
  a. development   c. washing
  b. fixing   d. drying
30 All but which of the following must be optimized to ensure best image quality?
  a. the concentration of the developer
  b. the temperature of the developer
  c. the time of fixation
  d. the time of development

WORSHEET 53

Processing the Latent Image

AUTOMATIC PROCESSING

Nearly all radiographs today are processed automatically. The time from insertion of the exposed radiograph into the processor to the appearance of the processed radiograph in the receiving bin—the dry-to-drop time—is 90 seconds. Such an automatic processor is an electromechanical device having four main systems: the transport system, the circulation system, the replenishment system, and the dryer system.

The transport system is a series of rollers, racks, and drive chains powered by an electric motor. This system takes the exposed radiograph and automatically feeds it through the four stations of the processor—the developing tank, the fixing tank, the wash tank, and the drying chamber.

The circulation system is powered by pumps that continuously circulate the chemistries in each tank to ensure complete chemistry mixing and uniform temperature of solution. The circulation system in the developing tank and the fixing tank is a closed loop, whereas that in the wash tank is a single-pass, flow-through system.

The replenishment system consists of a small pump, tubing, and a microswitch control. As the film is fed into the receiving tray of the automatic processor, the microswitch activates the pump to feed a measured amount of developer into the developing tank and fixer into the fixing tank. This replenishment of chemistry is necessary to maintain the chemical balance and concentration in those tanks.

As the film leaves the wash tank, it enters the drying system, which is a chamber where hot dry air is blown over both surfaces of the film to provide a dry, stable radiograph for easy handling and storage.

EXERCISES

1 An assembly consisting of one master roller, one planetary roller, and two guide shoes is called a
   a. transport rack.   c. detector assembly.
   b. roller subassembly.   d. crossover rack.

2 The time of developer immersion is critical. It should be within _____ of the manufacturer's recommendation.
   a. ±1%   c. ±10%
   b. ±2%   d. ±25%

3 Replenishment of which tank in the processing system is most important?
   a. developer   c. wash
   b. fixer   d. dryer

4 When films in the receiving bin are damp, the least likely cause is
   a. heater malfunction.
   b. blower malfunction.
   c. reduced transport time.
   d. depletion of glutaraldehyde.

5 When a large film is inserted into an automatic processor,
   a. a microswitch grips it.
   b. guide shoes grip it.
   c. the long dimension should be against the rail.
   d. the short dimension should be against the rail.

6 Adequate drying is necessary to
   a. complete development.
   b. complete fixation.
   c. reduce artifacts.
   d. reduce contrast.

7 Double-capacity processors can process a film in
   a. 90 seconds.   c. 5 minutes.
   b. 180 seconds.   d. 7 minutes.

8 The minimum flow rate for wash water is _____ gallon(s) per minute.
   a. 1   c. 5
   b. 3   d. 10

9 Between the fixing tank and the wash tank, the film passes through a
  a. transportation rack.
  b. crossover rack.
  c. drying chamber.
  d. receiving bin.

10 Which of the following is **not** one of the major systems of an automatic processor?
  a. the transport system
  b. the development system
  c. the drying system
  d. the replenishment system

11 The principal purpose of the circulation system is to
  a. agitate the chemistry.
  b. agitate the film.
  c. replenish the chemistry.
  d. control the chemistry temperature.

12 Which segment of the circulation system is most important to archival quality?
  a. developing   c. washing
  b. fixing   d. drying

13 Underreplenishment of the developer will result in a
  a. great increase in contrast.
  b. slight increase in contrast.
  c. slight decrease in contrast.
  d. great decrease in contrast.

14 Replenishment tanks should have close-fitting floating lids primarily
  a. to easily monitor fluid level.
  b. for control of replenishment rate.
  c. to control aerial oxidation.
  d. for control of replenishment temperature.

15 Dry-to-drop time refers to
  a. time in the pass box.
  b. time from feed tray to receiving bin.
  c. development time.
  d. exposure-to-view box time.

16 The segment of the circulation system most likely to contain a filter is
  a. the dryer.   c. the fixer.
  b. the wash cycle.   d. the developer.

17 If the power of the drive motor is transferred through a chain, the connecting device is usually a
  a. sprocket.   c. gear.
  b. pulley.   d. roller.

18 Control of the replenishment system is accomplished by a
  a. transport rack.   c. drive motor.
  b. timer.   d. microswitch.

19 The approximate developer conditions in a 90-s processor are
  a. 95° F, 22 s.   c. 85° F, 45 s.
  b. 95° C, 22 s.   d. 85° C, 45 s.

20 Circulation of the developer at the rate of approximately _____ will ensure adequate agitation.
  a. 1 l/m   c. 100 l/m
  b. 15 l/m   d. 150 l/m

21 The transport system includes all but the following:
  a. rollers.   c. drying chamber.
  b. transport racks.   d. drive motor.

22 The 3-in master roller is a part of a
  a. planetary roller.   c. turnaround assembly.
  b. guide shoe.   d. microswitch.

23 The replenishment system is critical. Therefore
  a. replenishment rates should be checked hourly.
  b. developer replenishment should be greater than fixer replenishment.
  c. fixer replenishment should be about 100 ml for each 14 in of film.
  d. decreased replenishment rate is acceptable. Increased replenishment rate is not.

24 Which of the following is not part of the transport system?
  a. 1-in roller   c. guide shoe
  b. fluid pump   d. crossover rack

25 Which of the following is likely to result in an increase in radiographic contrast?
  a. overreplenishment of fixer
  b. underreplenishment of fixer
  c. overreplenishment of developer
  d. underreplenishment of developer

Processing the Latent Image

An unwanted optical density on a radiograph constitutes an artifact. Artifacts are undesirable because they may obscure a meaningful optical density and therefore reduce diagnostic accuracy. Artifacts are identified according to three general classifications: processing artifacts, exposure artifacts, and handling and storage artifacts.

To minimize the generation of artifacts a program of quality assurance must be implemented. Most think of a quality assurance program associated only with the automatic processor. That certainly is important, but equally important are quality assurance programs associated with the imaging apparatus and with technologists' work habits.

EXERCISES

1 Which of the following artifacts might be associated with poor processing?
   a. crown static
   b. pi lines
   c. grid lines
   d. a kink

2 If a radiograph turns yellow during storage, it may be the result of
   a. developer retention.
   b. incomplete washing.
   c. wet pressure sensitization.
   d. presence of sodium sulfite.

3 Which of the following is **not** a necessary part of a quality assurance program?
   a. monitoring for darkroom light leaks
   b. periodic processor cleaning
   c. evaluation of film-screen contact
   d. determination of film-base thickness

4 Which of the following best describes an example of preventive maintenance?
   a. stopping smoking
   b. repairing a flat tire
   c. changing motor oil every 3,000 mi
   d. using gonadal shields in radiology

5 In establishing a processor maintenance program, which of the following would **not** normally be included?
   a. scheduled maintenance
   b. nonscheduled maintenance
   c. preventive maintenance
   d. productive maintenance

6 Which of the following artifacts is most likely to occur before processing?
   a. a small blur in an otherwise sharp radiograph
   b. dichroic stain
   c. wet pressure sensitization
   d. chemical fog

7 A quality assurance program for an automatic processor would include all except
   a. periodic cleaning.
   b. annual parts replacement.
   c. monthly monitoring.
   d. daily monitoring.

8 With a 90-s processor, immersion time in the developer is approximately
   a. 10 s.   c. 30 s.
   b. 20 s.   d. 40 s.

9 Most facilities would be sure that the automatic processor was
   a. monitored hourly.
   b. replenished daily.
   c. cleaned weekly.
   d. maintained annually.

10 The classification of artifacts includes all except
   a. exposure artifacts.
   b. processing artifacts.
   c. storage artifacts.
   d. location artifacts.

11 Which of the following would be identified as a handling artifact?
   a. motion
   c. curtain effect
   b. kink marks
   d. double exposure

12 The distinct patterns of static artifacts do **not** include
   a. finger static.
   b. tree static.
   c. crown static.
   d. smudge static.

13 Processor cleaning
   a. should be done bimonthly.
   b. takes no more than a few minutes.
   c. should be scheduled for a 4-hr interval.
   d. is unnecessary unless artifacts appear.

14 Scheduled maintenance does **not** include
   a. adjustment of pulleys.
   b. adjustment of gears.
   c. parts replacement.
   d. lubrication of moving parts.

15 Which of the following would be considered a storage artifact?
   a. wrong screen/film match
   b. warped cassette
   c. pi lines
   d. radiation fog

16 Failure of a system or subsystem of an automatic processor will result in
   a. scheduled maintenance.
   b. nonscheduled maintenance.
   c. preventive maintenance.
   d. none of the above.

17 Pi lines are so-called because
   a. they occur at 3.1416-in intervals.
   b. they occur at intervals of π times the roller diameter.
   c. they occur at principal intervals.
   d. they look like a slice of pie.

18 Which of the following types of artifact is most distinctive and identifiable?
   a. storage near radioactive material
   b. chemical fog
   c. light leaks
   d. pi lines

19 Artifacts caused by wet pressure sensitization usually occur
   a. before processing.
   b. in the developing tank.
   c. in the fixing tank.
   d. in the drying chamber.

20 Guide shoe artifacts will be found on the _____ of a radiograph.
   a. side
   b. leading edge
   c. trailing edge
   d. leading and trailing edges

Intensifying Screens

SCREEN CONSTRUCTION
·················
LUMINESCENCE
·················
SCREEN CHARACTERISTICS
·················

Radiographic intensifying screens are employed principally to reduce patient radiation dose. The use of screens degrades the final image quality when compared with direct-exposure techniques, but this degradation is slight and not objectionable. For this reason, intensifying screens have enjoyed widespread use, and today more than 99% of all radiographs are screen-film radiographs.

The intensifying screen is constructed by pasting a phosphor on a base material with a reflective layer between. The speed of a screen is a measure of its ability to reduce dose. Screen speed is identified by the intensification factor, which is the ratio of the exposures required to produce the same film density (OD = 1.0) with and without screens:

$$\text{Intensification factor} = \frac{\text{Exposure without screens}}{\text{Exposure with screens}}$$

The physical characteristics of intensifying screens are difficult to determine precisely. Speed and resolution are very much a function of the phosphor composition and thickness. Crystal size and concentration also affect speed and resolution. X-ray energy also affects screen speed; speed increases with increasing kVp.

EXERCISES

1 Intensifying-screen speed increases with increasing
  a. mAs.   **c.** atomic mass.
  b. phosphor thickness.   **d.** base thickness.

2 A nonscreen technique is used in radiography primarily because it
  a. produces higher contrast.
  b. results in less blur.
  c. results in less motion blur.
  d. reduces scatter radiation.

3 Afterglow is a property of intensifying screens that
  a. enhances resolution.
  b. reduces screen speed.
  c. tends to increase image blur.
  d. is enhanced at high kVp.

4 The resolution achievable with intensifying screens is approximately
  a. 1 lp/mm.
  b. 10 lp/mm.
  c. 1 lp/cm.
  d. 10 lp/cm.

5 Which of the following factors controlled by the technologist affects screen speed the most?
  a. process temperature
  b. room temperature
  c. kVp
  d. mAs

6 When screen film is the image receptor, image quality is a trade-off among speed, resolution, and radiographic noise. In general,
  a. as speed increases, resolution improves.
  b. as speed increases so does noise.
  c. as noise increases, resolution improves.
  d. as quantum mottle increases, resolution improves.

7 When discussing intensifying screens, which one of the following statements is true?
  a. Phosphorescence and fluorescence are the same.
  b. They neither phosphoresce nor fluoresce, only luminesce.
  c. They fluoresce but do not phosphoresce.
  d. They phosphoresce but do not fluoresce.

8 The intensification factor
  a. is greater for detail screens than for par speed screens.
  b. decreases with increasing kVp.
  c. increases with increasing temperature.
  d. is higher for rare earth screens than for calcium tungstate screens.

9 A phosphor currently used in radiographic intensifying screens is
  a. barium fluorochloride.
  b. cadmium tungstate.
  c. barium platinocyanide.
  d. calcium sulfate.

10 Screen unsharpness
  a. is the loss of sharpness of the image when screens are used.
  b. occurs because the light emitted is focused on the film.
  c. is greater with detail screens than with par speed screens.
  d. is less with rare earth screens.

11 Concerning luminescence, which of the following statements is true?
  a. There are two kinds: fluorescence and phosphorescence.
  b. Phosphorescence occurs only when a stimulus is applied.
  c. Materials that luminesce are called lumenites.
  d. Luminous watch dials that fade in the dark are fluorescent devices.

12 Intensifying screens are used with radiographic film to
  a. reduce exposure to the patient.
  b. increase radiographic latitude.
  c. improve definition.
  d. allow longer exposures.

13 Intensifying screens are used in conjunction with radiographic film to
  a. enhance patient motion.
  b. lower the mAs necessary to produce a proper radiograph.
  c. increase the latitude of the imaging system.
  d. increase the detail of the imaging system.

14 Which of the following properties is most important for intensifying screens?
  a. phosphor concentration
  b. phosphor crystal size
  c. reflective layer
  d. phosphor composition

15 Luminescence is a process that
  a. involves inner-shell electrons.
  b. involves outer-shell electrons.
  c. always requires x-ray attenuation.
  d. always requires x-ray absorption.

16 Since x-ray interaction with a phosphor produces light isotropically,
  a. a protective layer is required.
  b. a base is required.
  c. the light spreads out.
  d. the light is focused.

17 Which of the following is **not** a required characteristic of a base for an intensifying screen?
  a. rugges   c. chemically inert
  b. translucent   d. flexible

18 Quantum detection efficiency (QDE) refers to
  a. ability to absorb x rays.
  b. atomic number.
  c. mass density.
  d. light emission.

19 Phosphor afterglow
  a. results from fluorescence.
  b. is also called lag.
  c. is also called conversion efficiency.
  d. is helpful.

20 The patient exposure for a direct-exposure chest x-ray examination is 210 mR (54 µC/kg). If par speed screens are used, the exposure required is 15 mR (3.9 µC/kg). The intensification factor is
  a. 0.07.   c. 14.
  b. 7.   d. 3150.

21 A direct exposure radiograph requires 650 mR (169 µC/kg). If the intensification factor of rare earth screens is 200, what would the patient exposure be?
  a. 3.25 mR   c. 200 mR
  b. 6.5 mR   d. 1300 mR

22 Mammography conducted with detail screens results in exposures as low as 300 mR (77 µC/kg). The intensification factor for these screens is about 30. If such an examination were conducted as a nonscreen procedure, what would the patient exposure be?
  a. 100 mR   c. 1000 mR
  b. 900 mR   d. 9000 mR

23 Given the following information, calculate the intensification factor for the par speed screen:

	1000 x rays, direct exposure	1000 x rays, par screen film
Number absorbed in film	10	8
Number absorbed in screen	0	200
Number of visible light photons absorbed in film	0	25,000
Number of latent images formed	10	250

  a. 10   c. 31
  b. 25   d. 100

Intensifying Screens

Previously, calcium tungstate was the principal phosphor employed in radiographic intensifying screens. Now, however, newer and faster screens are available and have been incorporated into radiologic practice.

These screens are described as rare earth because the phorphors are compounds incorporating the rare earth elements gadolinium (Gd), lanthanum (La), and yttrium (Y). **The principal advantage of rare earth screens is speed.** They are approximately twice as fast as calcium tungstate screens. **The principal disadvantage is noise or quantum mottle.** Rare earth screens have resolution equal to that of calcium tungstate screens.

The increased speed of rare earth screens results from their ability to absorb more x rays than calcium tungstate screens. The absorption coefficient is higher, and once absorption has occurred, they convert more of the x-ray energy to light photons. The conversion efficiency is higher.

EXERCISES

1 Which of the following is **not** a rare earth element?
 a. gadolinium
 b. yttrium
 c. oxybromide
 d. lanthanum

2 In the formula La_2O_2S:Tb, the Tb
 a. stands for tungsten bromide.
 b. improves contrast.
 c. increases resolution.
 d. improves luminescence.

3 The principal advantage of rare earth screens over calcium tungstate screens is
 a. lower cost.
 b. better resolution.
 c. reduced noise.
 d. faster speed.

4 Rare earth screens exhibit higher x-ray absorption than calcium tungstate screens
 a. regardless of the x-ray energy.
 b. only at low x-ray energy.
 c. only over an intermediate x-ray energy range.
 d. only at high x-ray energy range.

5 Rare earth screens are most effective in reducing patient dose in
 a. mammography.
 b. abdominal radiography.
 c. 120 kVp chest radiography.
 d. xeromammography

6 Of the following elements, which has the highest atomic number?
 a. yttrium   **c.** gadolinium
 b. lanthanum   **d.** tungsten

7 Rare earth phosphors have conversion efficiencies _____ those of calcium tungstate.
 a. less than   **c.** twice
 b. equal to   **d.** four times

8 Which of the following contributes to the increased speed of rare earth screens?
 a. conversion efficiency
 b. phosphor thickness
 c. high atomic number
 d. longer wavelength emission

9 When using green-emitting rare earth screens,
 I. a green-sensitive film must be used.
 II. a red safelight is necessary
 III. northochromatic film is required.
 a. I only
 b. II only
 c. I and II
 d. I, II, and III

10 Which of the following spectra is discrete?
   a. calcium tungstate emission
   b. rare earth emission
   c. orthochromatic absorption
   d. panchromatic absorption

11 Rare earth screens
   a. show higher x-ray absorption in the diagnostic range than calcium tungstate screens.
   b. show higher absorption than calcium tungstate for x rays less than 25 keV.
   c. show higher absorption than calcium tungstate for x rays greater than 80 keV.
   d. are faster than calcium tungstate screens principally because of scatter radiation.

12 When diagnostic x rays interact with rare earth phosphors,
   a. the number of x rays absorbed is approximately the same as that for calcium tungstate.
   b. K-shell interaction will not occur at energies less than approximately 70 keV.
   c. the lower the x-ray energy the more probable is photoelectric absorption.
   d. it is possible that with increasing x-ray energy an abrupt decrease in x-ray absorption will occur.

13 When using rare earth intensifying screens,
   a. as x-ray energy increases up to the K-shell binding energy, absorption also increases.
   b. there is an abrupt reduction in x-ray absorption at an energy equal to the K-shell binding energy.
   c. the abrupt change in absorption at an energy equal to the K-shell binding energy is called the K-shell absorption edge.
   d. all rare earth elements have higher K-shell electron binding energy than tungsten.

14 By comparison with calcium tungstate, when an x ray is absorbed in a rare earth screen,
   a. more energy will be transferred.
   b. shorter wavelength light will be emitted.
   c. more light will be emitted.
   d. the ratio of visible light emitted to x-ray energy absorbed will be less.

15 In comparison with calcium tungstate screens, rare earth screens
   a. absorb one to two times as many x rays.
   b. absorb three to five times as many x rays.
   c. emit shorter wavelength light.
   d. emit higher energy light.

16 In comparison with calcium tungstate screens, rare earth screens
   a. emit more intense light.
   b. emit light in the blue-violet region.
   c. should be used with blue-sensitive radiographic film.
   d. may require a new darkroom.

17 Rare earth intensifying screens
   a. have better resolution than conventional calcium tungstate screens.
   b. have less quantum mottle than calcium tungstate screens.
   c. are more expensive than calcium tungstate screens.
   d. do not require good film-screen contact.

18 Which of the following statements concerning intensifying screens is correct?
   a. Par speed screens emit green light.
   b. Calcium tungstate screens emit green-yellow light.
   c. All have conversion efficiencies greater than one.
   d. Rare earth screens must be used in carbon fiber cassettes.

19 What is the principal limitation of the rare earth intensifying screen?
   a. quantum mottle
   b. decreased resolution
   c. an increased exposure factor
   d. decreased contrast

20 Stains in intensifying screens from processing chemicals are likely to result in _____ on the radiograph.
   a. increased base density
   b. an elevated fog level
   c. light blotches
   d. dark blotches

21 In the proper design and use of a film cassette,
   a. the front cover should be made of low Z material to minimize x-ray attenuation.
   b. the back cover should be made of low Z material to protect unexposed film while in the passbox.
   c. the back cover should be made of high Z material so it can function as a primary barrier for personnel protection.
   d. scratches on the front cover indicate that replacement is necessary.

22 Carbon fiber is particularly useful in x-ray imaging because of its
   a. flexibility.
   b. mass density.
   c. dimensional stability.
   d. low atomic number.

23 The routine care of screens requires that they be
   a. reinforced against radiation fatigue.
   b. replaced because of radiation fatigue.
   c. periodically cleaned.
   d. periodically calibrated.

Beam Restricting Devices

PRODUCTION OF SCATTER RADIATION

Scatter radiation is produced when the x-ray beam interacts with a patient. Scattered x-ray photons resulting from Compton interaction reach the film and decrease the quality and clarity of the image. Three principal factors influence the quantity of scatter radiation produced during a radiographic examination. The first two of these can be manipulated by the radiologic technologist.

1. **Kilovoltage (kVp).** Increasing kVp also increases the proportion of scatter radiation since the Compton effect predominates at higher energies.
2. **Field size.** The relative intensity of scatter radiation increases with increasing field size since more tissue is exposed to the x-ray beam.
3. **Patient thickness.** The total number of scattered photons increases proportionally to the thickness of the part to be radiographed.

EXERCISES

1 Remnant x rays include those that
   a. do not interact with the patient or the image receptor.
   b. are absorbed in the patient.
   c. exit the patient toward the image receptor.
   d. interact with the patient and are scattered laterally.
2 Which of the following factors can both affect the level of scatter radiation and be readily controlled by the radiologic technologist?
   a. inherent filtration
   b. added filtration
   c. patient thickness
   d. field size

3 As the kVp of operation increases, the absolute level of scatter radiation will
   a. decrease because of less Compton interaction.
   b. decrease because of less photoelectric interaction.
   c. increase because of more Compton interaction.
   d. increase because of more photoelectric interaction.
4 At 100 kVp what is the approximate percent of x rays that are transmitted through 10 cm of soft tissue?
   a. 0.5%   c. 5%
   b. 1%   d. 50%
5 At high kVp (i.e., 125 kVp) most x rays are
   a. transmitted through the body without interaction.
   b. transmitted through the body with interaction.
   c. not transmitted through the body.
   d. remnant x rays.
6 When kVp is increased with a compensating reduction in mAs, then _____ is reduced.
   a. scatter proportion   c. remnant radiation
   b. density   d. patient dose
7 If a constant radiographic density is maintained while increasing kVp,
   a. patient dose will increase.
   b. patient dose will decrease.
   c. collimation should be enlarged.
   d. collimation should be reduced.
8 As the field size is increased, scatter radiation
   a. is removed.   c. remains constant.
   b. is increased.   d. is reduced.
9 One factor that influences the production of scatter radiation that is generally not under the control of the technologist is
   a. kVp.
   b. use of grids.
   c. patient thickness.
   d. field size.

10 Which of the following is **not** a device designed to reduce the level of scatter radiation reaching the film?
   a. a test pattern
   c. a beam restrictor
   b. a compression device
   d. a diaphragm

11 Scatter radiation chiefly influences radiographic quality by reducing
   a. density.
   c. blurring.
   b. contrast.
   d. distortion.

12 In some radiographic techniques the primary purpose of adding a compensating filter is to
   a. change the distribution of radiation.
   b. increase overall radiation intensity.
   c. reduce the half-value layer of the radiation.
   d. control the production of scatter radiation.

13 The x-ray photons that the technologist would like to have interact with the image receptor are those that are _____ the body.
   a. absorbed within
   b. attenuated within
   c. transmitted through
   d. scattered within

14 As kVp is increased from 70 to 80,
   a. the mAs must be increased.
   b. the SID must be increased.
   c. there will be a lower proportion of scatter radiation.
   d. there will be a higher proportion of scatter radiation.

15 In conventional radiography, most of the photons that reach the image receptor are
   a. photoelectric photons.
   b. Compton-scattered photons.
   c. annihilation photons.
   d. classically scattered photons.

16 Remnant radiation consists of all _____ emerging from the patient in the direction of the image receptor.
   a. absorbed photons
   b. photoelectric photons
   c. Compton-scattered photons
   d. photons

17 As kVp increases from 70 to 90, all other factors remaining constant,
   a. the quantity of transmitted photons will decrease.
   b. the quantity of absorbed photons will decrease.
   c. the ratio of scattered-to-transmitted photons will increase.
   d. the ratio of absorbed-to-transmitted photons will increase.

18 As the field size of the x-ray beam increases, the _____ increases.
   a. kVp
   b. mAs
   c. total filtration
   d. patient exposure

19 In general, as the thickness of the part being radiographed increases,
   a. the kVp increases.
   b. the mAs decreases.
   c. the total filtration increases.
   d. the patient exposure increases.

20 Remnant x rays include those transmitted and _____ by the patient.
   a. absorbed
   b. scattered
   c. scattered forward
   d. absorbed back

21 In radiography, one would like to employ very low kVp because
   a. patient dose would be low.
   b. scatter radiation would be low.
   c. transmitted radiation would be high.
   d. Compton effect would be high.

22 In fact, it is necessary to use higher kVp in order that _____ be at an acceptable level.
   a. scatter radiation
   b. photoelectric effect
   c. Compton effect
   d. patient dose

23 As kVp increases, the absolute number of x rays that undergo
   a. photoelectric and Compton interaction increases.
   b. photoelectric interaction increases and Compton interaction decreases.
   c. photoelectric interaction decreases and Compton interaction increases.
   d. photoelectric and Compton interactions decreases.

24 In general, if an increase in radiographic technique is required because of patient size, patient dose will be lowest if
   a. only mAs is increased.
   b. only kVp is increased.
   c. both mAs and kVp are increased.
   d. mAs is increased and kVp decreased.

25 X-ray beam restriction to the area of interest is principally required to reduce
   a. patient dose.
   c. mAs.
   b. scatter radiation.
   d. kVp.

WORKSHEET 58

Beam Restricting Devices

CONTROL OF SCATTER RADIATION

Beam-restricting devices are employed in radiology to limit the volume of tissue irradiated in order to reduce patient dose and scatter radiation reaching the film. Three types of beam-restricting devices exist:

1. **Aperture diaphragm**—a fixed-aperture device consisting of a lead or lead-lined metal diaphragm attached to the head of the x-ray tube.
2. **Cones and cylinders**—a fixed-aperture device consisting of an extended metal structure attached to the x-ray tube head.
3. **Variable-aperture collimator**—a device consisting of two pairs of lead shutters that are independently adjustable. Square or rectangular fields are possible, and the x-ray field can be illuminated by a coincident light field. Positive beam limiting **(PBL)** variable-aperture collimators are required on all general purpose x-ray equipment sold in the United States.

EXERCISES

1 Which of the following is **not** a beam-restricting device?
   a. an aperture diaphragm
   b. a PBL device
   c. added filtration
   d. a cone

2 An aperture diaphragm should allow x rays to expose an area
   a. just larger than the image receptor.
   b. equal to the image receptor.
   c. just smaller than the image receptor.
   d. that varies according to patient size.

3 When an aperture diaphragm is used,
   a. grid cutoff can occur if the diaphragm is not properly positioned.
   b. x-ray field cutoff can occur if the diaphragm is not properly positioned.
   c. added filtration is more important.
   d. a PBL device is required.

4 Dental radiographic cones are usually designed for either _____ or _____ source-to-image receptor distance (SID).
   a. 10 in, 12 in
   b. 14 in, 17 in
   c. 20 cm, 40 cm
   d. 40 cm, 80 cm

5 The **least** desirable dental cone is a
   a. long, plastic, open-end cone.
   b. long, lead-lined, open-end cone.
   c. short, lead-lined, open-end cone.
   d. short, plastic pointer cone.

6 Off-focus radiation
   a. degrades the radiographic image.
   b. reduces patient dose.
   c. improves image contrast.
   d. originates from outside the x-ray tube.

7 In a light-localizing, variable-aperture collimator,
   a. periodic checks of x-ray beam and light-field coincidence are necessary.
   b. if the light bulb burns out, the graduated scale on the adjusting mechanism is correct.
   c. it is not necessary that the cross hairs in the light beam be centered.
   d. equipped with a PBL device, light-field illumination is unnecessary.

8 The simplest of all beam-restricting devices is
   a. an aluminum filter.
   b. a radiographic cone.
   c. an aperture diaphragm.
   d. a fluoroscopic collimator.

9 Which of the following devices is normally designed to limit off-focus radiation?
   a. fixed-aperture circular diaphragms
   b. fixed-aperture rectangular diaphragms
   c. first-stage shutters of a variable-aperture collimator
   d. second-stage shutters of a variable-aperture collimator

10 Off-focus radiation
   a. consists of scattered electrons.
   b. improves image quality.
   c. results when projectile electrons do not strike the focal spot.
   d. consists of electrons as well as x rays.

11 Which of the following could be considered a beam-restricting device?
   a. a dental pointer cone without an integral diaphragm
   b. a rectangular film mask on a radiographic head stand
   c. 2.5 mm Al added filtration
   d. fluoroscopic shutters

12 Cone cutting
   a. occurs when the tip of the cone is too close to the patient.
   b. occurs when the edge of the cone intercepts the scattered x ray beam.
   c. occurs if the axis of the cone, tube, and image receptor are not aligned.
   d. is useful in most radiographic examinations.

13 If a fixed-aperture, rectangular, beam-restricting device is used, then
   a. an unexposed border should be visible on at least two sides of the radiograph.
   b. an unexposed border should be visible on all four sides of the radiograph.
   c. the central axis of the aperture diaphragm must be centered somewhere on the image receptor.
   d. added filtration is unnecessary.

14 A properly designed light-localizing, variable-aperture collimator will
   a. have field-defining shutters of aluminum.
   b. be designed to reduce off-focus radiation.
   c. concentrate off-focus radiation onto the image receptor.
   d. have no added filtration.

15 Radiographic cones and cylinders are employed principally to reduce
   a. the need for added filtration.
   b. the radiographic technique required.
   c. the intensity of scatter radiation.
   d. patient dose.

16 In dental radiography
   a. the x-ray beam diameter must not exceed 7 cm.
   b. the x-ray beam diameter must not exceed 20 cm.
   c. the SID must not exceed 7 cm.
   d. the SID must not exceed 20 cm.

17 Which of the following is most useful in dental radiography?
   a. light-localizing, variable-aperture diaphragm
   b. circular-aperture diaphragm
   c. rectangular-aperture diaphragm
   d. a plastic pointer cone

18 The two general types of devices designed to control scatter radiation are
   a. filtration and diaphragms.
   b. filtration and beam restrictors.
   c. grids and beam restrictors.
   d. grids and filtration.

19 When a diaphragm is used,
   a. a 3 cm unexposed border should be visible on at least three sides.
   b. a 1 cm unexposed border should be visible on two sides.
   c. a 1 cm unexposed border should be visible on all sides.
   d. an unexposed border is not necessary.

20 PBL stands for
   a. photon beam limitation.
   b. positive beam limiting.
   c. photon beam level.
   d. photon border level.

21 One helpful feature of a light localizing collimator is increased
   a. kVp.   c. distance.
   b. mAs.   d. filtration.

22 A diaphragm is machined to just match image receptor size. If an unexposed border is required on the radiograph, the diaphragm opening will
   a. have to be enlarged.
   b. remain the same.
   c. have to be reduced.
   d. require more information before change.

23 A dental cone diaphragm assembly must restrict the circular x-ray beam to 7 cm diameter at the tip of the cone. If the source-to-cone tip distance is 20 cm and the source-to-diaphragm distance is 4 cm, what should the diameter of the diaphragm be?
   a. 0.7 cm   c. 2.1 cm
   b. 1.4 cm   d. 2.8 cm

24 An aperture diaphragm is designed for 10×12 in film. If the SID is 36 in and the source-to-diaphragm distance is 4 in, what size should the opening of the diaphragm be?
   a. 1.1 in $\times$ 1.3 in   c. 1.6 in $\times$ 1.9 in
   b. 1.3 in $\times$ 1.6 in   d. 1.3 in $\times$ 1.9 in

25 A room to be used exclusively to produce 14 in $\times$ 17 in chest radiographs is being installed. The SID is 180 cm, and the source-to-diaphragm distance is 10 cm. What size should the opening of the diaphragm be?
   a. 0.4 cm $\times$ 0.8 cm   c. 0.8 cm $\times$ 0.9 cm
   b. 0.4 in $\times$ 0.8 in   d. 0.8 cm $\times$ 0.9 in

The Grid

X rays that leave a patient and are incident on the image receptor are called **remnant radiation.** There are two basic components to remnant radiation: (1) those x rays that have passed directly through the patient without interaction and (2) those x rays that have been scattered in the patient. Only the x rays that are not significantly scattered carry useful diagnostic information to the image receptor.

The scattered x rays are the result of Compton interaction. Since the image receptor is not capable of distinguishing primary from scatter x rays, it will image a scattered x ray as having come directly from the tube target, when in fact its direction was from the anatomic structure from which it was scattered. This scattered radiation reduces contrast and degrades the quality of the radiograph. The main device used to "clean up" the scatter radiation in the remnant beam is the grid. There are two principal characteristics of grid construction: the **grid ratio** is the thickness of the grid (the height of the grid strip) divided by the width of the interspace material; the **grid frequency** is the number of grid strips per inch or per centimeter.

EXERCISES

1 The principal reason for using a grid is to
   a. reduce patient dose.
   b. remove remnant radiation.
   c. enhance differential absorption.
   d. increase radiographic contrast.
2 Which of the following will **not** enhance radiographic contrast?
   a. a decrease in kVp
   b. the use of a grid
   c. the use of added filtration
   d. collimating the x-ray beam
3 If one had to select the single most important grid characteristic, it would be
   a. grid ratio.   **c.** grid height.
   b. grid frequency.   **d.** grid weight.
4 In a grid that has lead strips 0.5 mm apart and 4 mm high, the grid ratio is
   a. 4:1.   **c.** 8:1.
   b. 6:1.   **d.** 12:1.
5 In a grid that has lead strips 0.5 mm apart and 8 mm high, the grid ratio is
   a. 4:1.   **c.** 12:1.
   b. 8:1.   **d.** 16:1.
6 The use of a grid will result in:
   a. a lighter radiograph.
   b. a darker radiograph.
   c. control of scatter radiation.
   d. reduction in patient dose.
7 In the design of a radiographic grid, the
   a. interspace material is radiopaque.
   b. interspace material is radiolucent.
   c. grid strips are radiotransparent.
   d. grid strips are radiolucent.
8 X-ray grids are principally effective in attenuating
   a. photoelectrons.
   b. x rays following photoelectric interaction.
   c. x rays following Compton interaction.
   d. all remnant radiation.
9 If the interspace dimension is constant, increasing the grid ratio will
   a. make the grid thicker.
   b. make the grid lighter.
   c. require less grid strip material.
   d. require less interspace material.
10 As grid frequency increases,
   a. the number of grid strips per centimeter decreases.
   b. the patient dose is reduced.
   c. the interspace width becomes thinner if the width of the grid strip remains constant.
   d. the grid ratio will be reduced if the thickness of the grid remains constant.

11 Which of the following would be most acceptable grid strip material from the standpoint of x-ray attenuation?
a. tungsten
b. wood
c. barium
d. copper

12 Which of the following would be most radiolucent as interspace material?
a. lead
b. aluminum
c. paper fiber
d. copper

13 Grids with a high ratio
a. are more effective than those with a low ratio.
b. are easier to manufacture than are those with a low ratio.
c. can be created by increasing interspace width.
d. can be created by increasing grid strip width.

14 The efficiency of a grid for reducing scatter radiation is related principally to the
a. grid ratio.
b. grid radius.
c. grid frequency.
d. grid mass.

15 The patient dose increases as
a. grid ratio decreases.
b. grid frequency decreases.
c. the width of the grid strips decreases.
d. the atomic number of the interspace material increases.

16 Radiographic grids
a. can be placed between the source and the patient.
b. must be placed between the source and the patient.
c. can be placed between the patient and the image receptor.
d. must be placed between the patient and the image receptor.

17 The construction of a radiographic grid
a. usually incorporates aluminum or copper as the grid strip material.
b. usually incorporates high Z interspace material.
c. is easier with an aluminum interspace.
d. has an aluminum cover for filtration.

18 Use of which of the following devices will reduce radiographic contrast?
a. intensifying screens
b. collimators
c. grids
d. filters

19 Added filtration influences selection of
a. x rays from a particular machine.
b. scattered x rays.
c. low energy x rays.
d. high energy x rays.

20 If only scatter radiation reached the image receptor,
a. radiographic contrast would be very high.
b. radiographic contrast would be very low.
c. image receptor speed would be very high.
d. image receptor speed would be very low.

21 A grid has the following characteristics: grid ratio = 10:1, grid strip = 25 μm, interspace width = 300 μm, contrast improvement factor = 1.8. What percentage of the incident radiation will be intercepted?
a. 3.3%
b. 7.7%
c. 8.3%
d. 83%

22 A grid has the following characteristics: grid frequency = 55 lines/cm, grid width = 33 μm, grid height = 3.3 mm, interspace width = 300 μm. What is the grid ratio?
a. 4.5:1
b. 10:1
c. 11:1
d. approximately 16:1

23 A grid has the following characteristics: grid ratio = 10:1, grid height = 4.5 mm, grid strip width = 40 μm, interspace width = 450 μm. What is the grid frequency?
a. 20 lines/cm
b. 22 lines/cm
c. 40 lines/cm
d. 45 lines/cm

24 A grid has the following characteristics: grid frequency = 40 lines/cm, grid strip width = 30 μm, grid height = 3.0 mm. The grid ratio is approximately
a. 8:1.
b. 10:1.
c. 12:1.
d. 14:1.

25 A grid has the following characteristics: grid ratio = 8:1, grid strip width = 50 μm, grid height = 3.2 mm. The grid frequency is approximately
a. 22 lines/cm.
b. 25 lines/cm.
c. 40 lines/cm.
d. 50 lines/cm.

The Grid

MEASURING GRID PERFORMANCE

The principal function of radiographic grids is to absorb scatter radiation from the remnant beam before it reaches the film. If scatter radiation does reach the film, the film is fogged and radiographic contrast is reduced. Stated differently, the function of radiographic grids is to increase contrast.

Generally speaking, the higher the grid ratio and the higher the grid frequency, the higher the radiographic contrast will be. The principal measure of grid performance is called the **contrast improvement factor,** which equals the following:

$$\frac{\text{Radiographic contrast with a grid}}{\text{Radiographic contrast without a grid}}$$

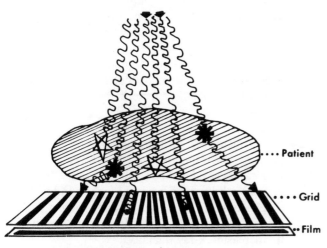

- **T** = Transmitted x rays
- **S** = Compton-scattered x rays
- **P** = X rays absorbed photoelectrically

Another measure of grid performance closely related to the contrast improvement factor is **selectivity:**

$$\text{Selectivity} = \frac{\text{Transmitted primary x rays}}{\text{Transmitted scattered x rays}}$$

The contrast improvement factor and selectivity depend on the characteristics of the x-ray beam and the construction characteristics of the grid. However, the contrast improvement factor depends more on the characteristics of the x-ray beam, whereas selectivity is primarily a function of the construction of the grid.

EXERCISES

1 Which of the following is the **least** important indicator of grid performance?
   a. grid ratio
   b. contrast improvement factor
   c. grid frequency
   d. grid-strip height

2 The contrast improvement factor is defined as the radiographic contrast obtained
   a. at a density of 1.
   b. with a grid compared to that obtained without one.
   c. with a screen compared to that obtained without one.
   d. without a grid compared to that obtained with one.

3 As the ratio of grids increases, the _____ also increases.
   a. system speed
   b. intensification factor
   c. contrast improvement factor
   d. thickness of interspace material

4 The use of high-frequency grids results in
   a. reduced patient dose
   b. increased contrast improvement factor.
   c. reduced spatial resolution.
   d. increased visualization of grid lines.

5 Radiographic grids with high contrast improvement usually

a. increase radiographic contrast.

b. are low ratio grids.

c. reduce patient dose.

d. transmit more scatter radiation.

6 A radiograph is made at 76 kVp and 25 mAs without a grid. If an 8:1 ratio grid is added, the mAs required would then be approximately.

a. 25 mAs.   c. 75 mAs.

b. 50 mAs.   d. 150 mAs.

7 The simplest type of grid is the

a. zero frequency grid   c. focused grid.

b. high ratio grid.   d. linear grid.

8 The undesirable absorption of primary-beam x rays by a grid is called

a. primary-beam scatter.   c. upside-down grid.

b. grid cutoff.   d. malpositioned grid.

9 Which of the following would be included in the three major classifications of moving grids?

a. crossed grid   c. zero-frequency grid

b. focused grid   d. reciprocating grid

10 If one had two grids whose characteristics were unknown, but grid B weighed twice as much as grid A, one might conclude that grid B would have a

a. lower grid ratio.

b. lower grid frequency.

c. higher contrast improvement factor.

d. lower selectivity.

11 Focused grids

a. reduce the amount of scatter radiation reaching the patient.

b. reduce the radiation exposure to the patient when compared with no grid.

c. cut off the four edges of an image if placed too close to the source.

d. cut off two edges of an image if placed too far from the tube.

12 One factor that does **not** affect the percentage of scatter radiation reaching the image receptor is

a. patient thickness.   c. kVp.

b. grid ratio.   d. mAs.

13 The efficiency of a grid for scatter radiation cleanup is related principally to the grid

a. ratio.   c. frequency.

b. radius.   d. interspace.

14 Which of the following would principally reduce the **production** of scatter radiation?

a. use of a grid   c. a decrease in SID

b. use of a filter   d. a decrease in kVp

15 Radiographic grids

a. usually have contrast improvement factors from 0 to 1.0.

b. may have aluminum step wedges incorporated into them.

c. usually have grid ratios between 5:1 and 16:1.

d. have reduced selectivity as the mass is increased.

16 A crosshatched radiographic grid

a. allows considerable positioning latitude when compared with linear grids.

b. reduces scatter radiation along two axes.

c. has a contrast improvement factor equal to a linear grid of equal ratio.

d. is said to have a grid ratio of 10:1; therefore it consists of two 5:1 linear grids.

17 Which of the following is a disadvantage of moving grids?

a. They require thinner strips.

b. They require higher grid frequency.

c. They may result in decreased magnification.

d. They may produce motion unsharpness.

18 The contrast improvement factor

a. increases with decreasing grid frequency.

b. increases with decreasing grid ratio.

c. varies with the kVp of operation.

d. is equal to 1.0 for a 10:1 grid.

19 Generally the selectivity of a grid will depend principally on

a. grid radius.   c. grid mass.

b. grid frequency.   d. contrast improvement factor.

20 With the moving-grid technique, the appearance of grid lines could indicate that

a. the kVp is too low.

b. the exposure started before the grid moved.

c. the exposure stopped before the grid stopped.

d. the grid frequency is too low.

21 If all other factors remain the same and the grid strip width is reduced,

a. grid ratio will increase.

b. grid frequency will decrease.

c. contrast improvement factor will increase.

d. selectivity will decrease.

22 Selectivity is principally a function of grid

a. radius.   c. frequency.

b. mass.   d. height.

23 The average gradient of an image receptor is 2.1. With a 10:1 grid having 50 lines/cm frequency, the average gradient is increased to 3.2. What is the contrast improvement factor?

a. 0.4   c. 2.0

b. 1.5   d. 6.7

24 Bucky factor is a measure of

a. x-ray beam quality.

b. x-ray beam quantity.

c. penetrability of a beam through a grid.

d. penetrability of a beam through the patient.

25 The value of the Bucky factor increases with

a. increasing x-ray quantity.

b. increasing x-ray quality.

c. decreasing grid ratio.

d. decreasing contrast improvement factor.

Name _____

Date _____

The Grid

TYPES OF GRIDS
....
USE OF GRIDS
....
GRID SELECTION
....

If the construction and performance characteristics of a grid are unknown and understood, grid selection and use will be more accurate. Selection of a grid generally requires that one specify the type of grid (linear, crossed, focused, or moving), the ratio of the grid, and the grid frequency.

Such selection is made on the basis of the types of radiographic examinations to be performed. If grid lines are objectionable, moving grids should be employed. If a high degree of cleanup is required, crossed grids should be employed. Cerebral angiography often requires crossed grids so that the contrast is maximized for imaging small vessel detail. Low kVp techniques would generally demand low ratio grids, and high kVp techniques generally need high ratio grids. For general purpose radiographic rooms, focused grids with ratios approximately 8:1 to 12:1 are usually employed.

Focused grids are **normally** preferred to linear grids because with linear grids there is a limit to the size of the radiograph that can be made because of grid cutoff. The following formula can be used for estimating grid cutoff.

$$\text{Distance to grid cutoff} = \frac{\text{Source-to-image receptor distance}}{\text{Grid ratio}}$$

Once the grid is selected, it must be properly positioned. This positioning is particularly important with focused grids. Focused grids that are off level, off center, off focus, or upside down will result in grid cutoff.

EXERCISES

1 Which of the following is **not** a grid positioning error?
   a. off-focus grid
   b. off-level grid
   c. off-center grid
   d. air-gap grid

2 In designing radiographic techniques, the most common practice is to use a
   a. focused stationary grid.
   b. linear stationary grid.
   c. focused moving grid.
   d. linear moving grid.

3 Which of the following techniques will result in the highest patient dose if mAs is changed to maintain optical density?
   a. 10:1 grid, 70 kVp
   b. 10:1 grid, 90 kVp
   c. 5:1 crossed grid, 70 kVp
   d. 5:1 crossed grid, 90 kVp

4 The radiologic technologist should remember that grids generally
   a. require less mAs.
   b. result in increased patient dose.
   c. must be cleaned on schedule.
   d. require periodic replacement because of radiation fatigue.

5 Which of the following is an undesirable characteristic of linear grids compared with focused grids?
   a. lower grid ratios
   b. lower grid frequencies
   c. higher grid cutoff
   d. increased patient dose

6 Grid cutoff
   a. occurs only with focused grids.
   b. never occurs with focused grids.
   c. is more pronounced with low ratio grids.
   d. is more pronounced with high ratio grids.

7 Air-gap technique
   a. requires that the grid and film be separated by at least 30 cm.
   b. results in magnification.
   c. results in approximately the same patient dose as nongrid techniques.
   d. reduces contrast by absorption of scatter radiation in the air.

8 If radiographic grids are used and technique is compensated, patient exposure
   a. remains unchanged from nongrid techniques.
   b. increases with increasing grid ratio.
   c. increases with increased kVp.
   d. is independent of grid frequency.

9 Bedside examinations require a wide range of SIDs. Which of the following linear grids would be most likely to produce grid cutoff?
   a. 5:1   **c.** 8:1
   b. 6:1   **d.** 12:1

10 In general, which of the following has the greatest contrast improvement factor?
   a. linear grids   **c.** crosshatched grids
   b. focused grids   **d.** moving grids

11 When producing comparable radiographs, which of the following combinations will result in the lowest patient dose?
   a. low kVp and low ratio grids
   b. high kVp and low ratio grids
   c. low kVp and high ratio grids
   d. high kVp and high ratio grids

The following four radiographs represent examples of grid use. In answering exercises 12 through 15 assume that a constant technique was employed.

12 Which of the radiographs was probably taken with no grid?

_____

13 Which of the radiographs was probably taken with a focused grid?

_____

14 Which of the radiographs was probably taken with an off-level focused grid?

_____

15 Which of the radiographs was probably taken with a cross-hatched grid?

_____

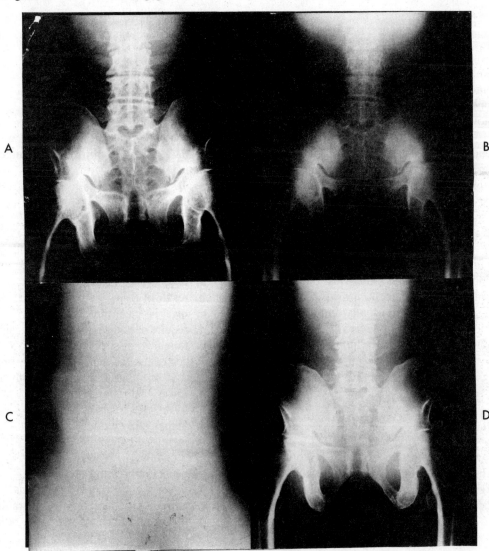

Radiographic Quality

FILM FACTORS

The optical density produced on a radiographic film by a known radiation dose can be predicted if the characteristic curve for the film is known. Such a characteristic curve, sometimes called an **H & D curve,** describes the relationship between **optical density** and **radiation intensity.** To construct the characteristic curve for a particular film, the film must be irradiated through a penetrometer and then processed and analyzed with a densitometer and the data plotted logarithmically.

The characteristic curve is helpful in predicting a number of image receptor factors such as density, contrast, speed, and latitude. Density is short for optical density (OD) and describes the degree of blackening on a film. It is related to the fraction of light transmitted through the exposed and processed film. Film contrast is shown visibly as the difference between light and dark areas on a radiograph. High contrast radiographs are nearly white on black whereas low contrast radiographs are very gray. Latitude is nearly the opposite of contrast.

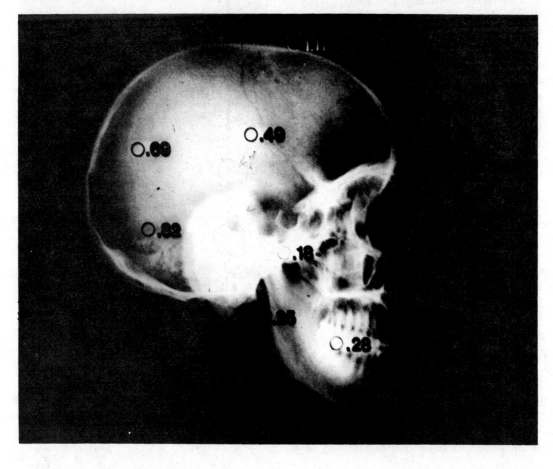

It describes the range of exposures over which an acceptable radiograph can be made. Speed is a measure of the sensitivity of the film to radiation.

In the following radiograph, the optical density of each encircled region is indicated.

EXERCISES

1. Which of the following items is **not** necessary for constructing an H & D curve?
   a. step wedge
   b. spinning top
   c. processor
   d. densitometer

2. The diagnostically useful portion of a characteristic curve includes the
   a. shoulder.
   b. straight-line portion.
   c. toe.
   d. base density plus fog.

3. If the density of a radiograph is such that only 1% of incident light is transmitted, the density has a value of
   a. 0.01.
   b. 0.1.
   c. 1.0.
   d. 2.0.

4. The generally accepted range of useful densities on a radiograph is
   a. 0.1 to 0.3.
   b. 1.0 to 3.0.
   c. 0.5 to 2.5.
   d. 1.5 to 4.0.

5. Which of the following radiographic techniques should result in the greatest latitude?
   a. high kVp, screen film, high grid ratio
   b. low kVp, screen film, low grid ratio
   c. low kVp, direct exposure, high grid ratio
   d. high kVp, latitude film, low grid ratio

6. As the time of development is increased beyond the manufacturer's recommendations, the
   a. speed decreases.
   b. fog increases.
   c. contrast increases.
   d. latitude decreases.

7. An exposure of 100 mR is equal to _____ log relative exposure.
   a. 0.2
   b. 2.0
   c. 0.3
   d. 3.0

8. When one increases the exposure by four times, that is an increase in log relative exposure of
   a. 0.1.
   b. 0.3.
   c. 0.6.
   d. 2.0.

9. Base density refers to
   a. the optical density of the base.
   b. the physical density of the film.
   c. a log relative exposure of 0.25.
   d. a log relative exposure of 0.5.

10. The main component of radiographic noise is
    a. structure mottle.
    b. quantum mottle.
    c. random mottle.
    d. graininess.

11. An average density of 3 on a radiograph
    a. indicates underexposure.
    b. must be viewed with a hot light.
    c. is usually on the toe of the characteristic curve.
    d. indicates higher radiopacity than a density of 4.

12. Unexposed but processed film may appear cloudy because of
    a. base density.
    b. contrast.
    c. latitude.
    d. average gradient.

13. One component of radiographic contrast is
    a. base contrast.
    b. fog contrast.
    c. film contrast.
    d. source contrast.

14. Radiographic noise increases with an increase in
    a. exposure time.
    b. image receptor distance.
    c. mAs.
    d. phosphor thickness.

15. As the temperature of the developer of an automatic processor increases above the recommended level, _____ increases.
    a. base density
    b. fog density
    c. contrast
    d. quantum mottle

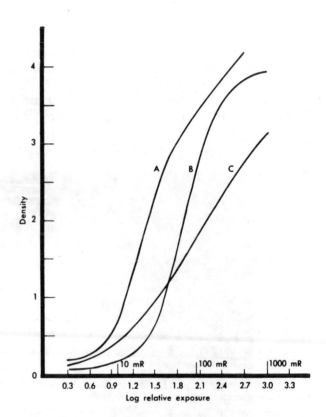

Answer the following questions with reference to the above illustration:

16. Which film is fastest? _____

17. Which film has the highest contrast? _____

18. Which film has the widest latitude? _____

19. Which film has the highest base plus fog density? _____

20. If only one curve was obtained using rare earth screens and the other two curves represent the use of calcium tungstate screens, which curve probably represents the rare earth screen film? _____

WORKSHEET 63

Radiographic Quality

GEOMETRIC FACTORS

....

To obtain a high quality radiograph, an understanding of geometry is necessary. The x-ray source, the anatomic object, and the image receptor all lie in different planes; therefore the image size will never precisely equal the object size. The image will always be larger than the object—a condition called **magnification.** Under some circumstances magnification is desired and planned (e.g., cerebral angiography, mammography). Normally however, it is preferable to have as little magnification as possible.

The extent of magnification is identified by the magnification factor (MF).

$$MF = \frac{\text{Image size}}{\text{Object size}} = \frac{\text{Source-to-image receptor distance (SID)}}{\text{Source-to-object distance (SOD)}}$$

The size of the object is rarely accessible for measurement; consequently, the MF is generally determined by the ratio of SID to SOD. The SOD can usually be estimated accurately.

Image **distortion** occurs when the object is not positioned in a plane that is parallel to the plane of the film. This situation occurs frequently in clinical practice and is one of the principal reasons that precise patient positioning is necessary.

EXERCISES

1 Magnification increases with increasing
   a. OID.   **c.** SID.
   b. SOD.   **d.** object size.
2 Distortion primarily occurs
   a. because objects are thick rather than thin.
   b. because objects are inclined.
   c. when objects are flat.
   d. when objects lie parallel with the film.

3 Distortion
   a. never accompanies magnification.
   b. can be corrected by proper positioning.
   c. occurs only when the image is inclined.
   d. occurs only lateral to the central axis of the x-ray beam.
4 Some radiologists object to anteroposterior (AP) rather than posteroanterior (PA) chest radiographs because
   a. higher kVp is necessary.
   b. the heart shadow is magnified.
   c. patient exposure is higher.
   d. the heel effect is more pronounced.
5 If the SID is 100 cm and an object is placed 20 cm from a film, what is the MF?
   a. 0.8   **c.** 1.25
   b. 1.0   **d.** 1.4
6 In a particular radiographic examination, the SID is 100 cm and the SOD is 86 cm. The image size–to–object size ratio is approximately
   a. 0.86:1.   **c.** 1.16:1.
   b. 1.12:1.   **d.** 2.14:1.
7 An x-ray field that is 25×30 cm at 100 cm SID is projected at 180 cm SID. The area of the projected field is
   a. 750 cm^2.   **c.** 2430 cm^2.
   b. 1350 cm^2.   **d.** 13,500 cm^2.
8 An x-ray field of size A at 80 cm SID is projected to 160 cm SID. The size of the projected field is _____ the size of A.
   a. twice
   b. four times
   c. eight times
   d. sixteen times
9 Distortion of an x-ray image results from unequal
   a. exposure of the object.
   b. SID.
   c. magnification.
   d. heel effect.

10 In magnification radiography, when the object is placed equidistant between the source and the image receptor, the size of the image will be
a. one half the object size.
b. the same size as the object.
c. 1.33 times the object size.
d. 2.0 times the object size.

11 A 20 cm object is radiographed at 40 cm from the focal spot, and the SID is 60 cm. The size of the image will be
a. 30 cm.
b. 40 cm.
c. 50 cm.
d. 60 cm.

12 When an object lies off to one side of the central axis of the x-ray beam,
a. the magnification factor will be larger.
b. the magnification factor will be smaller.
c. the magnification factor will remain unchanged.
d. subject contrast will remain unchanged.

13 Under normal circumstances, magnification is undesirable. To obtain minimum magnification, a technologist should
a. use maximum collimation.
b. make sure the object is positioned on the central axis.
c. select a short SID.
d. position the object close to the image receptor.

14 In dental radiography, two SIDs, 20 and 40 cm, are generally used. Usually,
a. magnification is greater at 40 cm SID.
b. distortion is greater at 20 cm SID.
c. distortion occurs only off the central axis of the x-ray beam.
d. distortion occurs only if a tooth is inclined.

15 Which of the following conditions contributes **least** to image distortion?
a. angling the central ray
b. object position
c. a thin object at a long SID
d. a thick object at a short SID

16 To minimize magnification, one should
a. place the x-ray tube as close to the patient as practical.
b. place the object as close to the film as practical.
c. use the small focal spot station.
d. use low kVp.

17 A foreshortened image
a. can never be smaller than the object.
b. results from an inclined object.
c. can usually be corrected by reducing SID.
d. can usually be corrected by reducing kVp.

18 Magnification in a radiograph can be reduced by the use of
a. a cone.
b. increased filtration.
c. shorter SID.
d. shorter OID.

19 Which of the following would **not** be included in the principal geometric factors affecting radiographic quality?
a. collimation
b. distortion
c. magnification
d. focal spot size

20 The magnification factor is **not** dependent on
a. SID.
b. SOD.
c. OID.
d. focal spot size.

21 The magnification factor increases with increasing
a. SOD and decreasing OID.
b. SOD and OID.
c. OID.
d. SID.

22 To minimize magnification, one should
a. use the small focal spot station.
b. use better collimation
c. reduce SID.
d. reduce OID.

23 Which of the following does **not** contribute to image distortion?
a. focal spot size
b. object size
c. object shape
d. object position

24 Which of the following anatomic objects is likely to be most magnified?
a. mammary microcalcifications
b. carotid artery
c. femur
d. lateral cervical spine

25 The magnification factor is equal to
a. SOD ÷ SID.
b. OID ÷ SID.
c. image size ÷ object size
d. object size ÷ image size.

WORKSHEET 64

Radiographic Quality

FOCAL SPOT BLUR

Focal spot size is very important in radiographic examinations. The smaller the focal spot size, the sharper the image. Conversely, the larger the effective focal spot, the greater the image blur or loss of detail. This blur is called *focal spot blur* (FSB) because the focal spot is not a point but an area.

The extent of FSB is also affected by the spatial relationship among source, object, and image in a way similar to the relationships influencing magnification and distortion. Mathematically, the FSB can be calculated as follows:

$$FSB = \text{Effective focal spot} \times \frac{OID}{SOD}$$

Although measurements of FSB are usually made on the central axis, it should be apparent that this blur off of the central axis varies. FSB on the cathode side will be larger than that on the anode side. This phenomenon is a consequence of the **line-focus principle.**

EXERCISES

1 In mammography, which of the following conditions would be most effective in improving the sharpness of detail of microcalcifications near the chest wall?
   a. positioning the anode on the same side as the chest wall
   b. positioning the cathode on the same side as the chest wall
   c. using a short SID
   d. using a long OID
2 Which of the following makes the most significant geometric contribution to image quality?
   a. SID   **c.** film graininess
   b. screen mottle   **d.** use of a grid

3 The sharpness of detail in a radiograph is best increased by the use of
   a. high speed screens.
   b. medium speed screens.
   c. large effective focal spot.
   d. small effective focal spot.
4 A radiograph showing a relative lack of focal spot blur would be called
   a. sharp in detail.   **c.** high in contrast.
   b. low in density.   **d.** magnified.
5 An intravenous pyelogram (IVP) is routinely done with an AP projection
   a. to minimize the focal spot blur of the kidneys.
   b. to maximize the effect of the contrast medium.
   c. to use the lowest kVp possible.
   d. to reduce the dose.
6 Geometric blur is principally controlled by a system's
   a. sensitivity.   **c.** resolution.
   b. noise.   **d.** contrast.
7 The best way to control focal spot blur without affecting optical density would be to use a very
   a. high contrast image receptor.
   b. short SID.
   c. long OID.
   d. small focal spot.
8 Another term for focal spot blur is
   a. umbra.   **c.** disumbra.
   b. penumbra.   **d.** effective focal spot.
9 A radiograph of the abdomen is taken at 100 cm SID with a 2.0 mm effective focal spot tube. If the OID is 10 cm, what is the focal spot blur?
   a. 0.1 mm   **c.** 0.1 cm
   b. 0.2 mm   **d.** 0.2 cm
10 When one images an object lateral to the central axis of the x-ray beam, the focal spot blur will be
   a. the same as on the central axis.
   b. larger on the cathode side.
   c. larger on the anode side.
   d. independent of OID.

11 Increasing the _____ is effective in reducing focal spot blur.
- **a.** SID
- **b.** OID
- **c.** focal spot size
- **d.** object size

12 If during a radiographic examination, the x-ray tube is switched from the large to the small focal spot station, then
- **a.** the penumbra will be reduced.
- **b.** the focal spot blur will be greater on the anode side.
- **c.** motion blur will be enhanced.
- **d.** mAs must be increased for the same radiographic density.

13 Focal spot blur can be reduced by
- **a.** increasing processing time or temperature.
- **b.** increasing focal spot size.
- **c.** decreasing SID.
- **d.** decreasing OID.

14 Image blur is decreased by
- **a.** the use of intensifying screens.
- **b.** decreasing OID.
- **c.** increasing SOD.
- **d.** increasing kVp.

15 High spatial resolution is affected principally by which of the following?
- **a.** kVp
- **b.** mAs
- **c.** focal spot size
- **d.** type of film

16 When proper radiographic detail cannot be obtained because of excessive OID, what change in technique may be used to improve the detail?
- **a.** decrease in kVp
- **b.** increase in time
- **c.** decrease in mAs
- **d.** increase in SID

17 For a radiograph with magnification of 3, which of the following focal spot sizes will limit the focal spot blur to 0.4 mm or less?
- **a.** 0.2 mm
- **b.** 0.3 mm
- **c.** 0.4 mm
- **d.** 0.5 mm

18 Which of the following conditions will result in a large focal spot blur?
- **a.** large focal spot station
- **b.** high ratio grid
- **c.** slow intensifying screen
- **d.** long SID

19 On the anode side of the central axis,
- **a.** effective focal spot size is smaller.
- **b.** magnification is greater.
- **c.** distortion is greater.
- **d.** radiation intensity is more.

20 The normal shape of the effective focal spot is a
- **a.** point.
- **b.** line.
- **c.** circle.
- **d.** rectangle.

21 Focal spot blur principally results in a reduction of
- **a.** density.
- **b.** contrast.
- **c.** sharpness of detail.
- **d.** shape distortion.

22 Those radiographic techniques that cause magnification of an image will usually reduce
- **a.** density.
- **b.** contrast.
- **c.** noise.
- **d.** sharpness of detail.

23 The heel effect results in all except
- **a.** reduced dose on the anode side.
- **b.** increased focal spot blur on the cathode side.
- **c.** reduced focal spot size on the cathode side.
- **d.** increased focal spot blur on the cathode side.

24 Which of the following conditions will result in the least focal spot blur?
- **a.** small target angle, long SID, short SOD
- **b.** small target angle, long SID, long SOD
- **c.** large target angle, long SID, short SOD
- **d.** large target angle, short SID, short SOD

25 Image contrast is the product of film contrast and
- **a.** screen contrast.
- **b.** subject contrast.
- **c.** grid contrast.
- **d.** resolution.

Name _____

Date _____

Radiographic Quality

SUBJECT FACTORS
....

Maximizing radiographic contrast and detail within the limitations of the examination are principal objectives of the radiologic technologist. The radiographic contrast is the product of the film contrast and the subject contrast.

Subject contrast varies with tissue thickness, density, and atomic number. The greater the difference in each of these factors for adjoining regions of the patient, the greater will be the subject contrast. The shape of the anatomic structure under examination will also affect subject contrast. These factors influencing subject contrast can only be manipulated for improvement by the radiologic technologist with the use of a contrast agent.

Two factors that can be controlled by the technologist are tube potential (kVp) and motion. Generally, as tube potential increases, subject contrast decreases. Blur

caused by motion of patient, tube, or film is called **motion blur** and results in loss of subject contrast as well as loss of sharpness.

EXERCISES

1 Which of the following radiographic techniques is likely to produce the best visualization of low contrast structures?
   a. 72 kVp, 100 mA, 100 ms
   b. 84 kVp, 200 mA, 100 ms
   c. 93 kVp, 400 mA, 50 ms
   d. 107 kVp, 800 mA, 25 ms
2 Short exposure times are recommended for radiography of the stomach in order to
   a. minimize geometric blur.
   b. decrease magnification.
   c. enhance contrast.
   d. reduce motion unsharpness.
3 An upper gastrointestinal image demonstrates motion blur. To increase sharpness, the technologist could
   a. decrease SID.
   b. increase kVp and exposure time.
   c. increase grid ratio.
   d. decrease exposure time.
4 Certain areas in a radiograph appear blurred while others are sharp. The technologist can adjust for this by
   a. using a smaller focal spot.
   b. increasing SID.
   c. reducing mAs and increasing kVp.
   d. using a different cassette.
5 Absorption blur can be reduced by
   a. use of contrast media.
   b. patient compression.
   c. increasing OID.
   d. increasing kVp.
6 Motion blur increases with increasing
   a. screen speed.   **c.** patient motion.
   b. grid ratio.   **d.** field size.

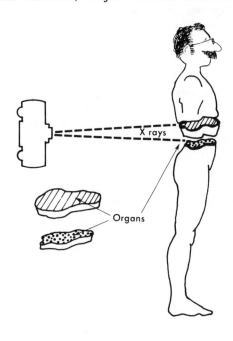

X rays

Organs

7 Subject contrast is
  a. radiographic contrast times film contrast.
  b. the sum of radiographic contrast and film contrast.
  c. radiographic contrast divided by film contrast.
  d. the difference between radiographic contrast and film contrast.

8 Which of the following factors **does not** affect subject contrast?
  a. kVp
  b. mAs
  c. object shape
  d. object size

9 Imaging microcalcifications is important during mammography. Which of the following factors most affects subject contrast in this examination?
  a. breast thickness
  b. breast density
  c. density of the microcalcification
  d. atomic number of the microcalcification

10 Which of the following anatomic structures should exhibit the highest subject contrast with muscle?
  a. kidney
  b. bladder
  c. heart
  d. lung

11 Absorption blur is most closely related to
  a. screen blur.
  b. film blur.
  c. focal spot blur.
  d. motion blur.

12 Extremity exposures result in
  a. short-scale contrast.
  b. long-scale contrast.
  c. high distortion.
  d. high noise.

13 Subject contrast is enhanced with the use of contrast media because
  a. absorption blur is reduced.
  b. focal spot blur is reduced.
  c. photoelectric interaction is increased.
  d. Compton effect is increased.

14 The principal cause of motion blur is movement of the
  a. x-ray tube.
  b. patient.
  c. table.
  d. image receptor.

15 Which of the following will **not** normally reduce motion blur?
  a. proper patient instructions
  b. a long SID
  c. a short exposure time
  d. a restraining device

16 To improve bony detail in a radiograph, the technologist could
  a. decrease kVp and mAs.
  b. decrease SID and decrease mAs.
  c. use a faster screen.
  d. use a smaller focal spot.

17 Which factor principally degrades the visualization of low contrast structures on a properly exposed radiograph?
  a. focal spot size
  b. patient motion
  c. type of screens
  d. type of film emulsion

18 Sharpness of detail on a radiograph is principally improved by
  a. increasing kVp.
  b. increasing scatter radiation.
  c. reducing radiation dose.
  d. reducing patient motion.

19 Sharp resolution of detail in a radiograph is improved by the use of
  a. a larger focal spot.
  b. a grid.
  c. a reduction of kVp.
  d. slower screens.

20 Which of the following controls subject contrast?
  a. SID
  b. OID
  c. effective atomic number
  d. atomic number

21 Which of the following radiographic factors is most determined by subject characteristics in an abdominal radiograph?
  a. visualization of high contrast tissues
  b. visualization of low contrast tissues
  c. speed resolution
  d. noise resolution

22 The density of a tissue affects subject contrast because of
  a. its thickness.
  b. its mass.
  c. the number of electrons per cm^3.
  d. the effective atomic number.

23 The effective atomic number of tissue is important to subject contrast because of
  a. photoelectric effect.
  b. Compton scattering.
  c. its change with kVp.
  d. its change with mAs.

24 Which of the following organ shapes would exhibit the least absorption blur?
  a. inclined wedge
  b. truncated wedge
  c. square
  d. sphere

25 One reason that low kVp is not used for all radiographic examinations is
  a. high patient dose.
  b. low patient dose.
  c. excessive scatter radiation.
  d. excessive scale of contrast.

Name _____

Date _____

Radiographic Quality

CONSIDERATIONS FOR IMPROVED RADIOGRAPHIC QUALITY

The radiologic technologist has many decisions to make before patient examination, each of which will influence the quality of the resulting radiographic image. These decisions relate to choice of equipment, patient preparation and positioning, and selection of radiographic factors from the operating console. Generally, a change in the selection of one factor will influence the selection of other factors; however, this is not always the case.

EXERCISES

1 Magnification is reduced by
  a. increasing screen speed.
  b. increasing SID and OID.
  c. increasing SID while maintaining OID constant.
  d. reducing focal spot size.
2 Absorption blur can be reduced by
  a. patient compression.
  b. increasing the OID.
  c. increasing kVp.
  d. increasing mAs.
3 When radiographic technique factors are adjusted to provide an acceptable radiograph and then filtration is added to the x-ray tube, which of the following will increase?
  a. patient dose   **c.** radiographic contrast
  b. radiographic density **d.** average energy of the beam
4 Assuring good screen-film contact also assures reduced
  a. patient dose.   **c.** magnification.
  b. blur.   **d.** radiographic noise.
5 Use of contrast media principally affects
  a. unsharpness.   **c.** contrast.
  b. density.   **d.** speed.

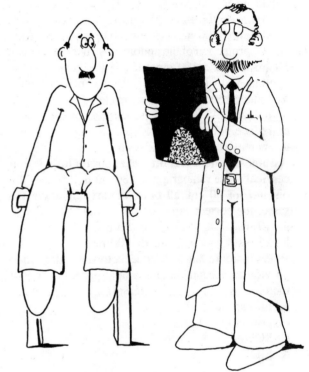

"Which technologist took this chest film? It only shows the top of his head."

6 Reducing the field size through proper collimation generally results in reduced
  a. patient dose.   **c.** contrast.
  b. magnification.   **d.** blur.
7 Reducing the field size through proper collimation generally results in improved
  a. patient dose.   **c.** contrast.
  b. density.   **d.** penumbra.
8 In a radiographic examination of the lumbar spine, which of the following techniques would result in the greatest exposure to the patient?
  a. 70 kVp/200 mAs   **c.** 95 kVp/50 mAs
  b. 80 kVp/100 mAs   **d.** 110 kVp/25 mAs

9 Which of the following **does not** affect image unsharpness?
   a. focal spot size
   b. SID
   c. kVp
   d. OID

10 Which of the following is the principal reason for using direct-exposure radiography?
   a. higher contrast
   b. less patient dose
   c. better spatial resolution
   d. better resolution of low contrast tissues

11 If other factors remain constant, which of the following would result in highest radiographic density?
   a. 100 mA, 750 ms, 90 cm SID
   b. 200 mA, 500 ms, 90 cm SID
   c. 300 mA, 300 ms, 100 cm SID
   d. 400 mA, 200 ms, 100 cm SID

12 An AP projection of the abdomen is taken at 80 kVp, 50 mAs, and a 100 cm SID. If the gray scale of contrast is to be shortened, the technologist must
   a. reduce kVp and increase mAs.
   b. reduce mAs and increase kVp.
   c. reduce both mAs and kVp.
   d. increase both mAs and kVp.

13 Assume that the usual time of exposure for a lateral cervical spine radiograph at 180 cm is 100 ms. At a distance of 90 cm, all other factors remaining the same, the correct exposure time would be
   a. 10 ms.   **c.** 50 ms.
   b. 25 ms.   **d.** 200 ms.

14 When radiographic technique factors are adjusted to provide an acceptable radiograph, patient dose will increase as _____ increases.
   a. film speed
   b. grid ratio
   c. SOD
   d. SID

15 Geometric blur can be reduced by
   a. increasing processing time or temperature.
   b. reducing focal spot size.
   c. increasing SID and OID.
   d. poor film-screen contact.

16 When technique factors are adjusted to provide an acceptable radiograph, motion blur may increase with
   a. slow screens (compared to fast screens).
   b. low ratio grid (compared to high ratio grid).
   c. increased field size.
   d. reduced total filtration.

17 With other factors constant, radiographic density will increase with increasing
   a. grid ratio.
   b. mAs.
   c. focal spot size.
   d. SID.

18 Radiographic contrast is increased by
   a. decreasing film speed.
   b. increasing grid ratio.
   c. reducing the air gap.
   d. reducing the heel effect.

19 When the mAs is adjusted to provide an acceptable radiograph following an increase in kVp,
   a. motion blur is reduced if the same mA is used.
   b. absorption blur is reduced.
   c. geometric blur is reduced.
   d. latitude is reduced.

20 Increasing the SID will
   a. increase motion blur.
   b. decrease geometric blur.
   c. decrease motion blur.
   d. decrease radiographic contrast.

21 Which of the following is most influenced by focal spot size?
   a. patient dose   **c.** geometric blur
   b. absorption blur   **d.** motion blur

Name _____

Date _____

Radiographic Exposure

FIFTEEN PERCENT RULE FOR kVp
....

The mathematical problems each radiologic technologist faces in daily practice include (1) mentally applying the 15% rule for kVp to adjust radiographic technique, (2) having a desired total mAs in mind and trying to mentally determine an mA-time combination that will yield that total, and (3) mentally applying the inverse square law for distance changes.

The following exercises will give you an idea of how well you are able to solve these types of problems in your head. If you have trouble with any of them, turn to Part 2 of the "Math Tutor Section" of this workbook and complete the related drills there; try this worksheet again.

EXERCISES

To obtain the greatest benefit from the following problems, solve them mentally, without a calculator or pencil and paper. If you have trouble with any of these, turn to Part 2 of the "Math Tutor Section" of this workbook for review.

1 What is 5% of 40?
2 What is 5% of 70?
3 What is 5% of 90?
4 What is 5% of 110?
5 What is 15% of 50?
6 What is 15% of 80?
7 What is 15% of 100?
8 What is 15% of 120?
9 What is one half of 15% of 60?

10 What is one half of 15% of 80?
11 Starting at 60 kVp, what new kVp would result in an optical density one half as dark as the original?

NOTE: Remember that application of the 15% rule must be done in "steps" for accuracy. For example, to quadruple the optical density starting at 80 kVp, do not simply increase kVp by 30%. Rather, think of the change as two doublings of the optical density (OD), or two steps of 15%. The first doubling is accomplished with an increase of 12 kVp (15% of 80); but the second doubling must be obtained with an increase of 14 kVp (15% of 92), for a total of 106 kVp.

12 Starting at 70 kVp, what new kVp would result in an OD four times greater than the original?
13 Starting at 100 kVp, what new kVp would result in an OD one eighth as great as the original?
14 Starting at 80 kVp, what new kVp would result in an OD 50% darker than the original, or halfway to double the original?
15 Starting at 70 kVp, what new kVp would result in an OD approximately 75% (halfway to one half) of the original?

Fill in the kVp in the following problems that would maintain equal OD with the original technique (listed first):

16 100 mA ½ s   60 kVp
     200 mA ⅛ s   ___ kVp
17 300 mA 1/60 s   120 kVp
     400 mA 1/20 s   ___ kVp
18 400 mA 1/120 s   40 kVp
     50 mA 1/60 s   ___ kVp
19 400 mA 1/30 s   80 kVp
     300 mA 1/30 s   ___ kVp
20 300 mA 1/30 s   70 kVp
     150 mA 1/10 s   ___ kVp

Name _____

Date _____

Radiographic Exposure

Each of the following problems has two answers: solve the first answer for a fraction timer, and fill in the second blank with the decimal answer. If you need additional help with technique math, turn to the "Math Tutor Section" of this workbook. To get the greatest benefit from this worksheet, try to solve the problems mentally, without writing them down or using a calculator.

EXERCISES

NOTE: *The fractional time for those problems marked with an asterisk (*) must have a numerator greater than 1, such as 3/10, 7/20, or 2/5.*

Total mAs = mA × s

1 2.5 mAs = 100 mA × _____ _____
2 5 mAs = 100 mA × _____ _____
3 33 mAs = 100 mA × _____ _____
4 15 mAs = 100 mA × _____ _____

5 12.5 mAs = 100 mA × _____ _____
6 7.5 mAs = 150 mA × _____ _____
7 0.8 mAs = 50 mA × _____ _____
8 20 mAs = 400 mA × _____ _____
9 *160 mAs = 400 mA × _____ _____
10 40 mAs = 200 mA × _____ _____
11 7 mAs = 100 mA × _____ _____
12 8 mAs = 100 mA × _____ _____
13 20 mAs = 300 mA × _____ _____
14 1.25 mAs = 50 mA × _____ _____
15 25 mAs = 200 mA × _____ _____
16 *80 mAs = 200 mA × _____ _____
17 *160 mAs = 200 mA × _____ _____
18 4 mAs = 200 mA × _____ _____
19 *14 mAs = 200 mA × _____ _____
20 60 mAs = 300 mA × _____ _____
21 5 mAs = 300 mA × _____ _____
22 15 mAs = 300 mA × _____ _____
23 *120 mAs = 300 mA × _____ _____
24 *90 mAs = 300 mA × _____ _____
25 *120 mAs = 200 mA × _____ _____
26 1.25 mAs = 100 mA × _____ _____
27 1.6 mAs = 100 mA × _____ _____
28 *180 mAs = 300 mA × _____ _____
29 80 mAs = 400 mA × _____ _____
30 *240 mAs = 400 mA × _____ _____

WORSHEET 69

Radiographic Exposure

ADJUSTING FOR CHANGE IN DISTANCE
....

The first 14 exercises below are for mental practice. All present distance changes that can be solved in your head if you are comfortable with the inverse square law. The applicable rules of thumb are discussed in Part 2 of the "Math Tutor Section" of this workbook. Exercises 15 to 25 employ the "square law" to find a new mAs that will compensate for a change in distance. Whereas the **inverse square law** is used to predict optical density, the **square law** is used to compensate technique so that optical density is maintained when distance changes. The formula for the square law is as follows:

$$\frac{mAs_2}{mAs_1} = \frac{(SID_2)^2}{(SID_1)^2}$$

where mAs_1 is the original mAs used at SID_1 (the original SID), and mAs_2 is the new mAs needed to maintain equal optical density (OD) if the SID is changed to SID_2. The solutions to square law problems are always the inverse of those for solving inverse square law problems. For example, if a distance change would result in twice as dark a film by the inverse square law, then the technique that would be required to maintain the original OD at the new distance would be one half the mAs. If the density change can be predicted, simply invert this change to find the technique adjustment.

Do the first 14 exercises mentally, without a pencil or calculator. Think of the distance changes in factors of 2: doubling, halving, halfway to doubling, or halfway to halving the original distance. If you have trouble with any of these, refer to the "Math Tutor Section" of this workbook.

EXERCISES

Use the technique rules of thumb to solve these problems:

	From:		To Maintain OD:
1	30 mAs, 100 cm SID	$\frac{30}{x} = \frac{100^2}{75^2}$	_____mAs, 75 cm SID
2	12.5 mAs, 100 cm SID		_____mAs, 150 cm SID
3	10 mAs, 100 cm SID		_____mAs, 180 cm SID
4	5 mAs, 100 cm SID		_____mAs, 240 cm SID
5	48 mAs, 80 cm SID		_____mAs, 90 cm SID
6	22.5 mAs, 100 cm SID		_____mAs, 200 cm SID
7	36 mAs, 150 cm SID		_____mAs, 113 cm SID
8	10 mAs, 150 cm SID		_____mAs, 225 cm SID
9	60 mAs, 70 kVp, 150 cm SID		15 mAs, _____kVp, 113 cm SID

Use the OD rules of thumb to solve these problems:

	From:	To:
10	150 cm SID, OD = 1	75 cm SID, OD = _____
11	100 cm SID, OD = 1	75 cm SID, OD = _____
12	36-in SID, OD = 1	180 cm SID, OD = _____
13	40-in SID, OD = 1	150 cm SID, OD = _____
14	40-in SID, OD = 1	180 cm SID, OD = _____

...llowing may be done with paper and calculator. ...you have trouble with any of these, or for a full explanation of the "square law," refer to the "Math Tutor Section" of this workbook.

Use the square law to solve these problems:

	From:	To Maintain OD:
15	7 mAs, 60-in SID	_____mAs, 100-in SID
16	8 mAs, 72-in SID	_____mAs, 50-in SID
17	3 mAs, 96-in SID	_____mAs, 40-in SID
18	1.5 mAs, 50-in SID	_____mAs, 20-in SID
19	2.5 mAs, 80 kVp, 72-in SID	2.5 mAs, _____kVp, 51-in SID
20	60 mAs, 20-in SID	15 mAs, _____SID
21	80 mAs, 80-in SID	5 mAs, _____SID
22	25 mAs, 25-in SID	100 mAs, _____SID
23	10 mAs, 30-in SID	90 mAs, _____SID
24	25 mAs, 96-in SID	_____mAs, 72-in SID
25	100 kVp, 80-in SID	72 kVp, _____SID

Use the inverse square law to solve these problems:

26	40-in SID, OD = 1	50-in SID, OD = _____
27	36-in SID, OD = 1	60-in SID, OD = _____
28	96-in SID, OD = 1	40-in SID, OD = _____
29	36-in SID, OD = 1	96-in SID, OD = _____

Radiographic Exposure

IMAGER CHARACTERISTICS

Proper radiographic exposure must take into account several variable characteristics of the x-ray imager. Perhaps the most important characteristic is the type of high voltage generator incorporated into the imager. In general, when compared to single-phase generators, full-wave rectified and more complex waveform generators will require a lower kVp and less mAs to produce acceptable radiographs. The radiologic technologist has no control over this characteristic.

Essentially all x-ray imagers now have selectable added filtration. The choices of added filtration available to the radiologic technologist usually range from 0 to 4 mm Al, resulting in total filtration of 1.5 to 5.5 mm Al. In general, when one increases added filtration, a reduction in kVp or an increase in mAs, or both are required to maintain image quality.

EXERCISES

1 A popular focal spot combination for a dedicated mammography machine is (small/large)
   a. 0.05 mm/0.2 mm.
   b. 0.1 mm/4.0 mm.
   c. 0.3 mm/1.0 mm.
   d. 0.6 mm/1.2 mm.
2 The approximate filtration of the x-ray beam contributed by the light-localizing collimator is
   a. 0.1 mm Al.   **c.** 1.0 mm Al.
   b. 0.5 mm Al.   **d.** 2.5 mm Al.
3 The radiologic technologist cannot change the type of high voltage generation because
   a. the service engineer determines that at installation.
   b. it is fixed and determined at the time of purchase.
   c. only the radiologist can make that change.
   d. only the service engineer can make that change.

4 Compared to half-wave rectification for a fixed exposure time,
   a. full-wave rectification can take four times the number of pulses.
   b. three phase will have four times the number of pulses.
   c. three phase will have at least six times the number of pulses.
   d. high frequency will have six times the number of pulses.
5 The principal advantage of a large focal spot compared to a small focal spot is
   a. better spatial resolution.
   b. less voltage ripple.
   c. more x rays can be produced.
   d. faster image receptors can be used.
6 The principal advantage of a small focal spot compared to a large focal spot is
   a. better spatial resolution.
   b. less voltage ripple.
   c. more x rays are produced.
   d. faster image receptors can be used.
7 General purpose x-ray tubes usually have inherent filtration of
   a. 0.1 mm Al.
   b. 0.5 mm Al.
   c. 1.0 mm Al.
   d. 2.5 mm Al.
8 Which of the following are basic types of x-ray generators?
   I. zero phase   **III.** single phase
   II. halt phase   **IV.** high frequency
   a. only I and II
   b. only II and III
   c. only III and IV
   d. only I and IV
9 Three-phase power is produced with
   a. 3 pulses per cycle.
   b. 6 pulses per cycle.
   c. 9 pulses per cycle.
   d. 12 pulses per cycle.

10 An acceptable radiograph is made with the large focal spot. If the examination were repeated with the small focal spot,
  a. mAs should be reduced.
  b. kVp should be reduced.
  c. mAs and kVp should be reduced.
  d. no technique change is required.
11 An acceptable radiograph is made with the large focal spot. If the examination were repeated with the small focal spot using the same technique,
  a. the image would be lighter.
  b. the image would be darker.
  c. the image would be sharper.
  d. the image would have better contrast.
12 An acceptable radiograph is made with 1.0 mm Al added filtration. If the examination were repeated with 3.0 mm Al added filtration, what would be the most likely technique change?
  a. Increase SID.
  b. Increase kVp.
  c. Increase mAs.
  d. Increase kVp and mAs.
13 Increasing filtration is most appropriate for examination of the
  a. skull.   c. abdomen.
  b. chest.   d. pelvis.
14 An acceptable radiograph is produced with a half-wave rectified x-ray machine. If the examination is repeated on a full-wave unit, what should be changed?
  a. SID   c. mAs
  b. OID   d. kVp
15 An acceptable radiograph is made with 1.0 mm Al added filtration. If the examination were repeated with 3.0 mm Al added filtration and appropriate technique changes made,
  a. image blur would be reduced.
  b. image contrast would be improved.
  c. patient dose would be reduced.
  d. such exposure would not be possible.

16 An acceptable radiograph is made with a single-phase generator. If a repeat examination is made with a three-phase generator, what technique change should be made?
  a. Reduce kVp.
  b. Increase mAs.
  c. Reduce kVp and mAs.
  d. Increase kVp and mAs.
17 What is the principal advantage of high voltage generators?
  a. reduced radiation quantity
  b. increased radiation quality
  c. reduced radiation quantity and quality
  d. increased radiation quantity and quality
18 An acceptable radiograph is made with a three-phase generator. If a repeat examination is made with a high frequency generator, what technique change should be made?
  a. Reduce kVp.
  b. Increase mAs.
  c. Reduce kVp and mAs.
  d. Increase kVp and mAs.
19 A small focal spot would yield the greatest benefit with
  a. examination of the skull.
  b. examination of the chest.
  c. stereoscopic examination.
  d. magnification examination.
20 When a radiologic technologist changes filtration before examination,
  a. the supervisor must be notified.
  b. the patient must be notified.
  c. it should be left that way for subsequent examinations.
  d. it should be returned to its original position after the examination.

Radiographic Technique

Producing a quality radiograph requires that the radiologic technologist have a firm understanding of radiographic technique. Radiographic technique is the selection of the proper x-ray exposure conditions with the x-ray machine necessary to produce that quality radiograph.

The radiologic technologist has control over the following: exposure technique factors, patient factors, and image quality factors. Exposure technique factors were covered in Worksheets 67 to 70.

The two principal patient factors are the thickness of the body part being examined and its composition. Generally, the thicker the part and the more dense the part, the higher should be the kVp and mAs.

EXERCISES

1 The chest represents high contrast anatomy (high subject contrast). Therefore which of the following is most appropriate?
  a. low kVp   **c.** low mAs
  b. high kVp   **d.** high mAs

2 The anatomic part to be examined must be measured because
  a. the selected radiographic technique depends on thickness.
  b. a different image receptor may be required.
  c. the density of the part is determined by thickness.
  d. a change of focal spots may be required.

3 When using fixed kVp technique a change will be required in
  a. SID.   **c.** kVp.
  b. added filtration.   **d.** mAs.

4 The anatomic part must be measured because for variable kVp technique a change will be required in
  a. SID.
  b. added filtration.
  c. kVp.
  d. mAs.

5 In the diagnostic range (60-100 kVp) what is the smallest change in kVp that can be perceived on the radiograph?
  a. 1 kVp   **c.** 8 kVp
  b. 3 kVp   **d.** 12 kVp

6 For a given anatomic part what is the smallest change in mAs that can be perceived on the radiograph?
  a. 5%   **c.** 30%
  b. 15%   **d.** 60%

7 Knowledge of the composition of the anatomic part is necessary because various tissues have different mass density. Match the following:
  a. lung tissue   **I.** 0.001 g/cm^3
  b. soft tissue   **II.** 0.85 g/cm^3
  c. fat   **III.** 1.0 g/cm^3
  d. bone   **IV.** 1.85 g/cm^3

8 Knowledge of the composition of the anatomic part is necessary because various tissues have different effective atomic numbers. Match the following:
  a. lung tissue   **I.**   6.3
  b. soft tissue   **II.**   7.4
  c. fat   **III.** 7.6
  d. bone   **IV.** 13.8

9 In general, a chest radiograph should be made with
  a. low kVp and low mAs.
  b. low kVp and high mAs.
  c. high kVp and low mAs.
  d. high kVp and high mAs.

10 In general, a mammogram should be made with
  a. low kVp and low mAs.
  b. low kVp and high mAs.
  c. high kVp and low mAs.
  d. high kVp and high mAs.

Radiographic Technique

Radiographic technique factors are the selections on the control panel of the x-ray machine made by the radiologic technologist. They are milliamperage (mA), time (ms), and kilovoltage (kVp). Some also include source-to-image distance (SID; cm) in such factors. These factors determine the basic characteristics of the radiation exposure of the patient and therefore also of the image receptor. The selected combination of these factors determines the acceptability of the finished radiograph.

Image quality factors refer to terms used to evaluate the characteristics of a radiograph. The principal terms are density, contrast, definition, and distortion. The radiologic technologist selects a combination of exposure technique factors to produce a radiograph with an acceptable scale of contrast, the correct density, the best sharpness of detail (definition), and minimum distortion of the image.

EXERCISES

1 One method to increase contrast is by selecting a
   a. smaller focal spot.
   b. shorter SID.
   c. lower grid ratio.
   d. smaller beam restrictor.
2 A longer gray scale on a radiograph can be obtained by
   a. decreasing kVp.   **c.** decreasing mAs.
   b. increasing kVp.   **d.** increasing mAs.
3 For a portable abdominal radiograph, contrast can be increased by
   a. using a grid.
   b. increasing the kVp and decreasing the mAs.
   c. increasing the SID.
   d. increasing the OID.

4 A radiograph that exhibits long gray scale contrast is one with _____ differences among them.
   a. many shades of gray having minimal
   b. few shades of gray having minimal
   c. many shades of gray having great
   d. few shades of gray having great
5 From the following set of exposure technique factors, select the set that is most likely to produce a radiograph with the **best** definition:

	mAs	kVp	Object-to-image distance (OID)	SID	Focal Spot	Screens
a.	10	60	8 cm	90 cm	2.0 mm	high speed
b.	20	68	10 cm	90 cm	2.0 mm	high speed
c.	25	72	5 cm	180 cm	1.0 mm	med. speed
d.	30	86	5 cm	90 cm	1.0 mm	med. speed

6 Rank the preceding exposure technique factors from best to worst for definition.
7 Size distortion (magnification) can be reduced by
   a. proper alignment of the grid.
   b. decreased field size with beam restrictor.
   c. decreased SID.
   d. decreased OID.
8 The function of contrast is to
   a. control detail sharpness.
   b. make detail visible.
   c. determine overall density.
   d. control quantum mottle.
9 A technique that would assure visibility of detail for a cervical spine is
   a. use of a beam restriction device
   b. lengthening the OID
   c. shortening the SID
   d. select the large focal spot

10 A radiograph was made using these factors: 200 mA, 300 ms, 70 kVp, 100 cm SID. A second radiograph is required, but the maximum possible SID is 75 cm. To maintain the same density, approximately _____ mAs should be selected.

a. 15   **c.** 28
b. 20   **d.** 34

Exercises 11 through 14 refer to the following exposure technique factors:

a.	100 mA	500 ms	60 kVp	par screens	no grid
b.	200 mA	750 ms	50 kVp	par screens	16:1 grid
c.	400 mA	100 ms	60 kVp	par screens	no grid
d.	600 mA	700 ms	70 kVp	par screens	8:1 grid

11 Which technique factors should result in greatest latitude?

12 Which technique factors should result in highest contrast?

13 Which technique factors should result in highest density?

14 Which technique factors should result in highest patient dose?

Exercises 15 through 25 refer to the following exposure technique factors:

100 mA	8:1 grid
1000 ms	par screens/film
100 cm SID	collimation to part
65 kVp	0.6 mm focal spot

For exercises 15 through 19, one factor is changed at a time. All other factors remain the same. Indicate "a" if the density will increase, "b" if the density will decrease, and "c" if there is no change in density.

15 Increase field size.
16 Switch to nongrid.
17 Change to 100 mA, 500 ms.
18 Use 120 cm SID.
19 Decrease kVp by 10.

For exercises 20 through 25, indicate "a" if the gray scale becomes shorter, "b" if the gray scale becomes longer, and "c" if there is no change in the gray scale.

20 Change to 1.2 mm focal spot.
21 Increase kVp by 10.
22 Use 50 mA, 2000 ms.
23 Switch to 16:1 grid.
24 Decrease field size.
25 Change to 110 cm SID.

Name _____

Date _____

Radiographic Technique

RADIOGRAPHIC TECHNIQUE CHARTS

Radiographic technique charts are guides that are prepared for specific radiographic rooms for the purpose of assisting radiologic technologists in selecting exposure factors for each radiographic procedure.

There are four general types of technique charts: variable kilovoltage, fixed kilovoltage, high kilovoltage, and automatic exposure. For the variable kilovoltage chart, kVp is adjusted for different tissue thickness. The fixed kilovoltage chart uses an optimum kVp selection for each body part, and the mAs is the variable used to accommodate for the differences in tissue thickness.

High kilovoltage means the kilovoltage selection is in excess of 100 kVp. Technique charts of this type are primarily used for barium studies and chest radiography. The automatic exposure chart serves as a guide for control panel selections when phototimers or other automatic exposure systems are used.

EXERCISES

1 The technique chart that provides the best protection for the patient with the least amount of radiation exposure is the
   a. variable kilovoltage.
   b. fixed kilovoltage.
   c. high kilovoltage.
   d. automatic exposure.
2 Accuracy in positioning of the patient would be most critical with the
   a. variable kilovoltage chart.
   b. fixed kilovoltage chart.
   c. high kilovoltage chart.
   d. automatic exposure.

3 Before preparing a radiographic technique chart, which of the following would be **most** important?
   a. Measure the part size with calipers.
   b. Calibrate x-ray equipment.
   c. Calculate mAs-distance rule.
   d. Mark all kVp stations on the control panel.
4 A basic characteristic for the variable kVp chart would be
   a. short exposure times.
   b. low mAs selections.
   c. short scale of contrast.
   d. long scale of contrast.
5 The basic principle in selecting the kVp for a body part when using the variable kVp chart should be
   a. measure the part, multiply by 5, and then add 40.
   b. measure the part, multiply by 2, and then add 40.
   c. preselect the kVp, and multiply the mAs by 2.
   d. preselect the kVp, multiply by 2, and then add 20.
6 Which of the following will increase exposure latitude?
   a. fixed kilovoltage chart
   b. variable kilovoltage chart
   c. automatic exposures
   d. a combination of fixed and variable kilovoltage
7 Which of the following procedures is best accommodated by the use of fixed kilovoltage charts to assure adequate penetration?
   a. shoulder   c. wrist
   b. skull   d. ribs
8 The density present on the radiograph can best be controlled by
   a. kVp.   c. measurement of the part.
   b. mAs.   d. collimation.
9 Penetration of the part by the x-ray beam can best be controlled by
   a. tissue thickness.
   b. mAs.
   c. calibration of the equipment.
   d. kVp.

10 Which of the following procedures would best utilize a high kilovoltage chart?
   a. barium enema   **c.** pelvis
   b. knee   **d.** mammography

For exercises 11 through 20, match the following sets of statements:

11 requires accurate measurement _____

12 higher patient dose of radiation _____

13 shortest scale of contrast _____

14 least exposure latitude _____

15 requires accurate positioning _____

16 recommends a 2 kVp change for each centimeter of thickness _____

17 requires no specific mAs selection _____

18 higher contrast _____

19 longest gray scale _____

20 assures adequate penetration _____

a. fixed kilovoltage

b. variable kilovoltage

c. high kilovoltage

d. automatic exposure

e. combination fixed and variable

Name _____

Date _____

Other Radiographic Procedures

TOMOGRAPHY
....

STEREORADIOGRAPHY
....

MAGNIFICATION RADIOGRAPHY
....

Tomography is the x-ray examination that produces an image of a plane in the body. Overlying and underlying tissues, which could mask the plane of interest, are blurred. Tomography requires deliberate, controlled motion unsharpness. Conventional tomography in its simplest form involves a linear tube and film motion. Complex multidirectional tomography includes circular, elliptic, hypocycloidal, and trispiral forms of motion. Generally, as x-ray tube motion increases in complexity, image contrast increases as well as patient dose.

Stereoradiography requires two exposures of the same anatomic structure from slightly different angles. When processed and properly viewed side by side, the stereoradiographs can provide three-dimensional images with considerable depth perception. Stereoradiographs are made either by shifting the conventional radiograph tube head between exposures or with a specially constructed stereoradiographic tube. The former is technically somewhat difficult, and the latter is rather expensive.

Magnification radiography refers to the procedure of increasing the distance between the object and the image receptor in order to produce an enlarged or magnified image. The degree of magnification is given by the magnification factor (MF).

$$MF = \frac{\text{Image size}}{\text{Object size}} = \frac{\text{SID}}{\text{SOD}}$$

Magnification radiography requires the use of a small x-ray tube focal spot for best results. It can usually be performed without radiographic grids yet still results in a somewhat higher patient dose.

EXERCISES

1 During conventional tomography, the cassette can
   a. remain fixed.
   b. move opposite the tube in a seesaw motion.
   c. move with the tube like the tube-tower assembly in fluoroscopy.
   d. do all of the above.

2 During tomography, only structures lying in the object plane are imaged. Structures outside the object plane are blurred because of _____ blur.
   a. geometric   **c.** motion
   b. subject   **d.** absorption

3 Which of the following is **not** a multidirectional tomographic mode?
   a. linear   **c.** hypocycloidal
   b. elliptic   **d.** trispiral

4 Which of the following combinations determines the thickness of the cut in a tomograph?
   a. OID and length of tube travel
   b. SOD and length of tube travel
   c. OID and speed of tube travel
   d. SID and speed of tube travel

5 Conventional tomography employs the principle of
   a. stereoscopy.
   b. motion blur.
   c. random movement.
   d. a tridimensional image and an optical illusion.

6 During tomography the fulcrum is in the
   a. focal plane.   **c.** film plane.
   b. tomographic layers. **d.** image plane.

7 When the tomographic angle is 0 degrees, the tomographic layer will be
a. thin.   c. very thick.
b. thick.   d. infinite.

8 To obtain an approximately 1 mm tomographic layer, the tomographic angle should be about
a. 0 degrees.   c. 50 degrees.
b. 25 degrees.   d. 100 degrees.

9 The major disadvantage of tomography is
a. cost.   c. image blur.
b. patient dose.   d. enhanced contrast.

10 The major advantage of tomography is
a. cost.   c. image blur.
b. patient dose.   d. enhanced visibility.

11 Stereoradiography results in increased
a. patient dose.   c. image contrast.
b. spatial resolution.   d. contrast resolution.

12 To make stereoradiographs, the technologist can move
a. the patient.   c. the image receptor.
b. the x-ray tube.   d. all of the above.

13 The degree of shift in stereoradiography depends on
a. SID.   c. interpupillary distance.
b. viewing distance.   d. all of the above.

14 When viewing stereoradiographs, the technologist should position them
a. with the tube side of the film away from the viewer.
b. so they can be viewed as though the eyes were the x-ray tube.
c. perpendicular to the tube shift.
d. lateral to the tube shift.

15 A patient is positioned for a lateral view of the skull. Stereoradiographs are to be taken using the following technique: 78 kVp/100 mA/200 ms/100 cm SID. The amount of tube shift should be
a. 4 cm.   c. 15 cm.
b. 10 cm.   d. 20 cm.

16 Magnification radiography is normally used to image _____ structures.
a. small   c. low contrast
b. large   d. moving

17 The magnification factor is equal to
a. SOD + SID.   c. SID + SOD.
b. SOD + OID.   d. SID + OID.

18 For magnification cerebral angiography, which of the following focal spot sizes would be best?
a. 0.3 mm   c. 1.0 mm
b. 0.6 mm   d. 10 mm

19 The major disadvantage of magnification radiography is increased
a. cost.   c. unsharpness.
b. patient dose.   d. noise.

20 If the MF is 1.5 and the image size is 9 cm, what is the object size?
a. 3 cm   c. 12 cm
b. 6 cm   d. 13.5 cm

21 The tomographic angle is
a. equal to the anode angle.
b. determined by the table top angle.
c. that of maximum tube movement.
d. that between the vertical and the image plane.

22 The thickness of tissue imaged during tomography is called the
a. tomographic angle.
b. image plane.
c. tomographic layer.
d. tomographic motion.

23 The thickness of tissue imaged is determined by the
a. SID.
b. source-to-fulcrum distance.
c. fulcrum–to–image receptor distance.
d. tomographic angle.

24 Which of the following tomographic angles would be considered for use in zonography?
a. 5 degrees   c. 25 degrees
b. 15 degrees   d. 35 degrees

25 Simultaneous multifilm nephrotomography
a. increases patient dose when compared with a radiograph of the abdomen.
b. increases patient dose when compared with conventional tomography of an equal number of planes.
c. results in better image quality when compared with single-frame tomography.
d. requires a rapid film changer.

26 Tomography has also been called
a. the line-focus principle.   c. myelography.
b. laminography.   d. cisternography.

27 An attempt at stereoradiography is made at a SID of 90 cm. What should the total tube shift be?
a. 4.5 cm   c. 13.5 cm
b. 9 cm   d. 18 cm

28 The SID is 100 cm, the SOD is 80 cm, and the OID is 20 cm. What is the magnification factor?
a. 0.75   c. 4
b. 1.25   d. 5

29 During stereoradiography if the SID equals the viewing distance, the tube shift should equal the _____ distance.
a. SOD   c. SID
b. OID   d. interpupillary

30 To do adequate magnification radiography, a large _____ is required.
a. focal spot   c. OID
b. SID   d. SOD

31 The tomographic angle is the angle of tube movement during
a. anode preparation.
b. cathode boost.
c. radiographic exposure.
d. fulcrum adjustment.

Mammography

Mammography is an examination of the breast using lower energy x rays than those used in routine radiography. General purpose x-ray apparatus incorporates a tungsten targeted x-ray tube. When operated at low kVp, the x-ray emission spectrum from such a target is broad, consisting mostly of bremsstrahlung radiation and useless L-characteristic x rays. Such general purpose x-ray apparatus **cannot** be used successfully for mammography; it is necessary to employ a specially designed and dedicated x-ray machine.

The mammographic x-ray machine must be capable of the accurate production of x rays in the 25 to 50 kVp

range. Radiographic equipment that is especially dedicated to screen-film mammography should have a molybdenum targeted x-ray tube. Such a tube emits radiation that is rather intense, especially with K-characteristic x rays at 20 keV. A tungsten targeted tube is acceptable with the proper thickness of molybdenum or rhodium filter. Rhodium targets are also acceptable. Units designed for xeromammography should have a tungsten targeted tube although molybdenum is acceptable. Some dedicated units have targets fabricated of alloys of tungsten and molybdenum.

Because of the low filtration of mammography machines, the radiation intensity and exposure to the patient can be considerably higher than in general purpose radiography. Regardless of the type of target employed, when operated at 50 kVp or less, the x-ray beam must be filtered by **at least 0.5 mm Al equivalent.** Molybdenum filtration of 30 μm is required when molybdenum tubes are used for screen-film imaging. Patient compression devices are necessary for reducing motion and absorption blur.

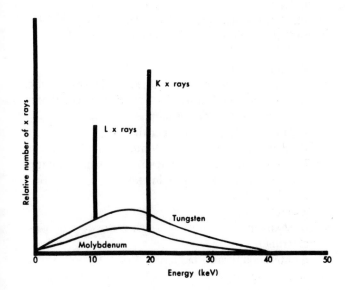

Relative number of x rays / Energy (keV)
K x rays — L x rays — Tungsten — Molybdenum

EXERCISES

1 Low kVp is required for mammography because of
 a. the type of image receptor employed.
 b. the varying thickness of breast tissue.
 c. patient positioning and compression.
 d. the composition of breast tissue.
2 When molybdenum is used for the tube target,
 a. no added filtration is required.
 b. useful characteristic x rays are produced.
 c. no bremsstrahlung x rays are produced.
 d. kVp can be higher.
3 If the cathode of the x-ray tube is positioned toward the chest wall during a cranial-caudad view,
 a. absorption unsharpness will be reduced.
 b. geometric unsharpness will be greater toward the chest wall.
 c. exposure time will be reduced.
 d. the density on the nipple side will be greater.

4 In mammography a low kVp is selected to
   a. reduce skin reaction.
   b. reduce patient dose.
   c. increase photoelectric absorption.
   d. increase Compton absorption.
5 When comparing a mammogram taken at 30 kVp with one taken at 50 kVp,
   a. for the same exit dose the 50 kVp examination will require a higher entrance dose.
   b. radiographic contrast will be enhanced at 50 kVp.
   c. the ratio of entrance dose to exit dose will be higher at 30 kVp.
   d. if the mAs is held constant, the number of photons reaching the image receptor will be the same.
6 The principal reason molybdenum targeted tubes are employed in mammography is that molybdenum has a
   a. higher heat capacity.
   b. high melting point.
   c. high atomic number.
   d. useful characteristic x-ray emission.
7 Successful mammography could not be done at 90 kVp because
   a. exposure time would be too long.
   b. patient dose would be too high.
   c. differential absorption would be too low.
   d. Compton interactions are too few.
8 During mammography
   a. the half-value layer is relatively low.
   b. the radiation quality is relatively high.
   c. x-ray transmission predominates.
   d. radiographic contrast is low.
9 Regarding the incidence of breast cancer in women, which of the following is correct?
   a. Each year about 10,000 new cases appear in the United States.
   b. The odds of developing breast cancer are 1 in 10.
   c. The most critical decade is the 30- to 40-year interval.
   d. More than 80% of breast cancer results in death.
10 Disadvantage(s) to mammography is (are)
   I.   long exposure time.
   II. high patient dose.
   III. patient discomfort.
   a. I   c. II and III
   b. II   d. I, II, and III
11 Tube potential below 20 kVp is not used because
   a. there are no x rays below 20 keV.
   b. generators are not available for such low voltage.
   c. Compton interaction predominates.
   d. x-ray penetration is not sufficient.

12 X-ray machines specially designed for mammography
   a. have tube target angles less than 10 degrees.
   b. have SIDs that are more than 100 cm.
   c. employ large focal spot x-ray tubes.
   d. have devices to reduce motion and absorption blur.
13 If an x-ray tube is positioned so that the anode is toward the chest wall during a cranial-caudad view,
   a. the radiation exposure will be higher at the nipple than at the chest wall.
   b. the exposure time will be about one half.
   c. image quality will be improved toward the thicker part of the breast because of increased penumbra.
   d. remnant radiation will have more uniform intensity over the image receptor.
14 The current widespread use of mammography is principally because
   a. it is easy.
   b. it is inexpensive.
   c. of the incidence of breast cancer.
   d. the radiation dose is low.
15 Which of the following is **not** a type of normal breast tissue?
   a. muscle
   b. fat
   c. fibrous
   d. glandular
16 Which of the following tissues is most susceptible to the induction of breast cancer?
   a. muscle
   b. fat
   c. fibrous
   d. glandular
17 Compression during mammography is necessary in order to
   a. comfort the patient.
   b. reduce geometric unsharpness.
   c. increase SID.
   d. increase OID.
18 Use of grids during mammography is designed to
   a. reduce patient dose.
   b. reduce geometric unsharpness.
   c. improve radiographic density.
   d. improve radiographic contrast.
19 If a 4:1 ratio grid is used during mammography, patient dose will be approximately _____ compared to nongrid.
   a. half
   b. doubled
   c. tripled
   d. not enough information

Mammography

IMAGE RECEPTORS
....

Three types of image receptors are available for mammography: direct exposure film, screen film, and a Xerox image receptor. Differences in image quality occur among these three; however, screen film is now the image receptor of choice.

Differences in patient skin dose also occur. Direct exposure mammography results in the highest patient dose, 5 to 15 rad per view, and for that reason **it should not be used.** Xeromammography requires from 0.5 to 1 rad per view. The use of a screen film combination results in the lowest patient dose—0.1 to 0.5 rad per view.

It is generally recognized that xeromammography is better able to detect and image microcalcifications than screen film combinations because of the property of edge enhancement. Screen film image receptors, on the other hand, are generally recognized to be more effective in detecting rounded and nodular types of structures. Of critical importance is the proper matching of the image receptor with the appropriate radiographic equipment.

EXERCISES

1 During a mammographic examination, it is important that
  a. the SID be as short as practicable.
  b. a kVp above 50 be selected.
  c. 2.5 mm Al filtration be used.
  d. at least 0.5 mm Al filtration be used.

2 Currently two image receptors are used. Comparing the two,
  a. the patient dose is somewhat higher with xeromammography.
  b. screen film techniques show better edge enhancement.

  c. the type of tube target is less important for screen film mammography.
  d. generally, xeromammography is performed at a lower kVp.

3 An advantage to the use of a molybdenum targeted tube for mammography is that
  a. it is recommended for all types of image receptors.
  b. its emission spectrum is better for differential absorption in soft tissue.
  c. the radiation dose is less than one half that from a tungsten targeted tube.
  d. Bremsstrahlung radiation predominates over characteristic radiation.

4 In choosing a tube for mammography,
  a. if a Xerox plate is the image receptor, molybdenum is preferred.
  b. if screen film is the image receptor, molybdenum is preferred.
  c. if a Xerox plate is the image receptor, a tungsten-molybdenum alloy is preferred.
  d. both types of targets are equally suited to both types of receptors.

5 Xeroradiography is
  a. the system used to duplicate radiographic film.
  b. based on certain properties of silver halide.
  c. based on the principle that x rays will neutralize a charged plate.
  d. useful in procedures requiring high contrast.

6 During the Xerox process the relaxation station
  a. charges the selenium plate.
  b. processes the film emulsion.
  c. removes residual charge.
  d. flows toner onto the plate.

7 The **single** principal advantage to xeroradiography when compared with conventional radiography is
  a. high contrast.
  b. blue tint.
  c. edge enhancement.
  d. increased sensitivity.

8 During xeroradiography the uniform electrostatic charge is placed on the image receptor
a. in the relaxation oven.
b. by corona effect.
c. by edge enhancement.
d. at the image transfer station.

9 Which of the following statements regarding xero-mammography is correct when compared to screen film mammography?
a. Patient dose is somewhat higher.
b. Lower kVp should be used.
c. A molybdenum-targeted tube should be used.
d. Total filtration should be less.

10 In xeroradiography the latent image
a. is contained in exposed silver crystals.
b. is visible.
c. is electrostatic.
d. appears during conditioning.

11 Which of the following techniques is most appropriate to xeromammography?
a. tungsten target, long SID, 30 kVp
b. molybdenum target, short SID, 30 kVp
c. tungsten target, long SID, 50 kVp
d. molybdenum target, long SID, 30 kVp

12 When comparing screen film to Xerox image receptors, it should be remembered that
a. microcalcifications are best visualized with Xerox.
b. a screen film receptor is a photoconductor.
c. a molybdenum target tube must be used with a Xerox receptor.
d. a screen film receptor has wider latitude.

13 When film is loaded for mammography,
a. the base should be in contact with the screen.
b. the emulsion should be in contact with the cover.
c. the film should be on the tube side of the screen.
d. the resolution is about the same as for routine radiography with screen films.

14 When one considers the three possible image receptors for mammography,
a. direct exposure receptor has the widest latitude.
b. Xerox receptor is the fastest.
c. screen film receptor has the highest contrast.
d. screen film receptor has the widest latitude.

15 The image receptor in xeromammography is
a. aluminum.   c. selenium.
b. molybdenum.   d. an electrostatic charge.

16 A material that is photoconductive is
a. an insulator when irradiated.
b. an insulator when illuminated.
c. a semiconductor.
d. a conductor when illuminated.

17 Which of the following is **not** a stage in the Xerox conditioner?
a. plate-charging station
b. fuser
c. storage elevator
d. relaxation oven

18 Image contrast in xeroradiography can be controlled by the
a. relaxation oven.
b. voltage at the plate-charging station.
c. speed of the conditioner.
d. speed of the processor.

19 Xeroradiographic toner is
a. a powder of charged particles.
b. introduced in the relaxation oven.
c. introduced at the transfer station.
d. the result of a corona discharge.

20 In xeroradiography, toner robbing results in a
a. corona.
b. fusion.
c. halo.
d. photoconductor.

21 Which of the following techniques is most appropriate to screen film mammography?
a. tungsten target, long SID, 20 kVp
b. tungsten target, long SID, 50 kVp
c. molybdenum target, short SID, 28 kVp
d. molybdenum target, long SID, 28 kVp

22 Poor mammographic screen film contact will result in
a. lower patient dose.
b. higher patient dose.
c. small region blurring.
d. large region blurring.

23 Use of screen film for mammography
a. requires more mAs than xeromammography.
b. produces better contrast than direct exposure.
c. results in improved edge enhancement over xeromammography.
d. requires that a higher kVp be used than xeromammography.

24 The characteristic curve for xeromammography clearly shows its superior
a. patient dose.
b. contrast.
c. latitude.
d. edge enhancement.

25 To do xeromammography, one must have a
a. processor.
b. conditioner.
c. conditioner and processor.
d. darkroom.

Name _____

Date _____

Fluoroscopy

The fluoroscopic examination has undergone continuing improvement since its first demonstration in 1896. In earlier times fluoroscopy required dark adaptation for scotopic vision (rod vision). Now all fluoroscopes are image intensified and produce images that can be viewed under photopic vision (cone vision).

To appreciate the implications of image intensified fluoroscopy, some understanding of general fluoroscopic equipment and visual physiology is required.

EXERCISES

1 In a modern fluoroscope, the fluoroscopic x-ray tube
  a. is always under the table.
  b. is always over the table.
  c. can be either under or over the table.
  d. is always the same as the radiographic tube.

2 The fluoroscope was invented by
  a. Thomas Edison.   c. Alexander Bell.
  b. Wilhelm Roentgen.   d. Hollis Potter.

3 The primary purpose of a fluoroscopic examination, compared with a radiographic examination, is to visualize _____ images.
  a. static   c. cross-sectional
  b. dynamic   d. longitudinal

4 The purpose of angiography is to
  a. perform tomography.
  b. produce stereoradiographs.
  c. obtain 3D images.
  d. visualize vessels.

5 During a fluoroscopic examination, static images are obtained on a
  a. tomogram.   c. spot film.
  b. video monitor.   d. charged plate.

6 Compared with image-intensified fluoroscopy, conventional fluoroscopy
  a. should not be done.
  b. is faster.
  c. requires less patient dose.
  d. is higher contrast.

7 Fluoroscopy normally requires a tube current of
  a. 0.1 to 1.0 mA.   c. 5 to 10 mA.
  b. 1 to 5 mA.   d. 10 to 100 mA.

8 Compared with radiography, the x-ray technique required for fluoroscopy calls for
  a. higher kVp.   c. higher mA.
  b. lower kVp.   d. lower mA.

9 Automatic brightness stabilization (ABS) is designed to compensate for changes in
  a. examination time.   c. patient positioning.
  b. technique selection. d. patient dose.

10 The Bucky slot cover of a fluoroscope is a
  a. protective device.
  b. film transport device.
  c. film support device.
  d. cassette holder.

11 Which of the following units of measurement is used to express image brightness?
  a. roentgen   c. coulomb/kilogram
  b. coulomb   d. lambert

12 Which of the following normally produces the brightest images?
  a. conventional fluoroscopy
  b. image-intensified fluoroscopy
  c. radiography
  d. a spot film

13 Which of the following structures is most sensitive to colors?
  a. rods   c. the cornea
  b. the iris   d. cones

14 It is known that radiation can cause cataracts in which structure of the eye?
  a. lens   c. iris
  b. rods   d. cornea

15 The function of the iris is to
   a. protect the eye.
   b. sense visible light photons.
   c. control the light level.
   d. focus the light onto the retina.

16 The cones are
   a. located on the periphery of the retina.
   b. used for photopic vision.
   c. very sensitive to light.
   d. essentially color blind.

17 The fovea centralis is
   a. next to the lens.   c. the disclike structure.
   b. the blind spot.   d. part of the retina.

18 Visual acuity is the ability to
   a. perceive fine detail.
   b. control the amount of light entering the eye.
   c. detect differences in brightness.
   d. distinguish colors.

19 The rods are principally used for
   a. visual acuity.   c. dim vision.
   b. color perception.   d. bright vision.

20 In general, during fluoroscopy rather than radiography
   a. a smaller focal spot is used.
   b. the mA will be lower.
   c. the SID will be longer.
   d. patient dose will be less.

21 Which of the following describes the fluoroscopic system designed to maintain a constant image brightness?
   a. automatic brightness stabilization (ABS)
   b. positive beam limitation (PBL)
   c. automatic channel selector (ACS)
   d. automatic programmed radiography (APR)

22 Which of the following structures is responsible for the vision of dim objects?
   a. cornea   c. iris
   b. rod   d. pupil

23 Which of the following ocular structures immediately precedes the vitreous humor along the path of incident light?
   a. cone   c. iris
   b. cornea   d. lens

24 Which of the following properties is associated with rods but not cones?
   a. scotopic vision
   b. contrast perception
   c. color detection
   d. visual acuity

25 Radiographic images
   a. are viewed under scotopic conditions.
   b. are brighter than fluoroscopic images.
   c. are viewed under photopic conditions.
   d. require rod vision.

26 Whereas one would like to make radiographic images at high kVp and low mAs, generally during fluoroscopy _____ are preferred.
   a. low kVp and low mA
   b. high kVp and low mA
   c. low kVp and high mA
   d. high kVp and high mA

27 Dim objects can be viewed better
   a. under bright light.
   b. under dim light.
   c. by looking straight on.
   d. with peripheral vision.

28 Video viewing of the fluoroscopic image is advantageous because
   a. patient dose is less.
   b. the examination is quicker.
   c. the image is brighter.
   d. patient motion is less.

29 During fluoroscopic imaging
   a. increasing kVp increases image contrast.
   b. increasing mA reduces patient dose.
   c. reducing kVp increases patient dose.
   d. reducing mA increases image contrast.

30 Rank the following from least bright to most bright:
   a. full moon over Scenic Drive in El Paso _____
   b. movie screen showing "All in a Night's Work" with the Three Stooges _____
   c. threshold for cone vision _____
   d. this page under normal bathroom light _____

Fluoroscopy

IMAGE INTENSIFICATION
....

The image intensifier tube was introduced to radiology in the 1950s and has undergone many refinements since then. If an image intensifier is used during fluoroscopy, patient dose is lower, image quality is better, and diagnostic accuracy is improved. No fluoroscopic examination today should be conducted without image intensification.

The gain produced by the image intensifier is measured by the degree of amplification of the image when compared with that of a conventional fluoroscopic screen. It is the product of the geometric gain, or **minification,** and the **flux gain.**

The image intensifier has made possible a number of alternative methods of examination. Small format spot filming, cinefluorography, and remote television viewing are some. Until recently, the phosphor incorporated into image intensifier tubes was zinc cadmium sulfide. Newer tubes employ cesium iodide and have better gain and resolution.

EXERCISES

1 Photoemission
   a. is the emission of electrons from a heated wire.
   b. is the emission of electrons.
   c. occurs in the input phosphor of an image intensifier tube.
   d. occurs in the output phosphor of an image intensifier tube.
2 At what stage of image-intensified fluoroscopy is the number of photons lowest?
   a. entering the input phosphor
   b. leaving the input phosphor
   c. entering the photocathode
   d. leaving the output phosphor

3 Image intensifier brightness gain increases with increasing
   a. flux gain.
   b. output phosphor size.
   c. kVp.
   d. mA.
4 An image intensifier receives x rays at the input phosphor and emits _____ at the output phosphor.
   a. electrons
   c. ultraviolet light
   b. x rays
   d. visible light
5 The input phosphor of most modern image intensifiers is
   a. zinc cadmium sulfide.
   b. cesium iodide.
   c. sodium iodide.
   d. calcium tungstate.
6 The output phosphor of most modern image intensifiers is
   a. zinc cadmium sulfide.
   b. cesium iodide.
   c. sodium iodide.
   d. calcium tungstate.
7 The photocathode converts
   a. x rays into visible light.
   b. visible light into x rays.
   c. visible light into electrons.
   d. electrons into visible light.
8 The component of the image intensifier tube responsible for focusing the electron field is the
   a. input phosphor.
   b. electrostatic lens.
   c. photocathode.
   d. glass envelope.
9 The ability of an image intensifier to increase image illumination is called
   a. minification gain.
   b. flux gain.
   c. brightness gain.
   d. illumination gain.

10 The flux gain of an image intensifier tube increases with increasing

  a. mA.   **c.** input phosphor size.
  b. kVp.   **d.** tube voltage.

11 The minification gain of an image intensifier tube increases with increasing

  a. mA.   **c.** input phosphor size.
  b. kVp.   **d.** tube voltage.

12 Which of the following is a representative brightness gain for an image intensifier tube?

  a. 5000   **c.** 20,000
  b. 10,000   **d.** all of the above

13 If a tube is described as a 10/7 image intensifier tube, the 10/7 refers to the

  a. area of the input phosphor in square inches.
  b. diameter of the input phosphor in inches.
  c. radius of the input phosphor in inches.
  d. radius of the output phosphor in centimeters.

14 When a multifocus image intensifier tube is operated in the magnification mode,

  a. a larger area of input phosphor will be used.
  b. patient dose will be lower.
  c. image sharpness will be reduced.
  d. the electron focal point will be closer to the input phosphor.

15 An image that displays vignetting will

  a. be dim in the center.
  b. be dim around the periphery.
  c. have higher spatial resolution.
  d. have higher contrast resolution.

16 Which of the following is the principal advantage of image-intensified fluoroscopy?

  a. Dark adaptation is unnecessary.
  b. Photopic vision is possible.
  c. Patient dose is less.
  d. Grids are not necessary.

17 When using a multifocus image intensifier tube in the magnification mode,

  a. spatial resolution is improved.
  b. noise is increased.
  c. patient dose is reduced.
  d. the field of view is increased.

18 In a 10/7/5 image intensifier tube,

  a. spatial resolution is best in the 10 mode.
  b. there are three different input phosphors.
  c. there are three different output phosphors.
  d. the field of view is largest in the 10 mode.

19 An image intensifier tube has a 5 cm output phosphor and a 45 cm input phosphor. The brightness gain is 10,000. The flux gain is approximately

  a. 10.   **c.** 120.
  b. 80.   **d.** 1000.

20 Place the following in proper sequence for image-intensified fluoroscopy.

  a. electron-to-light conversion   _____
  b. x ray–to–light conversion   _____
  c. light-to-electric signal   _____
  d. light-to-electron conversion   _____
  e. electric signal to light   _____

Match the following components of an image intensifier tube with the appropriate type of radiation. Some answers may be used more than once or not at all.

21 output phosphor _____   **a.** light absorbed
22 input phosphor _____   **b.** light emitted
23 photocathode _____   **c.** electrons absorbed
24 glass envelope _____   **d.** electrons emitted
25 patient _____   **e.** x rays absorbed

Match the arrows labeled 26 to 30 in the diagram above with the following descriptions. Some answers may be used more than once.

26 _____   **a.** ultraviolet photons
27 _____   **b.** visible light photons
28 _____   **c.** infrared photons
29 _____   **d.** x-ray photons
30 _____   **e.** electrons

Fluoroscopy

IMAGE MONITORING

The fluoroscopic image produced at the output of an image intensifier tube is of high quality but of postage-stamp size and therefore cannot be viewed directly. Consequently, this image is manipulated for viewing, or **monitoring,** in any one of a number of different ways. The most popular method of monitoring the fluoroscopic image is with a closed circuit television system. The output image of the image intensifier tube is detected by a television camera tube, usually a **vidicon,** and then displayed on a television monitor that incorporates a television picture tube. Alternately, the image can be magnified by optical lenses and reflected through a series of mirrors for direct viewing.

These modes allow the dynamic, moving fluoroscopic images to be monitored. Such images can also be monitored with an optically coupled cine camera. Such cameras are usually restricted to specialized examinations, such as cardiac catheterization. If static images are required during the examination, they are made with an optically coupled spot film camera. Both the spot film and cine cameras employ single-emulsion photographic film having dimensional sizes from 16 mm to 105 mm. In addition to providing an alternate mode of image monitoring, these film cameras produce permanent images that can be retained in the patient's file.

EXERCISES

1 The most common position for the fluoroscopic x ray tube is
a. ceiling mounted.
b. wall mounted.
c. above the table.
d. below the table.

2 The use of television rather than optical monitoring of the fluoroscopic image results in a _____ image.
a. magnified   c. color
b. brighter   d. sharper

3 Which of the following is (are) a television camera tube(s)?
a. vidicon   c. image orthicon
b. plumbicon   d. all of the above

4 The electron beam in a television camera tube is produced by
a. thermionic emission.   c. electroemission.
b. photoemission.   d. photoconduction.

5 The electron beam in a television camera tube is controlled by
a. deflection coils.   c. focusing coils
b. electrostatic grids.   d. all of the above.

6 The target assembly of a television camera tube consists of
a. a window.   c. a signal plate.
b. a target.   d. all of the above.

7 Which of the following can be described as photo-conductive?
a. window   c. signal plate
b. target   d. electron gun

8 The principal disadvantage to coupling the television camera to the image intensifier by fiber optics is
a. reduced image quality.
b. increased fragility.
c. that a spot film camera cannot be used.
d. that a cassette-loaded spot film cannot be used.

9 In an optical coupling arrangement, which is nearest the television camera?
a. objective lens   c. beam splitter
b. camera lens   d. mirror

10 Which is a critical component in optically coupling the image intensifier to a spot film camera?
a. objective lens   c. face plate
b. subjective lens   d. signal plate

11 The most important component in a television monitor is the
  a. cathode ray tube.
  b. television camera tube.
  c. electromagnetic coils.
  d. coupling device.

12 When an electric signal is modulated, that means its _____ is changed in a controlled fashion.
  a. intensity   **c.** amplitude
  b. frequency   **d.** all of the above

13 The component of the television monitor that transfers the video signal into an image is the
  a. electron beam.   **c.** target assembly.
  b. electron gun.   **d.** fluorescent screen.

14 The electron beam of the television camera tube is
  a. modulated.   **c.** an area beam.
  b. a fan beam.   **d.** blanked.

15 One television frame is equivalent to
  a. one television field.   **c.** 262½ lines.
  b. two television fields.   **d.** 17 ms.

16 Fluoroscopic television operates at a frame rate of _____ frames per second.
  a. 30   **c.** 262½
  b. 60   **d.** 525

17 Vertical television resolution is limited principally by the
  a. frame rate.   **c.** bandpass.
  b. field rate.   **d.** lines per frame.

18 Horizontal television resolution is limited principally by the
  a. frame rate.   **c.** band pass.
  b. field rate.   **d.** lines per frame.

19 The weakest link in television fluoroscopy is the
  a. image intensifier.
  b. optical coupling device.
  c. television camera.
  d. television monitor.

20 The common frame rates during cinefluorography are 15, 30, and 60 frames/s
  a. because of the frame rate requirement of the television camera tube.
  b. because of the frequency of the power supply.
  c. because flicker is not observed at these rates.
  d. because the film format requires it.

21 When the electron beam of the CRT is blanked, it is
  a. in an active trace.
  b. in a vertical retrace.
  c. turned on.
  d. modulated.

22 The imaging system of commercial broadcast television in the United States has which of the following characteristics?
  a. 30 fields/s
  b. 33 ms/frame
  c. 625 lines
  d. two frames/field

23 Switching from a 70 mm to 105 mm spot film or from a 16 mm to 35 mm cine film will
  a. increase patient exposure.
  b. allow a faster frame rate.
  c. result in better radiographic quality.
  d. require better film.

24 Television fluoroscopic imaging systems have
  a. image intensifier tubes.
  b. contrast limited by the number of scan lines on the television monitor.
  c. mirror optics for viewing.
  d. better spatial resolution than cinefluorographic systems.

25 Which of the following is true about cineradiography?
  a. The x-ray beam is off when the shutter is closed to avoid damaging the film transport system.
  b. The x-ray beam is off when the shutter is closed as a patient protection measure.
  c. The x-ray beam is on during film transport.
  d. Patient exposure rates are lower than in fluoroscopy.

Match the following:

26 television camera tube _____   **a.** electrons from light
27 image intensifier input phosphor _____   **b.** vidicon
28 photoemission _____   **c.** synchronized
29 cinefluorography _____   **d.** cesium iodide
30 brightness gain _____   **e.** minification

Introduction to Computer Science

HISTORY OF COMPUTERS
....
ANATOMY OF A COMPUTER
....

The **hardware** of a computer is the nuts, bolts, and chips of the system. Everything visible and material about a computer is hardware. Hardware essentially exists in three stages: input devices, the central processing unit (CPU), and output devices.

The input and output devices, called I/O devices, are the most visible of the computer parts. Some serve as only input or output devices, but most perform a dual function. The most recognizable input device is the typewriter-like keyboard that is usually associated with

"Would you run through that again please?"

a cathode ray tube. Such an assembly is collectively called a **video display terminal (VDT).** The multiformat and laser cameras are widely used as output devices in radiology. Another common output device is a printer. Printers are necessary to provide hard copy of the output data generated by the computer. They are available as high speed line printers, dot matrix printers, and laser printers. Disk drives, whether floppy, hard, or optical, serve as I/O devices and, more importantly, as secondary memory modules.

Primary memory is provided by the least visible of all the hardware—small memory modules made up of very large scale integrated circuits on very small silicon chips. The central processing unit is also located on such a chip.

EXERCISES

1 Of the following, a _____ best represents an analog device.
  a. photograph
  b. gasoline pump register
  c. point of sale register
  d. raffle ticket

2 To the computer buff, LSI means
  a. large simple implementation.
  b. large scale integration.
  c. long slender implement.
  d. lazy Susan inside.

3 Which of the following printers is slowest?
  a. laser printer
  b. line printer
  c. laser printer
  d. dot matrix printer

4 One difference between random access memory (RAM) and read-only memory (ROM) is
  a. one cannot write to ROM.
  b. RAM is solid state and ROM is tape.
  c. RAM is hard disk and ROM is floppy disk.
  d. ROM is not found in primary memory.

5 Many milestones stand out in the development of the modern computer, but perhaps the most important is
  a. the discovery of x rays.
  b. the transistor.
  c. the flip-flop.
  d. ENIAC.

6 The arithmetic unit in a computer
  a. is synchronized by an electronic clock.
  b. contains the control unit.
  c. can be primary or secondary memory.
  d. is an I/O device.

7 Primary memory is usually found
  a. in the CPU.   **c.** on magnetic tape.
  b. on diskettes.   **d.** in a modem.

8 Which of the following has the largest memory capacity?
  a. floppy disk   **c.** optical disk
  b. Winchester disk   **d.** optical tape

9 A logic terminal is one that
  a. logically fits with the rest of the system.
  b. performs only logic functions.
  c. can be programmed.
  d. does not contain a microprocessor.

10 In which of the following is RAM located?
  a. the CPU   **c.** a magnetic tape
  b. a floppy disk   **d.** a modem

11 The CPU contains
  a. a control unit.
  b. memory.
  c. an arithmetic unit.
  d. all of the above.

12 The term *stored program* means
  a. the binary number system must be used.
  b. only binary data can be manipulated.
  c. digital instead of analog must be used.
  d. instructions can be placed in memory.

13 The control unit
  a. is synchronized by an electronic clock.
  b. contains the arithmetic unit.
  c. can contain primary or secondary memory.
  d. is an I/O device.

14 Which of the following is normally associated with the first generation of computers?
  a. peg wheels   **c.** an abacus
  b. vacuum tubes   **d.** transistors

15 Most primary memory devices consist of a
  a. tape.   **c.** magnetic core.
  b. disk.   **d.** semiconductor.

16 Which of the following is not an I/O device?
  a. a modem   **c.** a Winchester disk
  b. a memory module   **d.** the VDT

17 Most computer-assisted radiologic imaging devices incorporate a
  a. calculator.   **c.** minicomputer.
  b. microcomputer.   **d.** mainframe computer.

18 Optical character recognition (OCR) is a
  a. part of the CPU.   **c.** software system.
  b. part of the CRT.   **d.** hardware device.

19 The type of printer most likely to be used with a radiologic imaging system is a
  a. laser printer.   **c.** daisy wheel printer.
  b. line printer.   **d.** dot matrix printer.

20 Secondary memory is available as a
  a. VDT.   **c.** keypad.
  b. modem.   **d.** magnetic tape.

21 Which of the following would be found in the CPU?
  a. an arithmetic unit **c.** a modem
  b. a Winchester disk   **d.** secondary storage

22 Which of the following would **least** likely be a part of a radiologic imaging VDT?
  a. alphabetic keypad
  b. modem
  c. special function keypad
  d. CRT

23 Which of the following is an arithmetic function?
  a. and-or   **c.** session
  b. multiplication   **d.** transfer file

24 I/O devices employed in radiologic imaging include all except the
  a. CPU.   **c.** multiformat camera.
  b. Winchester disk.   **d.** floppy disk.

Name _____

Date _____

Introduction to Computer Science

COMPUTER SOFTWARE
....
PROCESSING METHODS
....

The written instructions that guide a computer through its various operations are called **computer programs.** These are the **software** of a computer. **Systems software** exists as instructions written in a very low level computer language based on the binary number system. Individual **application computer programs** are written in various computer languages. High level computer languages, e.g., FORTRAN, BASIC, and COBOL, are written in English-oriented symbols that can be assembled, compiled, or interpreted into a machine-oriented language.

Machine language is the lowest level language employed in computer programs. It consists of a series of **binary digits (bits)** assembled according to a code to represent instructions for the CPO or numeric and alphabetic characters. The binary code is based on the binary number system, which contains only two digits, zero and one. Eight bits make a **byte,** and two bytes make a **word.** It is the bits, bytes, and words that move through a computer operation from input to output.

EXERCISES

1 Software includes which of the following?
  a. the CPU   **c.** the operating system
  b. the ROM   **d.** the operating terminal
2 Which of the following can be expressed in the binary number system?
  a. duodecimal numbers **c.** logic functions
  b. alphabetic characters **d.** all of the above
3 The binary code for the decimal 18 is
  a. 10010.   **c.** 1001.
  b. 1010.   **d.** 10001.

4 The sum of $2^3 + 2^2 + 2^0$ is
  a. 8.   **c.** 84.
  b. 13.   **d.** 84^2.
5 The number 47 falls between
  a. 2^4 and 2^5.   **c.** 2^6 and 2^7.
  b. 2^5 and 2^6.   ,   **d.** 2^7 and 2^8.
6 Which of the following is a high level computer language?
  a. Display writer   **c.** Dbase
  b. Lotus 1-2-3   **d.** Fortran
7 Which of the following is an applications program?
  a. Basic   **c.** Wordstar
  b. Cobol   **d.** Logo
8 Alphabetic characters are usually encoded by how many bits?
  a. 2   **c.** 8
  b. 4   **d.** 16
9 The operating system
  a. is usually programmed in the highest level language.
  b. is usually in decimal form.
  c. organizes data flow through the system.
  d. is found in the modem.
10 Which of the following terms **does not** fit with the others?
  a. operating system **c.** compiler
  b. assembler   **d.** interpreter
11 Which of the following is a high level language?
  a. assembly   **c.** LOGO
  b. bootstrap   **d.** machine oriented
12 The oldest of currently employed computer languages is
  a. ADA.   **c.** PASCAL.
  b. BASIC.   **d.** FORTRAN.
13 An algorithm is
  a. a computer language.
  b. rarely used in diagnostic imaging.
  c. an equation in computer language.
  d. an operating system.

14 The computer language that is particularly suited to business is
 a. FORTRAN.   **c.** COBOL.
 b. BASIC.   **d.** PASCAL.

15 Which type of computer processing is used in radiologic imaging?
 a. real-time processing
 b. batch processing
 c. on-line processing
 d. time share processing

16 Which of the following equalities is correct?
 a. $2^8 = 512$ **c.** $12^3 = 1728$
 b. $10^4 = 1000$ **d.** $3^4 = 27$

17 Probably the programming language easiest to learn is
 a. PASCAL.   **c.** FORTRAN.
 b. BASIC.   **d.** COBOL.

18 The type of program that a user might write to classify radiologic images would be
 a. an applications program.
 b. a bootstrap program.
 c. an assembler program.
 d. an operating system.

19 The zero or one in the binary system is called a
 a. CPU.   **c.** bit.
 b. word.   **d.** byte.

20 Software would include all of the following except
 a. interpreters.
 b. interrogators.
 c. compilers.
 d. algorithms.

21 Which of the following number systems uses the most digits?
 a. binary   **c.** heximal
 b. decimal   **d.** duodecimal

22 Which of the following computer measures is the largest?
 a. bit   **c.** smack
 b. byte   **d.** chomp

23 To encode is to change from
 a. bits to bytes.
 b. bytes to bits.
 c. ordinary characters to binary digits.
 d. alphabetic characters to decimal characters.

24 When a computer is turned on, the first interaction is through the
 a. bootstrap.
 b. file manager and scheduler.
 c. memory manager.
 d. I/O manager.

Compute the following:
25 Change 6 to binary form.
26 Change 53 to binary form.
27 Change 147 to binary form.
28 Change 1163 to binary form.
29 Change 1671 to binary form.
30 What is the decimal equivalent of 1011?
31 What is the decimal equivalent of 10101?
32 What is the decimal equivalent of 110011?
33 What is the decimal equivalent of 1001001?
34 What is the decimal equivalent of 110110110?

Name _____

Date _____

Digital X-ray Imaging

Digital fluoroscopy has been developed as a replacement for some angiographic procedures. Whereas angiography, particularly subtraction angiography, requires considerable time to produce a final image, the images produced in digital fluoroscopy are available nearly instantaneously. Film subtraction techniques that accompany angiographic procedures are exceedingly difficult and time consuming to perform. With digital fluoroscopy, such subtraction images not only are relatively easy and quick to produce but also allow postexamination image processing and manipulation. Finally, digital fluoroscopy can be accomplished with a venous injection rather than the arterial injection required in conventional angiography.

In digital fluoroscopy a high signal-to-noise, high resolution video system is coupled to a computer. The video signal is digitized, manipulated in the computer by one of several techniques, and finally displayed on the video monitor. Each image is in digital form and therefore is subject to postexamination processing.

EXERCISES

1 The principal reason for image integration is to reduce
   a. patient dose.   **c.** examination time.
   b. image noise.   **d.** contrast.

2 The maximum frame acquisition rate in digital fluoroscopy is about
   a. 1 frame per second.
   b. 4 frames per second.
   c. 10 frames per second.
   d. 30 frames per second.

3 The signal-to-noise ratio of conventional TV camera tubes is about
   a. 100:1.   **c.** 1000:1.
   b. 200:1.   **d.** 2000:1.

4 Compared with conventional fluoroscopy, digital fluoroscopy is conducted
   a. at much lower x-ray tube currents.
   b. at much higher x-ray tube currents.
   c. with a different type of image intensifier.
   d. with a different type of video monitor.

5 The newest digital imaging systems display images on a 1024×1024 matrix. How many pixels are there in such a matrix?
   a. 1000   **c.** 2048
   b. 1024   **d.** $>10^6$

6 A conventional radiograph could be called
   a. an exponential image.
   b. a linear image.
   c. an analog image.
   d. a digital image.

7 Which of the following components will be found in digital fluoroscopy but not conventional fluoroscopy?
   a. a video monitor   **c.** an ADC
   b. an image intensifier   **d.** an ABS

8 During digital fluoroscopy, the image receptor is
   a. film.
   b. the video monitor.
   c. the cassette.
   d. the image intensifier tube.

9 A principal advantage of digital fluoroscopy over conventional fluoroscopy for subtraction studies is
   a. noise enhancement.
   b. contrast enhancement.
   c. low patient dose.
   d. less contrast material.

10 The approximate resolution limit for a 4-in image intensifier tube and a 256 reconstruction matrix is
   a. 0.4 mm.   **c.** 2.56 mm.
   b. 1.0 mm.   **d.** 4 mm.

11 During digital fluoroscopy,
   a. the x-ray beam is pulsed.
   b. the x-ray beam is continuous and at high mA.
   c. the x-ray beam is continuous and at low mA.
   d. each of the above modes can be used.
12 Digital fluoroscopy is conducted
   a. at relatively low mA.
   b. in the progressive TV mode.
   c. with low signal-to-noise ratio.
   d. with direct exposure film.
13 Image acquisition rate is determined by all of the following except the
   a. speed of the computer.
   b. image matrix size.
   c. computer architecture.
   d. size of the image intensifier.
14 Time interval difference mode is best used for
   a. extremities.   c. large fields.
   b. dynamic motion.   d. long exposure times.
15 Reregistration of an image is used to
   a. correct for motion.
   b. correct any error in patient identification.
   c. reduce noise.
   d. increase edge enhancement.
16 The combination of temporal subtraction and energy subtraction techniques is called
   a. resonance subtraction.
   b. radiographic subtraction.
   c. hybrid subtraction.
   d. no subtraction.
17 The minimum acceptable signal-to-noise ratio for digital fluoroscopy is
   a. 100:1.   c. 1000:1.
   b. 200:1.   d. 2000:1.
18 Interrogation time
   a. is the time spent questioning the patient.
   b. refers to the total examination time.
   c. is the time to switch on the x-ray tube.
   d. is the time to switch off the x-ray tube.
19 A digital imaging system with a dynamic range of 2^{10} will be able to reproduce _____ shades of gray.
   a. 32   c. 1024
   b. 256   d. 4096
20 The approach to digital radiography used in computed tomography (CT) is called
   a. digital vascular imaging.
   b. digital subtraction angiography.
   c. scanned projection radiography.
   d. area beam imaging.

21 An advantage of digital imaging over conventional imaging is
   a. reduced noise.   c. increased resolution.
   b. reduced speed.   d. increased latitude.
22 A pixel is
   a. a matrix of numbers.
   b. a two-dimensional representation.
   c. a three-dimensional representation.
   d. the unit of fluoroscopy dose.
23 Between the TV camera and the computer of a digital fluoroscopic system is
   a. an image-intensifier tube.
   b. an analog-to-digital converter.
   c. a digital-to-analog converter.
   d. a second video monitor.
24 The mask image is usually
   a. the first image.
   b. the last image.
   c. the image preceding the appearance of contrast.
   d. the image at the peak of contrast.
25 Energy subtraction is based on
   a. noise reduction.
   b. contrast enhancement.
   c. K-edge absorption.
   d. time differences.
26 As one integrates video frames in DF
   a. the signal-to-noise ratio increases.
   b. spatial resolution is improved.
   c. patient dose increases.
   d. video noise is enhanced.
27 Which of the following components is uniquely essential to digital fluoroscopy?
   a. CRT
   b. ADC
   c. TV camera pickup tube
   d. TV monitor
28 A misregistration artifact
   a. occurs when a patient moves.
   b. is not really an artifact.
   c. cannot be corrected or compensated.
   d. requires more hardware than is usually available.
29 Remasking
   a. will increase patient dose.
   b. requires a repeat examination.
   c. reduces spatial resolution.
   d. can correct for patient motion.
30 During DF _____ video monitor(s) is (are) required.
   a. one   c. three
   b. two   d. four

Digital X-ray Imaging

DIGITAL RADIOGRAPHY

Digital radiography is the process of producing a radiographic image utilizing digital technology. Images are obtained either with a finely collimated fan beam or with an area beam, and the image receptor can be any one of a number of different types of radiation detectors.

The principal advantage of the collimated fan beam is the inherent rejection of scatter radiation from the detector array. Such scatter rejection improves contrast. This approach to digital radiography is called **scanned projection radiography,** and its major disadvantage is that it can take several seconds to obtain.

Area beam digital radiography, on the other hand, can be conducted at exposure times measured in milliseconds, and therefore problems resulting from patient motion are minimized. However, image contrast is not as great because the remnant x-ray beam contains scatter radiation. Both fan and area beam approaches provide for postexamination processing of the image with the incorporation of image enhancement techniques.

EXERCISES

1 The principal disadvantage to the use of an area beam in digital radiography is
   a. short exposure time.
   b. increased patient dose.
   c. scatter radiation.
   d. no postexamination processing.
2 Rapid translation or sweep of the source-detector assembly across the patient during digital radiography will
   a. slow the examination.
   b. reduce spatial resolution.
   c. enhance contrast.
   d. reduce system noise.
3 Digital radiography
   a. employs film as the image receptor.
   b. requires computer processing.
   c. produces an initial image in analog form.
   d. is faster.
4 A scanned projection radiograph
   a. is virtually scatter free.
   b. removes superposition of structures.
   c. is like a tomograph.
   d. has worse contrast than digital fluoroscopy.
5 Which of the following would **not** be a part of scanned projection radiography?
   a. video monitor
   b. an analog-to-digital converter
   c. an area beam
   d. a detector array
6 The x-ray tube in digital radiography must have high heat capacity because of
   a. the time of image acquisition.
   b. high mA.
   c. high kVp.
   d. all of the above.
7 The principal advantage to the use of an area beam in digital radiography is
   a. short exposure time.
   b. low patient dose.
   c. scatter radiation rejection.
   d. postexamination processing.
8 Which of the following is an advantage of area digital beam radiography over scanned projection radiography?
   a. improved contrast
   b. improved resolution of detail
   c. reduced motion blur
   d. low noise
9 Which of the following is used as an image receptor in digital radiography?
   a. an image intensifier   c. $CaWO_4$
   b. film   d. $CdWO_4$

10 The principal disadvantage of area beam digital radiography is
  a. poor resolution of detail.
  b. poor contrast.
  c. edge enhancement.
  d. noise.

11 A digital image constructed on a 512×512 matrix will have how many pixels?
  a. 512
  b. 1024
  c. 2^9
  d. 2^{18}

12 The minimum matrix size for an acceptable radiographic image is probably
  a. $2^4 \times 2^4$.
  b. $2^6 \times 2^6$.
  c. $2^8 \times 2^8$.
  d. $2^{10} \times 2^{10}$.

13 Which of the following is normally unique to digital radiography?
  a. remasking
  b. reregistration
  c. area x-ray beam
  d. linear detector array

14 Which of the following is **not** necessary for a digital radiographic examination?
  a. an image intensifier tube
  b. an ADC
  c. a radiation detector
  d. memory

15 Which of the following is **not** used as a radiation detector in DR?
  a. xenon
  b. air
  c. BGO
  d. $CdWO_4$

16 The principal limitation to the SPR mode of DR is
  a. cost.
  b. patient dose.
  c. noise.
  d. examination time.

17 An x-ray system employed for DR must have
  a. a rapid film changer.
  b. a high heat capacity x-ray tube.
  c. at least two video monitors.
  d. a modem.

18 Spatial resolution is improved in SPR by
  a. speeding up the examination.
  b. using a higher heat capacity tube.
  c. employing more detectors per degree.
  d. using an image intensifier tube.

19 The principal advantage to a fan x-ray beam over an area x-ray beam is
  a. reduced patient dose.
  b. scatter rejection.
  c. hybrid images.
  d. examination time.

20 Temporal subtraction in DF
  a. requires rapid kVp switching.
  b. can produce misregistered images.
  c. results in higher dose than energy subtraction.
  d. uses alternating x ray beam filters.

Name _____

Date _____

Computed Tomography

Computed tomography (CT) represents one of the most important developments in x-ray imaging in the past 50 years. Many identify the method as a CAT scanner, but in fact, it is a CT scanner producing CT scans. The illustration on the right shows a CAT scanner.

The CT scanner differs from other x-ray imaging equipment principally because it uses a computer to reconstruct an image. The computer portion of the CT scanner consists of two components—hardware and software. The hardware is the computer itself. The software represents the mathematic computations in computer language or **algorithms** required to reconstruct an image from the data supplied by the detector assembly.

The CT scanner has three principal sections, which are not the same as those for a conventional x-ray system. The **gantry assembly** contains a high voltage generator, an x-ray tube, radiation detectors, and patient

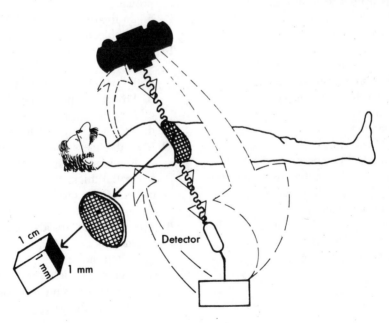

positioning apparatus. The **operating console** serves the same function as that for conventional x-ray systems. However, it is the **computer** that sets the CT scanner apart, assisting in the control of the scanner, receiving data from the detector assembly, and reconstructing the data into an image.

EXERCISES

1 A CT scanner produces which kind of image?
  a. axial
  b. biaxial
  c. transaxial
  d. orthoaxial

2 In its simplest configuration the CT scanner consists of an x-ray source and
  a. a detector.
  b. an image receptor.
  c. an image intensifier.
  d. a selenium plate.

3 Which of the following is (are) characteristic of first-generation CT scanners?
  a. a selenium or film image receptor
  b. multiple sources and multiple detectors
  c. a pencil x-ray beam
  d. rotate-only geometry

4 Newer developments in CT scanners incorporate
  a. light-localizing, variable-aperture collimators.
  b. charged electrostatic plates.
  c. multiple reconstruction algorithms.
  d. high-frequency radiographic grids.

5 Sensitivity profile in CT is determined by the _____ collimator.
  a. prepatient
  b. postpatient
  c. predetector
  d. postdetector

6 Which of the following is **not** a constituent of a CT scanner?
  a. an image intensifier
  b. a computer
  c. a television monitor
  d. an algorithm

7 Second-generation CT scanners
  a. use scan speeds from 1 to 5 minutes.
  b. have a multiple detector array.
  c. have rotate-only geometry.
  d. use increments of 1 degree per view.

8 Third-generation CT scanners have
  a. multiple detector, area beam geometry.
  b. single detector, fan beam geometry.
  c. rotate-only geometry.
  d. translate-only geometry.

9 Fourth-generation CT scanners
  a. incorporate area beam geometry.
  b. may use selenium or film as the image receptor.
  c. are faster than third-generation scanners.
  d. require prepatient collimation.

10 Which of the following subsystems would normally be associated with the gantry assembly?
  a. the physician's viewing console
  b. the algorithms
  c. the software
  d. the detector assembly

11 Which one of the following has been employed as detectors in a CT scanner?
  a. silver halide
  b. bismuth germanate
  c. selenium
  d. high pressure air

12 A comparison of scintillation and gas-filled detectors shows that
  a. both have approximately the same total detection efficiency.
  b. both rely heavily on Compton interaction.
  c. the scintillation detectors have higher geometric efficiency.
  d. the gas-filled detectors have higher intrinsic efficiency.

13 The operating console of a CT scanner will normally have controls for all of the following except
  a. kVp.
  b. exposure time.
  c. SID indicator.
  d. slice thickness.

14 CT images can be
  a. stored electronically.
  b. stored in the detector assembly.
  c. viewed on image intensifiers.
  d. viewed directly.

15 In a CT scanner, prepatient collimation
  a. determines patient dose.
  b. determines image noise.
  c. controls pixel size.
  d. controls scatter radiation reaching the detector.

16 In the translate-rotate mode
  a. data are collected only during the rotate portion.
  b. solid state is the only detector permitted.
  c. scan times as short as 1 s are routine.
  d. one finds both first- and second-generation CT scanners.

17 Each translation of a source-detector assembly produces
  a. an image.
  b. a projection.
  c. a pixel.
  d. a voxel.

18 _____ and _____ collimation are the same.
  a. Prepatient, postpatient
  b. Prepatient, predetector
  c. Predetector, postpatient
  d. Predetector, postdetector

19 Slice thickness can also be expressed as
  a. low contrast thickness.
  b. spatial thickness.
  c. sensitivity profile.
  d. dose profile.

20 The principal disadvantage of fourth-generation scanner is
  a. system noise.
  b. large slice thickness.
  c. excessive examination time.
  d. high patient dose.

Name_____

Date_____

Computed Tomography

IMAGE CHARACTERISTICS

IMAGE QUALITY

QUALITY ASSURANCE

When describing the quality of any imaging system, three principal characteristics need to be considered—high contrast or spatial resolution, low contrast resolution, or simply contrast, and noise. Every imaging system will have a number of other characteristics that may be unique to that system and should be considered in its overall evaluation. In CT the secondary image characteristics are linearity and uniformity.

Spatial resolution refers to the capacity of an imaging system to reproduce tiny objects that are radiopaque, such as a lead bar test pattern or calcifications in soft tissue. Spatial resolution is often quantified by **spatial frequency** or **modulation transfer function (MTF).**

Contrast refers to the ability of the imaging system to reproduce objects, such as cysts and tumors, that do not vary much in their x-ray absorption properties from surrounding tissue. The figure below represents the spatial resolution and contrast characteristics of a typical CT scanner.

When evaluating a conventional radiographic image, the **noise** or **quantum mottle** of the image may be bothersome, but it rarely obscures the detectability of the lesion. Noise has little effect on spatial resolution, but it is the limiting factor for imaging low contrast tissues.

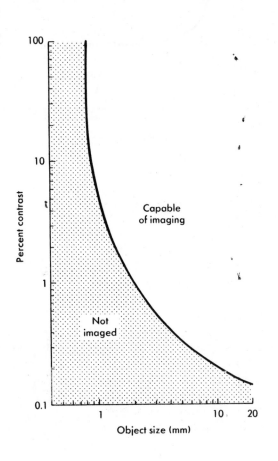

EXERCISES

1 A 120 by 120 matrix will consist of _____ pixels.

   a. 12   **c.** 625

   b. 144   **d.** 14,400

2 What is the pixel size of an image reconstructed from a 24 cm diameter region in a 320 by 320 matrix?

   a. 0.25 mm   **c.** 0.75 mm

   b. 0.5 mm   **d.** 1.5 mm

3 A CT scan is made with a 5 mm slice thickness and a 0.5 mm pixel size. What is the size of its voxel?

   a. 25 mm^3 **c.** 1.25 mm^3

   b. 1.5 mm^3 **d.** 1.00 mm^3

4 If a CT scanner is being calibrated, which of the following CT numbers most closely represents the value for blood?

   a. 100   **c.** −2

   b. 40   **d.** −40

5 A CT scanner has a limiting resolution of 7 lp/cm. What size object can be resolved?
   a. 0.35 mm   **c.** 1.4 mm
   b. 0.7 mm   **d.** 3.5 mm

6 Which of the following is characteristic of a CT image and not of conventional radiographs?
   a. Anatomic structures are superimposed on one another.
   b. CT images are more severely degraded because of scatter radiation.
   c. CT images have better contrast.
   d. Overlying and underlying tissues are blurred.

7 An image matrix contains
   a. silver halide information units.
   b. equations of information.
   c. picture elements.
   d. algorithms.

8 A Hounsfield unit (HU)
   a. is the numeric value of a pixel.
   b. is the numeric value of heat units.
   c. is the volume of a voxel expressed in mm^3.
   d. takes on values from −100 to +100.

9 The precise pixel value in HU depends on
   a. beam size.
   b. the attenuation coefficient of water.
   c. 32 shades of gray.
   d. light-field, x-ray beam coincidence.

10 Spatial resolution usually refers to the
   a. binary number system.
   b. ability to identify tissues of varying composition.
   c. constancy of the imaging system over time.
   d. ability to identify small radiopaque objects.

11 When describing a CT image, contrast
   a. means that contrast material was injected.
   b. is the same as spatial resolution.
   c. is limited by the noise of the system.
   d. is not as good as in conventional radiography.

12 The noise in a CT image is influenced by all of the following except
   a. quantum mottle.   **c.** slice thickness.
   b. pixel size.   **d.** patient dose.

Exercises 13 through 15 refer to the Figure below.

13 The MTF curves describe two imaging systems. Which of the following statements is true?
   a. System B has better contrast for coarse details than system A.
   b. System A has better spatial resolution than system B.
   c. System B has better spatial resolution than system A.
   d. System A detects smaller objects than system B.

14 A device has the MTF characteristics represented by B. Which of the following statements is true for that device?
   a. Its imaging ability increases with increasing spatial frequency.
   b. At 10 1p cm^{-1} the response is excellent.
   c. At 2 1p cm^{-1} only one half of an object can be imaged.
   d. It can image a 0.5 mm object.

15 The MTF characteristics of system A suggest that it
   a. is a better system than B.
   b. can image down to approximately 0.8 mm.
   c. can image down to approximately 6 cm.
   d. images small objects better than large objects.

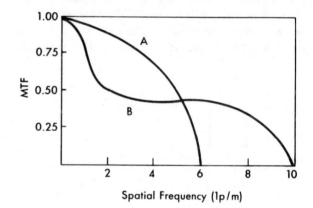

WORKSHEET 86

Quality Control

X-ray imaging equipment is becoming ever more sophisticated and complicated. Although the operation of such imaging equipment is often made easier by these continuing developments in design, the assurance that the equipment is functioning properly becomes more difficult to monitor. Such monitoring is called a **quality control program.**

A quality control program designed for an x-ray system involves a number of observations and measurements on the various parts and subsystems of the imager. Collectively, an assessment of imager performance is made to ensure that it continues to operate within the manufacturer's specifications. Most elements of such a quality control program are conducted annually or following any major repairs or alterations.

EXERCISES

1 Compared to a quality control program a quality assurance program
   a. deals with equipment.
   b. deals with people.
   c. is normally performed weekly.
   d. is normally performed annually.
2 Which of the following are essential elements of a quality control program?
   I. performance evaluation
   II. image interpretation
   III. error correction
   IV. scheduling performance
   a. I and II   **c.** II and III
   b. I and III   **d.** II and IV

3 Radiographic kVp should be evaluated
   a. weekly.   **c.** semiannually.
   b. monthly.   **d.** annually.
4 The variable aperture, light-localizing collimator must confine the x-ray beam to
   a. inside the light field. **c.** ±2% of the SID.
   b. the light field.   **d.** ±5% of the SID.
5 The actual kVp should be within _____ of the indicated kVp.
   a. ±1 kVp   **c.** ±4 kVp
   b. ±2 kVp   **d.** ±6 kVp
6 Which of the following devices may be used to assess the accuracy of the exposure timer?
   a. ion chamber   **c.** sensitometer
   b. densitometer   **d.** slit camera
7 If the automatic exposure timer fails, a backup timer should terminate the exposure at
   a. 3 s or 300 mAs. **c.** 9 s or 900 mAs.
   b. 6 s or 600 mAs. **d.** 12 s or 1200 mAs.
8 Output radiation exposure should be reproducible to within
   a. 1%.   **c.** 5%.
   b. 3%.   **d.** 10%.
9 During normal fluoroscopy the radiation intensity at the tabletop will result in dose rates of
   a. 0 to 2 mrad/min. **c.** 0 to 2 rad/min.
   b. 2 to 10 mrad/min. **d.** 2 to 10 rad/min.
10 When using cassette spot films instead of photofluoro spot films,
   a. patient dose is higher.
   b. patient dose is lower.
   c. a grid must be used.
   d. compression must be applied.
11 All fluoroscopic automatic exposure systems should be evaluated
   a. weekly.
   b. monthly.
   c. semiannually.
   d. annually.

12 Conventional tomography systems should produce images of tissue that lie within _____ of the indicated tomographic plane.
   a. ±5 mm
   b. ±10 mm
   c. ±15 mm
   d. a range of values (depending on tube motion)

13 Mammography kVp must be accurate within
   a. ±1 kVp.
   b. ±3 kVp.
   c. ±5 kVp.
   d. ±10 kVp.

14 A quality control program for computed tomography involves measurements at least
   a. daily.
   b. weekly.
   c. monthly.
   d. semiannual.

15 The patient couch of a CT scanner must move automatically with an accuracy of
   a. 1 mm.   c. 3 mm.
   b. 2 mm.   d. 5 mm.

16 When operated at 70 kVp, the minimum allowed HVL is
   a. 2.0 mm Al.   c. 2.3 mm Al.
   b. 2.1 mm Al.   d. 2.5 mm Al.

17 Which of the following organizations accredits hospitals?
   a. ACPM   c. CRCPD
   b. ACR   d. JCAHO

18 The total filtration required for general purpose radiography and fluoroscopy is
   a. 2.0 mm Al.   c. 2.3 mm Al.
   b. 2.1 mm Al.   d. 2.5 mm Al.

19 Which of the following can be used to measure effective focal spot size?
   a. ion chamber   c. sensitometer
   b. densitometer   d. slit camera

20 The ability of an x-ray machine to produce constant radiation output at various conditions of mA and exposure time producing the same mAs is called
   a. reproducibility.   c. accuracy.
   b. linearity.   d. precision.

Name _____

Date _____

Quality Control

Perhaps the most important quality control program is that associated with the automatic processor. Daily attention to the automatic processor is essential, and this attention should be properly recorded. The American College of Radiology (ACR) has developed a processor quality control program to be implemented by mammography facilities seeking its accreditation. Many elements of this program should also be implemented for all of radiology. Inadequate attention to the automatic processor can result in image degradation and artifacts.

An artifact is any irregular density on a radiograph that is not caused by the proper shadowing of the object by the primary x-ray beam. Processing, exposure, and handling and storage are the three types of artifacts a radiologic technologist is likely to encounter. Proper identification of the type of artifact produced will aid in its elimination.

EXERCISES

1 Patient motion during exposure will result in
   a. a processing artifact.   **c.** a handling artifact.
   b. an exposure artifact.   **d.** no artifact.
2 A guide shoe is a component of
   a. a cassette.
   b. a film bin.
   c. an automatic processor.
   d. a darkroom countertop.
3 A chemical fog artifact
   a. is an exposure artifact.
   b. appears as streaks.
   c. results in lower contrast.
   d. results in lower optical density.

4 A yellow appearance to a radiograph with time
   a. is a storage artifact.
   b. is a processing artifact.
   c. indicates that the developer was underreplenished.
   d. indicates that the developer was overreplenished.
5 Which of the following tasks should be performed daily?
   a. assess darkroom fog
   b. analyze fixer retention
   c. clean screens
   d. monitor automatic processor
6 Corrective action should be triggered whenever automatic processor monitoring shows a change in contrast exceeding an optical density of
   a. ±0.1.   **c.** ±0.3.
   b. ±0.2.   **d.** ±0.5.
7 The repeat rate
   a. should be determined monthly.
   b. is the number of repeated images.
   c. should not exceed 2%.
   d. should not exceed 4%.
8 Which of the following is a part of processor quality control?
   a. Assess x-ray reproducibility.
   b. Determine beam quality.
   c. Clean screens.
   d. Analyze fixer replenishment rate.
9 For most facilities the frequency of processor cleaning will be
   a. daily.   **c.** monthly.
   b. weekly.   **d.** semiannually.
10 The operation of the processor should be observed and the developer temperature recorded at least once each
   a. day.   **c.** month.
   b. week.   **d.** quarter.
11 Wet pressure sensitization would be classified as
   a. an exposure artifact.   **c.** a handling artifact.
   b. a processing artifact.   **d.** no artifact.

12 Pi lines are so-called because they
   a. appear as a section of pie.
   b. appear as a whole sliced pie.
   c. occur on the finished radiograph.
   d. occur at regular intervals.
13 Static artifacts appear most often during _____ temperature and _____ humidity.
   a. low, low   c. high, high
   b. low, high   d. high, low

14 If residual thiosulfate is not properly removed during washing, the radiograph will
   a. be underdeveloped.   c. turn blue.
   b. be overdeveloped.   d. turn yellow.
15 Which of the following is a source of fog?
   a. poor screen/film contact
   b. improper screen cleaning
   c. improper safelight
   d. excess hypo retention

Name_____

WORKSHEET 88

Date_____

Physical Principles of MRI

There are many reasons for the explosion in application of nuclear magnetic resonance (NMR) techniques to magnetic resonance imaging. Nonionizing radiation, multiplanar imaging, and freedom from x-ray induced artifacts are a few. The single most important reason, however, is enhanced contrast. In this regard, magnetic resonance imaging (MRI) is superior to every other imaging modality.

The most abundant atom in the human body is hydrogen. The hydrogen nucleus is a single proton that spins on its axis. This spinning charged particle creates a magnetic field that behaves much like a bar magnet. The proton in this state has a **magnetic dipole,** and it creates a magnetic field called a **magnetic moment.**

If there is a strong external magnetic field, some magnetic moments of hydrogen will align themselves with the field. While so aligned, if a radio frequency pulse (RF) is absorbed by the tissue, the magnetic moments will flip and align against the field. When the RF pulse is removed, the magnetic moments slowly flip back to their equilibrium state and emit an RF signal in the process. It is this signal that is used to make the MR image.

EXERCISES

1 The RF signal emitted by tissue following RF excitation is called
  a. tesla.
  b. free induction decay.
  c. gyromagnetic ratio.
  d. precession.

2 Which of the following is the principal advantage to MRI?
  a. scan time
  b. spatial resolution
  c. enhanced contrast
  d. nonionizing radiation

3 Precession is a
  a. magnetic field.
  b. dipole.
  c. wobble.
  d. top.

4 Relaxation time refers to the
  a. resonant frequency.
  b. time of the transmitted RF pulse.
  c. time required for nuclear spins to return to normal.
  d. time of the gyromagnetic ratio.

5 By convention, the long axis of the patient in an MR imager coincides with the
  a. X axis.
  b. Y axis.
  c. Z axis.
  d. It does not matter.

6 The free induction decay (FID) signal decays
  a. linearly.
  b. as time squared.
  c. as time cubed.
  d. exponentially.

7 Which of the following is measured in mT/cm?
  a. the gyromagnetic rotation
  b. the main magnetic field
  c. the Larmor frequency
  d. the gradient magnetic field

8 Given a strong external magnetic field, some nuclear magnetic dipoles align
  a. with the field.
  b. against the field.
  c. with and against the field.
  d. randomly.

9 _____ is to NMR as Roentgen is to x-ray imaging.
  a. Damadian
  b. Bloch
  c. Lauterbur
  d. Mistretta

10 The net magnetization of a sample
  a. represents all magnetic dipoles.
  b. is a macroscopic quantity.
  c. equals the sum of all nuclear magnetic moments.
  d. all of the above.
11 During nuclear relaxation
  a. the gyromagnetic ratio changes.
  b. radiation is absorbed.
  c. radiation is emitted.
  d. nuclei are stationary.
12 Which of the following would best be described by quantum mechanics?
  a. slipping down a water slide
  b. a gamma ray
  c. a plucked harp string
  d. a swinging pendulum
13 The nucleus of hydrogen has which of the following properties?
  a. mass   c. spin
  b. charge   d. all of the above
14 Net magnetization refers to the
  a. gyromagnetic ratio.
  b. sum of all magnetic moments.
  c. frequency of the Larmor precession.
  d. magnitude of a nuclear dipole.
15 The symbol that indicates the intense main magnetic field is
  a. B_0.   c. $B\gamma$.
  b. B_1.   d. γ.
16 The peaks in an MRI spectrum represent the
  a. Larmor frequency.
  b. gyromagnetic ratio.
  c. magnetic field.
  d. relaxation time.
17 The Larmor frequency is
  a. symbolized by ω.
  b. unique for each nucleus.
  c. a function of the magnetic field.
  d. all of the above.

18 Which of the following nuclei produce the most intense NMR signal?
  a. ^{1}H c. ^{39}K
  b. ^{13}C d. ^{31}P
19 The frequency of precession is
  a. indirectly related to the main magnetic field.
  b. directly related to the gyromagnetic ratio.
  c. indirectly related to the magnetic moment.
  d. indirectly related to the net magnetization.
20 Which of the following best illustrates "in phase"?
  a. a snow ball rolling down a hill
  b. race cars after 50 laps at Indianapolis
  c. a chord struck on a harp
  d. marching soldiers
21 The gyromagnetic ratio has units of
  a. mT/cm.
  b. mT/s.
  c. MHz/s.
  d. MHz/T.
22 Hydrogen nuclei are at equilibrium when
  a. they precess.
  b. they stop precessing.
  c. the relative number aligned with the field is fixed.
  d. they are in random motion.
23 Following RF transmission into the patient, nuclei
  a. are at equilibrium.
  b. stop precessing.
  c. start precessing.
  d. are in an excited state.
24 The gyromagnetic ratio is
  a. a constant regardless of MRI conditions.
  b. a relaxation time.
  c. measured in tesla.
  d. a function of the magnetic field.
25 In a superconducting MR imager the transaxial plane is the _____ plane.
  a. XY   c. YZ
  b. XZ   d. Z

Physical Principles of MRI

MRI PARAMETERS
....
IMAGING PRINCIPLES
....

The return to the normal state of equilibrium with the external magnetic field, B_0, and the accompanying RF emission can be analyzed in terms of three nuclear magnetic resonance imaging (MRI) parameters—spin density (SD), T_1 relaxation, and T_2 relaxation. Each of these parameters, or combinations thereof, can be employed to produce an MR image. This process only works at the resonance frequency of the tissue, called the **Larmor frequency,** which is given by the equation

$$\omega = \gamma B_0$$

where γ is the gyromagnetogyric ratio and B_0 is the external magnetic field strength.

EXERCISES

1 For the spin-lattice relaxation time, the lattice is
   a. an imaginary frame.
   b. the X, Y, Z coordinate system.
   c. surrounding tissue.
   d. a set of adjacent nuclei.
2 The T_2 relaxation time
   a. occurs when all dipoles are in phase.
   b. is due to dephasing magnetic moments.
   c. is caused by dipole-dipole interactions.
   d. is always longer than T_1.
3 The frequency of precession is given by
   a. γ/B.   **c.** $B./\gamma$.
   b. γB.   **d.** ωB.
4 The MR image appearance is determined by which of the following?
   a. T_1 relaxation time
   b. T_2 relaxation time
   c. spin density
   d. all of the above

5 The time required for interactions among nuclear spins to reduce the MRI signal to zero following RF excitation is called _____ time.
   a. T_1 relaxation   **c.** spin density
   b. T_2 relaxation   **d.** Larmor
6 Which of the following is proportional to the number of nuclei that contribute to the MRI signal?
   a. specific absorbed radiation
   b. gyromagnetic ratio
   c. spin density
   d. T_1 relaxation time
7 With a longer and stronger RF pulse,
   a. net magnetization will be shifted further away from the +Z axis.
   b. the volume of tissue imaged will be larger.
   c. scan time will be shorter.
   d. resolution will be better.
8 Which of the following tissues has the longest T_1?
   a. fat   **c.** muscle
   b. water   **d.** bone
9 Which of the following tissues has the shortest T_1?
   a. fat   **c.** muscle
   b. water   **d.** bone
10 Net magnetization can be shifted
   a. 10 degrees.   **c.** 135 degrees.
   b. 90 degrees.   **d.** all of the above.
11 Hydrogen concentration is best indicated by
   a. spin density.
   b. gyromagnetic ratio.
   c. T_1 relaxation.
   d. T_2 relaxation
12 Which of the following is **not** an MRI parameter?
   a. attenuation coefficient
   b. spin-spin relaxation
   c. spin-lattice relaxation
   d. spin density
13 The intensity of the MRI signal is proportional to
   a. temperature.
   b. voltage.
   c. frequency.
   d. magnetic field strength.

14 Spin density relates to hydrogen
  a. frequency.　　　c. density.
  b. gyromagnetic ratio.　d. field strength.
15 The main magnetic field in most imagers is oriented
   _____ to the patient.
  a. lateral　　　　c. transverse
  b. posteroanterior　d. longitudinal
16 To rotate the net magnetization
  a. the gyromagnetic ratio must be changed.
  b. an RF pulse is required.
  c. a gradient magnetic field is required.
  d. the spin density must be increased.
17 Return of M_z to M_0 is controlled by
  a. the spin density.
  b. the T_1 relaxation time.
  c. The T_2 relaxation time.
  d. all of the above.
18 Return of M_{xy} to zero is controlled by
  a. the spin density.
  b. the T_1 relaxation time.
  c. The T_2 relaxation time.
  d. all of the above.
19 After a 90-degree RF pulse
  a. $M_z = M_0$.　　　c. $M_{xy} = -M_0$.
  b. $M_z = -M_0$.　　d. $M_{xy} = M_0$.
20 After a 180-degree RF pulse
  a. $M_z = M_0$.　　　c. $M_{xy} = -M_0$.
  b. $M_z = -M_0$.　　d. $M_{xy} = M_0$.

21 An MRI signal is received from the patient only
   when
  a. the spins are at equilibrium.
  b. there is an M_{xy} greater than zero.
  c. there is an M_z greater than zero.
  d. the gyromagnetic ratio is changing.
22 FID
  a. stands for finally induced detection.
  b. is an RF signal.
  c. is a changing magnetic field.
  d. has units of mT/s.
23 Which of the following expressions is correct?
  a. $T_1 \geq T_2$
  b. $T_2 \geq T_1$
  c. $T_1 \geq SD$
  d. $T_2 \geq SD$
24 Transverse relaxation is also called
  a. gyromagnetic ratio.
  b. spin-lattice relaxation.
  c. lattice-lattice relaxation.
  d. spin-spin relaxation.
25 The principal difference between an MRI spectrometer and an MR imager is the
  a. gyromagnetic ratio.
  b. main magnetic field.
  c. gradient magnetic field.
  d. RF pulse.

MR Equipment and Images

IMAGING MAGNETS
....

SECONDARY COILS
....

The MR imager is similar to a CT scanner in that its three principal parts are the **gantry,** the **computer,** and the **operating console.** The computer is similar to that used in CT scanning except it is bigger and faster. The MRI operating console looks surprisingly similar. The gantry, however, is very different.

There are no moving parts in an MRI gantry. The principal component is the primary magnet. Positioned inside the patient aperture of the primary magnet are shim coils and gradient coils. Inside the gradient coils are a set of RF transmitting and receiving coils called the **RF probe.**

EXERCISES

1 Examination time in MRI is
   a. short compared with CT.
   b. controlled by the T_2 relaxation time.
   c. proportional to the number of signal acquisitions.
   d. proportional to the gyromagnetic ratio.

2 The MRI examination room is usually
   a. shielded to protect employees.
   b. shielded to protect the patient.
   c. shielded to protect the scanner.
   d. not shielded.

3 Some resistive imaging magnets produce fields of 0.2 T. What is the Larmor frequency for protons at this field strength?
   a. 4.3 MHz   **c.** 50 MHz
   b. 8.6 MHz   **d.** 100 MHz

4 Cryogenic refers to very
   a. strong magnetic fields.
   b. low temperatures.
   c. high power consumption.
   d. nonuniform magnetic fields.

5 Which of the following types of magnets is capable of producing the strongest magnetic field?
   a. resistive
   b. superconductive
   c. permanent
   d. it depends on the individual design

6 In the MRi gantry _____ move(s).
   a. the B_0 windings   **c.** the RF probe
   b. the B_1 windings   **d.** nothing

7 The localization of an anatomic structure during an MR examination
   a. requires that the magnetic field be nonuniform.
   b. occurs because the RF is swept through all frequencies.
   c. is better for longer scan times.
   d. is better for shorter scan times.

8 Nearly all MR imagers are of the _____ magnet variety.
   a. permanent   **c.** superconducting
   b. resistive   **d.** hybrid

9 Which of the following methods can be used by the computer to produce an image from the MRI signal?
   a. latent image formation
   b. resonance subtraction
   c. free induction decay
   d. 2DFT

10 Resistive imaging magnets usually have how many coils?
   a. one   **c.** three
   b. two   **d.** four

11 A dewar is associated with
   a. superconducting magnets.
   b. very cold temperatures.
   c. liquid helium.
   d. all of the above.

12 A superconducting magnet for small samples produces a field of 2.0 T. What is the proton Larmor frequency at this field strength?
   a. 12 MHz   **c.** 42 MHz
   b. 21 MHz   **d.** 86 MHz

13 The principal disadvantage to a resistive MR imager is
   a. poor spatial resolution.
   b. operating cost.
   c. low magnetic field.
   d. cryogen requirement.

14 The principal disadvantage to a superconducting MR imager is
   a. capital cost.
   b. operating cost.
   c. high magnetic field.
   d. cryogen requirement.

15 The vacuum chambers in a superconducting magnet provide _____ insulation.
   a. electric
   b. thermal
   c. magnetic
   d. frequency

16 Which of the following would **not** be considered a secondary magnetic coil?
   a. the superconducting magnet
   b. the gradient coils
   c. the RF probe
   d. the shim coils

17 Gradient coils are used to
   a. change a uniform field to nonuniform.
   b. change a nonuniform field to uniform.
   c. intensify the magnetic field.
   d. reduce the magnetic field.

18 Which is coldest?
   a. nitrogen
   b. liquid nitrogen
   c. helium
   d. liquid helium

19 Which type of magnet uses the most electric power?
   a. resistive
   b. superconductive
   c. permanent
   d. it depends on the individual design

20 In the computer an MRI spectrum is obtained from a free induction decay by
   a. subtraction.
   b. Fourier transformation.
   c. back projected reconstruction.
   d. direct imaging.

21 During MRI, the localization of an anatomic structure is due principally to
   a. the primary magnetic field.
   b. a gradient magnetic field.
   c. pulsed RF.
   d. continuous RF.

22 The power supply for an MR imager is most like a
   a. high voltage generator.
   b. high current generator.
   c. high time generator.
   d. all of the above.

23 Which type of magnet costs the most?
   a. resistive
   b. superconductive
   c. permanent
   d. it depends on the individual design

24 The coldest possible temperature is about
   a. −275° C.
   b. 0° K.
   c. −460° F.
   d. all of the above.

25 Most MR imagers have
   a. a single gradient coil.
   b. two gradient coils.
   c. three gradient coils.
   d. three pairs of gradient coils.

Name _____

Date _____

MR Equipment and Images

The images produced in an MR imager are somewhat similar to those obtained with a CT scanner. The spatial resolution is approximately the same, but the contrast for soft tissues is considerably better with MRI. The principal disadvantage to MRI is the examination time, which can extend to 1 hour or more. However, it is possible to obtain data from a total volume of tissue during an examination scan and reconstruct that data in transverse, coronal, sagittal, and oblique planes.

There are no direct biologic hazards to MRI. The three fields used in MRI—the static magnetic field, the time-varying gradient magnetic fields, and the RF pulse—have been studied extensively and show no ill effects at the levels employed.

EXERCISES

1 Which characteristic of an MRI spectrum is used to indicate distance between objects?
   a. its frequency
   b. the distance between peaks
   c. the height of the peaks
   d. the width of the peaks
2 To produce an MRI spectrum,
   a. long scan times are necessary.
   b. short scan times are used.
   c. a nonuniform magnetic field is required.
   d. a uniform magnetic field is required.
3 During MRI the radiologic technologist
   a. must not be in the scan room.
   b. must wear a lead apron.
   c. should wear a wire mesh apron.
   d. may remain in the room.

4 In a normal MR image,
   a. fat will appear black.
   b. skin will appear white.
   c. bone will appear white.
   d. gray/white matter contrast is absent.
5 A hypothesized bioeffect of MRI is
   a. heating.   **c.** conduction.
   b. ionization.   **d.** skin erythema.
6 The spatial resolution of an MR image
   a. is much worse than a CT image.
   b. can be improved by detecting more MRI signals.
   c. is limited by the long scan times.
   d. is reduced with increasing magnetic field strength.
7 The intrinsic contrast of tissue MRI parameters is closest to
   a. 1%.   **c.** 10%.
   b. 5%.   **d.** 20%.
8 Which of the following will always appear black on MRI regardless of the pulse sequence?
   a. kidney   **c.** cortical bone
   b. bone marrow   **d.** skin
9 The fields employed in MRI can be
   a. ionizing.   **c.** distorting.
   b. thermalizing.   **d.** none of the above.
10 Which of the following is **not** one of the physical fields of MRI?
   a. static magnetic field
   b. time varying magnetic field
   c. electromagnetic radiation
   d. ultrasonic radiation
11 Which of the following is **not** a major criterion for evaluating an MR image?
   a. spatial resolution   **c.** quantum mottle
   b. contrast   **d.** noise
12 The main reason to keep MRI examinations short is to minimize _____ unsharpness.
   a. motion   **c.** contrast
   b. geometric   **d.** quantum

13 Acceptable examination time for MRI is principally controlled by
   a. T_1 relaxation time
   b. T_2 relaxation time
   c. spin density
   d. B_0 field intensity

14 Which of the following statements best characterizes MRI?
   a. There are hazardous early effects.
   b. There are hazardous late effects.
   c. It is risky to personnel.
   d. It is safe for personnel.

15 Which of the following is **not** a possible harmful MRI field?
   a. electric field
   b. stationary magnetic field
   c. electromagnetic field
   d. time-varying magnetic field

16 The possible harmful effects of high field MRI are best described by _____ dose-response relationships.
   a. linear, nonthreshold
   b. linear, threshold
   c. nonlinear, nonthreshold
   d. nonlinear, threshold

17 Which MRI field is measured in W/kg?
   a. electric field
   b. stationary magnetic field
   c. electromagnetic field
   d. time-varying magnetic field

18 Which of the following will improve MRI spatial resolution?
   a. higher kVp
   b. more data acquisitions
   c. smaller gantry
   d. larger pixel size

19 MRI should prevail over all other imaging modalities in imaging
   a. an extremity fracture.
   b. cystic lesions of the liver.
   c. microcalcifications.
   d. the lung fields.

20 Probably the greatest hazard associated with MRI is
   a. the main magnetic field.
   b. RF energy.
   c. a projectile.
   d. a cryogen leak.

Name _____

Date _____

Physical Principles of Diagnostic Ultrasound

NATURE OF ULTRASOUND
....
ACOUSTIC INTENSITY AND POWER
....

Diagnostic ultrasound is radiation in the sense that it is energy emitted from a source, transferred through a medium, and attenuated or absorbed by an object. The principal difference between ultrasound and x radiation is ionization. Diagnostic ultrasound is not capable of ionization and therefore, when used for medical imaging, is essentially harmless. That is a major reason for its widespread use in diagnosis.

EXERCISES

1 Which of the following frequencies would include diagnostic ultrasound?
   a. 10 Hz   **c.** 100 kHz
   b. 10 kHz   **d.** 10 MHz

2 Which of the following statements about diagnostic ultrasound is true?
   a. The velocity and frequency are constant regardless of the wavelength.
   b. The velocity is constant regardless of the wavelength.
   c. Velocity increases with increasing frequency.
   d. Velocity decreases with increasing density.

3 Which of the following characteristics of diagnostic ultrasound applies also to x radiation?
   a. It is a wave phenomenon.
   b. Its velocity and frequency are inversely proportional.
   c. Matter must be present for transmission.
   d. Molecular compression and rarefaction occur.

4 Given the various physical characteristics of audible sound, then it is true that
   a. its velocity is the same in all materials.
   b. its velocity depends on its pitch or tone.
   c. the smaller the source, the more collimated the sound.
   d. the higher the frequency, the more collimated the sound.

5 When two ultrasound waves exist in the same medium at the same time,
   a. they will interfere constructively if traveling with the same direction and phase.
   b. standing waves will be produced if they are traveling with the same direction and phase.
   c. standing waves will be produced if they are traveling in the same direction but out of phase.
   d. beat frequencies result from two very different frequencies.

6 Diagnostic ultrasound intensity is measured in
   a. W/cm^2.
   b. rad.
   c. grays.
   d. decibels.

7 If the intensity of beam A is compared with that of beam B, its value in decibels will be
   a. $10 e^{-\mu x}$.
   b. 10 In (A/B).
   c. 10 (log A–log B).
   d. 10 (log B–log A).

8 At audible sound levels,
   a. the threshold of sound is 70 dB.
   b. the threshold of pain is 70 dB.
   c. normal office sounds should be 70 dB.
   d. 0 dB means no sound.

9 Diagnostic ultrasound resonance does **not**
   a. occur in ¼ wavelength.
   b. occur when reflecting surfaces are separated by a ½ wavelength.
   c. occur when reflecting surfaces are separated by any number of ½ wavelengths.
   d. occur when destructive interference patterns exist.

10 Amplitude
   a. increases with increasing frequency.
   b. is a measure of particle displacement in the conducting medium.
   c. is measured in MHz/cm^2.
   d. is the same as ultrasonic power.

11 As ultrasound is transmitted through tissue, its intensity is reduced by all **except**
   a. excitation.   c. scattering.
   b. absorption.   d. divergence.

12 Sound emitted with a frequency of 10 Hz would be called
   a. subsonic.   c. audible.
   b. supersonic.   d. piezo.

13 A 5 μs pulse is emitted every 500 μs. What is the pulse repetition period?
   a. 0.5 ms   c. 500 pulses/s
   b. 5.0 ms   d. 2000 pulses/s

14 Five cycles of 2 MHz ultrasound are emitted per pulse. What is the pulse duration?
   a. 0.5 μs   c. 2.5 μs
   b. 1.0 μs   d. 5.0 μs

15 Five cycles of 1 MHz ultrasound are emitted per pulse with a pulse repetition rate of 1000 pulses/s. What is the duty factor?
   a. 0.001   c. 0.01
   b. 0.005   d. 0.05

16 Ultrasound and x rays differ in which of the following ways?
   a. One is transverse, and the other is phased.
   b. One requires matter, and the other does not.
   c. One has constant frequency, and the other has variable frequency.
   d. One has constant wavelength, and the other has variable wavelength.

17 In which of the following materials is the velocity of ultrasound fastest?
   a. air   c. steel
   b. bone   d. soft tissue

18 A 4.5 MHz ultrasound beam will have a period of
   a. 0.2 μs.   c. 0.4 μs.
   b. 0.22 μs.   d. 0.45 μs.

19 When radiation is emitted isotropically, it is emitted
   a. as a highly collimated beam.
   b. as a broad scattering beam.
   c. with equal intensity in all directions.
   d. with equal velocity in all directions.

20 Which of the following designations will have the highest value for pulse echo ultrasound?
   a. SATA   c. SATP
   b. SPTA   d. SPTP

Physical Principles of Diagnostic Ultrasound

ACOUSTIC REFLECTION
....

ACOUSTIC ABSORPTION AND ATTENUATION
....

Diagnostic ultrasound requires matter such as air or tissue for transmission, whereas x radiation does not. Diagnostic ultrasound is transmitted with a velocity that varies with the transmission medium; x rays have constant velocity. Both types of radiation obey the wave equation so that frequency and wavelength are inversely proportional. However, diagnostic ultrasound is a longitudinal wave, whereas x rays are transverse waves. As the frequency of diagnostic ultrasound increases, its penetrability decreases. The opposite is true with x rays. X-ray intensity is measured in units of roentgens (coulombs/kilogram) and rad (grays), whereas ultrasound intensity is measured in units of milliwatts per square centimer (mW/cm^2) and decibels (dB).

EXERCISES

1 As the frequency of ultrasound increases, its _____ increases.
   a. resolving power
   b. velocity
   c. penetration in tissue
   d. wavelength

2 Acoustic impedance as applied to diagnostic ultrasound increases with increasing
   a. frequency.
   b. wavelength.
   c. mass.
   d. density.

3 When a diagnostic ultrasound beam is incident on a tissue interface,
   a. none of the beam will be transmitted.
   b. none of the beam will be reflected.
   c. reflection can occur only when the beam is at right angles to the interface.
   d. at an angle greater than the critical angle, there will be total reflection.

4 When an acoustic wave is transmitted through soft tissue,
   a. there will be no reduction in intensity.
   b. attenuation will occur.
   c. energy will be transferred by way of ionization and excitation.
   d. energy will be transferred by way of Compton scattering.

5 When an ultrasound beam is attenuated while passing through tissue,
   a. a 3 dB loss is equivalent to a 50% reduction.
   b. a 6 dB loss is equivalent to a 100% reduction.
   c. a 100 dB loss is equivalent to a 100% reduction.
   d. the normal rate is 10 dB/cm/MHz.

6 When a transmitted ultrasonic beam changes direction while passing from one medium to another, this is called
   a. reflection.   **c.** refraction.
   b. diffraction.   **d.** scattering.

7 Which of the following statements is true regarding ultrasound attenuation in matter?
   a. A good rule of thumb is 1 HVL/mm/MHz.
   b. The principal attenuating effects are called recombinant effects.
   c. Acoustic impedance is the produce of density and velocity.
   d. The units of acoustic impedance are mW/cm^2.

8 In the exposure of tissue to ultrasound,

  a. the units of intensity are mW/cm^2.

  b. the unit of ultrasound dose is the rad.

  c. if a beam has a 30 dB gain, that means it is 30% more intense.

  d. if the reflected beam is –40 dB, it is only 0.1% of the transmitted beam.

9 If a reflected wave has to be amplified by a factor of 20 in order to have the same intensity as the transmitted wave, it will be amplified

  a. 3 dB.   **c.** 13 dB.

  b. 10 dB.   **d.** 20 dB.

10 Acoustic reflectivity is expressed by which of the following equations?

  a. $R = \dfrac{Z_1 \times Z_2}{Z_1 + Z_2}$ **c.** $R = \dfrac{Z_1 - Z}{Z_1 + Z_2}$

  b. $R = \left(\dfrac{Z_1 \times Z_2}{Z_1 + Z_2}\right)^2$ **d.** $R = \left(\dfrac{Z_1 - Z_2}{Z_1 + Z_2}\right)^2$

11 Acoustic reflectivity

  a. is equal to density times velocity.

  b. equals 100 if $Z_1 = Z_2$.

  c. is higher for an air-soft tissue interface than for a bone-soft tissue interface.

  d. increases with increasing frequency.

12 The decibel is defined as

  a. 1/10 log (Ir/It).   **c.** 1/10 log (It/Ir).

  b. 10 log (Ir/It).   **d.** 10 log (It/Ir).

13 The threshold for pain induced by audible sound is approximately

  a. 70 dB.   **c.** 120 dB.

  b. 100 dB.   **d.** 140 dB.

14 One rayl is equal to 1

  a. kg m^{-3}.   **c.** kg m^{-2}s^{-1}.

  b. kg m^{2}s^{-1}.   **d.** kg m^{-3}s^{-1}.

15 What is the percent reflectivity at a blood-brain interface if the acoustic impedance of blood is 1.61×10^6 rayl and brain is 1.58×10^6 rayl?

  a. 0.00009%   **c.** 0.9%

  b. 0.009%   **d.** 9%

16 The critical angle of the incident ultrasound beam is

  a. 0 degrees.

  b. 90 degrees.

  c. totally transmitting.

  d. dependent on the velocity of sound in each medium.

17 Reflections from a smooth interface are called

  a. backscatter.

  b. isotropic.

  c. specular.

  d. initial.

18 Which of the following terms is **not** employed to describe both MRI and diagnostic ultrasound?

  a. scattering   **c.** transverse

  b. relaxation time   **d.** frequency

19 Ultrasound attenuation occurs because of all the following except

  a. electronic excitation.   **c.** scattering.

  b. absorption.   **d.** divergence.

20 Which of the following tissues will attenuate ultrasound the most?

  a. lung   **c.** muscle

  b. fat   **d.** bone

Name _____

Date _____

Diagnostic Ultrasound Instrumentation and Operation

THE ULTRASOUND TRANSDUCER
....
ULTRASONIC BEAM
....

A diagnostic ultrasound unit has two principal parts—the transducer assembly and the console. The transducer assembly contains the piezoelectric crystals properly encased in its support mechanism for hand-held manipulation and orientation. The console contains the associated electronics for operational control and image display.

The ultrasound transducer emits either a continuous wave or pulsed ultrasound. Both types of ultrasound beams have characteristically shaped fields, consisting of a near field and a far field. The size and shape of both fields are controlled by the diameter of the transducer and its frequency of operation. The fields can also be controlled by shaping the transducer face and by using an acoustic lens. The shape of the ultrasound beam and its frequency of operation determine the resolution capabilities of the system. **Axial resolution** is the ability to identify closely separated objects that lie on the axis of the ultrasound beam. **Lateral resolution** refers to the plane perpendicular to the axis of the beam. Typically, abdominal ultrasound systems have an axial resolution of 2 mm and a lateral resolution of 2 cm.

EXERCISES

1 The principle on which the ultrasound transducer operates is the _____ effect.
   - **a.** photoelectric
   - **b.** crystalline
   - **c.** piezoelectric
   - **d.** transducer
2 The piezoelectric crystal is often made of
   - **a.** aluminum.
   - **b.** calcium tungstate.
   - **c.** PZT.
   - **d.** lithium fluoride.

3 Which of the following is a component of an ultrasound transducer?
   - **a.** an antiscatter grid
   - **b.** beam-defining collimator
   - **c.** backing material
   - **d.** gadolinium oxysulfide
4 A pulse echo system is designed to emit a pulse 3 μs long followed by a 497 μs dead time. What is the pulse repetition rate?
   - **a.** 1 kHz
   - **b.** 2 kHz
   - **c.** 3 kHz
   - **d.** 3 μs
5 The resolution of a diagnostic ultrasound system is
   - **a.** usually best perpendicular to the central axis at the beam.
   - **b.** usually best along the central axis of the beam.
   - **c.** independent of the length of the ultrasound pulse.
   - **d.** independent of the frequency of operation.
6 The thickness of a piezoelectric crystal is closest to
   - **a.** 10 μm.
   - **b.** 100 μm.
   - **c.** 1 mm.
   - **d.** 10 mm.
7 Best image resolution is obtained
   - **a.** in the near field.
   - **b.** at the near field–far field transition.
   - **c.** in the far field.
   - **d.** beyond the far field.
8 The Fraunhofer zone is the
   - **a.** image plane.
   - **b.** image focus.
   - **c.** near field.
   - **d.** far field.
9 Best axial resolution is obtained with
   - **a.** highest frequency and shortest pulse width.
   - **b.** highest frequency and longest pulse width.
   - **c.** lowest frequency and shortest pulse width.
   - **d.** lowest frequency and longest pulse width.
10 Best lateral resolution is obtained with
   - **a.** highest frequency and smallest transducer.
   - **b.** highest frequency and largest transducer.
   - **c.** lowest frequency and smallest transducer.
   - **d.** lowest frequency and largest transducer.

11 The active element of the diagnostic ultrasound transducer

   I. converts electric energy into mechanical energy.

   II. converts mechanical energy into electric energy.

   III. converts frequency into wavelength.

   a. I   **c.** I and II

   b. II   **d.** I, II, and III

12 Which of the following statements **best** characterizes the ultrasound beam?

   a. If the crystal diameter is large, a plane wave front is formed.

   b. Best resolution is obtained in the far field.

   c. As frequency is increased, the near field is lengthened.

   d. As the transducer diameter is increased, the near field shrinks.

13 The lateral resolution of the diagnostic ultrasound system is

   a. called the azimuthal resolution.

   b. better in the near field.

   c. better with lower frequency.

   d. better than axial resolution.

14 In fabricating a transducer,

   a. the piezoelectric crystal is exposed bare for maximum skin coupling.

   b. electrodes are wired to one face of the piezoelectric crystal.

   c. a backing block is used to reduce reverberation.

   d. a backing block is used to increase intensity.

15 Ultrasonic pulses are

   a. poorly transmitted by liquids.

   b. poorly transmitted by solids.

   c. partially reflected at interfaces between two liquids.

   d. totally transmitted at interfaces between two liquids.

16 The intensity of ultrasound is most uniform

   a. just beyond the transducer face.

   b. in the near field.

   c. at the near field–far field transition.

   d. in the far field.

17 The quality factor is principally a function of

   a. resonant frequency and acoustic impedance.

   b. resonant frequency and bandwidth.

   c. bandwidth and pulse duration.

   d. bandwidth and acoustic impedance.

18 Which of the following primarily depends on the pulse duration?

   a. axial resolution

   b. lateral resolution

   c. contrast resolution

   d. reflectivity

19 A necessary condition to produce diagnostic ultrasound echoes is

   a. sound frequency of 1 to 15 mHz.

   b. sound wavelength less than 1 mm.

   c. differences of acoustic impedance.

   d. differences in atomic number.

20 A diagnostic ultrasound beam passing through the body can

   a. be totally attenuated.

   b. be totally transmitted.

   c. produce fever.

   d. produce ionization.

Diagnostic Ultrasound Instrumentation and Operation

OPERATIONAL MODES
....
BIOLOGIC EFFECTS
....

There are four principal modes that are employed in diagnostic ultrasound. **A-mode** was the first to be developed and measures distance much like SONAR. **B-mode** is the imaging mode that is nearly universally employed. **M-mode** is used to evaluate interface motion as in echocardiography. **Doppler mode** is also used for motion studies as in fetal heart monitoring and blood flow studies.

The biologic response of tissue to ultrasound follows a threshold, nonlinear dose-response relationship. The threshold is at least 10 times the intensity employed in diagnostic ultrasound. No adverse human responses have ever been observed following diagnostic ultrasound.

EXERCISES

1 When operating in the M-mode, M stands for
  a. module.
  b. major.
  c. motion.
  d. magnitude.
2 When operating in the Doppler mode,
  a. one is employing the pulse-echo technique.
  b. meaningful information can only be obtained from moving interfaces.
  c. the principal application is the measurement of midline shifts of the brain.
  d. the equipment is more expensive than B-mode imaging.

3 Of the number of techniques for displaying an ultrasound signal,
  a. abdominal imaging is usually done real time.
  b. echocardiography usually employs B-mode.
  c. A-mode is most often used in obstetrics.
  d. Doppler mode produces the best image.
4 In pulse-echo A-mode, which of the following represents the distance between blips?
  a. velocity $\times$ ½ time to interface
  b. velocity $\times$ time to interface
  c. velocity $\times$ 2 times to interface
  d. velocity $\times$ 4 times to interface
5 What is the Doppler shift frequency in soft tissue when the transmitted frequency is 3 MHz and the interface has a velocity of 10 cm/s?
  a. 20 Hz
  b. 154 Hz
  c. 390 Hz
  d. approximately 3MHz
6 A-mode display stands for _____ mode.
  a. axial   **c.** alternate
  b. amplitude   **d.** action
7 In compound B-mode imaging, the B stands for
  a. brightness.   **c.** bulk.
  b. body.   **d.** bistable.
8 Real-time ultrasound imaging
  a. shows better lateral resolution than B-mode.
  b. cannot be accomplished with a single transducer.
  c. cannot be accomplished with a sequential linear array.
  d. requires multiple transducers if a phased array is used.
9 Which of the following images **does not** use pulse-echo ultrasound?
  a. real-time   **c.** A-mode
  b. Doppler mode   **d.** B-mode

10 Which type of scan image is a sector type?
   a. linear scan   c. compound scan
   b. phased array scan d. Doppler scan
11 Bistable is a term that refers to
   a. electronic drift. c. black and white.
   b. transducer drift. d. gray scale.
12 Gray scale imaging is possible principally because of the
   a. microprocessor.   c. D/A convertor.
   b. A/D convertor.   d. scan converter.
13 According to the Doppler effect, objects that are moving toward each other appear to have
   a. higher frequency. c. lower frequency.
   b. equal frequency.   d. negative frequency.

14 A 2.25 MHz transducer detects reflected radiation at 2.20 MHz. The Doppler shift frequency is _____, and the interface is moving _____.
   a. 4.45, closer
   b. 4.45, away
   c. 0.05, closer
   d. 0.05, away
15 A duplex scanner is one that incorporates
   a. real time and dead time.
   b. real time and Doppler.
   c. Doppler and segmental arrays.
   d. segmental and sequential arrays.

Name _____

Date _____

Fundamental Principles of Radiobiology

FROM MOLECULES TO HUMANS
....
HUMAN BIOLOGY
....

To understand the effects of radiation on the body, one needs a basic knowledge of human anatomy and physiology. The body is an extremely organized system that is composed mostly of water. Radiation interactions at the atomic level are transferred through the various levels of organization and can result in visible radiation effects.

The single most important molecule in the body is deoxyribonucleic acid (DNA). DNA contains all of the genes and is the single molecule responsible for controlling the body's growth, development, and function. Nevertheless, if water and oxygen were not present, it would take considerably more radiation than it does to produce damage in the DNA molecule.

It is assumed that the principal type of radiation damage is to the cell's control center, the DNA, resulting in errors in metabolism that can produce a visible radiation effect. Disruption or alteration in macromolecular synthesis is presumed to be the principal effect of this type.

EXERCISES

1 An example of a macromolecule is
   a. water.
   b. salt.
   c. a lipid.
   d. an amino acid.

2 The breaking down of macromolecules into eventual end products, water and carbon dioxide, is
   a. anabolism.
   b. catabolism.
   c. metabolism.
   d. homeostasis.

3 In the normal configuration of the human cell,
   a. both the cytoplasm and the nucleus are surrounded by membranes.
   b. macromolecules are synthesized in the mitochondria.
   c. macromolecules are digested in the ribosomes.
   d. lysosomes contain nucleic acid.

4 Which of the following is part of interphase?
   a. prophase
   b. protein synthesis phase
   c. DNA synthesis phase
   d. telophase

5 The body is organized in such a way that
   a. organs combine to form tissues.
   b. tissues and organs are integrated into an organ system.
   c. mature cells are called stem cells.
   d. epithelial cells are usually found inside organs.

6 Which of the following molecules is a protein?
   a. a salt
   b. an amino acid
   c. a nucleic acid
   d. an enzyme

7 Lipids are
   a. an energy storehouse.
   b. electrical conductors.
   c. micromolecules.
   d. inorganic compounds.

8 In metaphase, the chromosomes
   a. split apart to form sister members.
   b. line up along the equator of the cell.
   c. remain dominant.
   d. ooze through the cellular membrane.

9 Lipids store
   a. salt.
   b. antibodies.
   c. enzymes.
   d. fat.

10 At what phase in mitosis are the chromosomes most visible?
   a. interphase   **c.** prophase
   b. anaphase   **d.** metaphase

11 Messenger RNA (mRNA) moves from _____ to _____.
   a. cytoplasm, nucleus
   b. cytoplasm, mitochondria
   c. nucleus, mitochondria
   d. nucleus, ribosome

12 Which element is most abundant in the body?
   a. calcium   **c.** hydrogen
   b. carbon   **d.** oxygen

13 Organic molecules
   a. are not essential for life.
   b. contain nitrogen.
   c. contain carbon.
   d. include DNA.

14 The principal component of a protein is
   a. an amino acid.   **c.** a lipid.
   b. a peptide bond.   **d.** an enzyme.

15 Which kind of molecule is most abundant in the body?
   a. water   **c.** lipids
   b. proteins   **d.** carbohydrates

16 The general formula $(C_nH_nO_n)$ represents
   a. carbohydrates.   **c.** nucleic acids.
   b. lipids.   **d.** proteins.

17 Polysaccharides are
   a. carbohydrates.   **c.** nucleic acids.
   b. lipids.   **d.** proteins.

18 Which of the following base pairs is allowed?
   a. adenine-cytosine   **c.** thymine-guanine
   b. cytosine-thymine   **d.** guanine-cytosine

19 The nucleolus, in particular, contains
   a. DNA.   **c.** proteins.
   b. RNA.   **d.** lipids.

20 Which of the following is **not** part of mitosis?
   a. anaphase   **c.** metaphase
   b. interphase   **d.** prophase

21 The nitrogenous organic base found in RNA but not in DNA is
   a. adenine.   **c.** cytosine.
   b. guanine.   **d.** urocil.

22 The nucleic acids of the human body
   a. are found only in the nucleus.
   b. consist of DNA and RNA.
   c. are macromolecules.
   d. consist of peptide bonds.

23 Which of the following is **not** associated with carbohydrates?
   a. glucose   **c.** monosaccharides
   b. starch   **d.** protein

24 In describing the various cells of the body, which of the following is false?
   a. Hair and nail cells are somatic.
   b. The oogonium undergoes meiosis.
   c. Skin cells proliferate by means of meiosis.
   d. The spermatogonium is a genetic cell.

25 Which of the following types of tissue would be classified as highly radiosensitive?
   a. skin   **c.** bone marrow
   b. muscle   **d.** growing bone

26 The first step in producing a radiation response is
   a. molecular alteration.
   b. latent effect.
   c. ionization.
   d. manifest lesion.

27 Human responses to radiation that do not appear for years are called _____ effects.
   a. late   **c.** linear
   b. law   **d.** large

28 Most radiobiologic research is conducted with animals. Approximately how many human population groups have shown radiation effects?
   a. none
   b. less than 5
   c. 10
   d. more than 10

29 Homeostasis refers to the _____ of the body.
   a. atomic composition
   b. molecular composition
   c. constancy of the internal environment
   d. water content

30 Which of the following is **not** a protein?
   a. hormone
   b. glycerol
   c. antibody
   d. enzyme

Fundamental Principles of Radiobiology

LAW OF BERGONIÉ AND TRIBONDEAU
....
PHYSICAL FACTORS AFFECTING RADIOSENSITIVITY
....

Linear energy transfer (LET) expresses numerically in keV/μm the rate at which energy is transferred from ionizing radiation to soft tissue. In general, high LET radiation is more damaging than low LET radiation.

Different types of ionizing radiation have different LET, and the efficiency for producing a given response is related to LET. Such efficiency is measured by the relative biologic effectiveness (RBE), which is determined experimentally. Generally, radiations with a high LET have high RBE. The precise definition of RBE follows:

$$RBE = \frac{\text{Dose of standard radiation necessary to produce a given effect}}{\text{Dose of test radiation necessary to produce the same effect}}$$

EXERCISES

1 Which of the following is **not** part of the law of Bergonié and Tribondeau?
   a. Stem cells are radiosensitive.
   b. A fetus is less radiosensitive than an adult.
   c. When metabolism is high, so is radiosensitivity.
   d. When proliferation rate is high, so is radiosensitivity.
2 The law of Bergonié and Tribondeau states that
   a. the older a cell, the more radiosensitive it is.
   b. metabolic activity results in radioprotection.
   c. radiosensitivity increases with proliferation rate.
   d. radiosensitivity increases with increasing hypoxia.

3 The response of tissue to radiation is principally a function of
   a. dose.
   b. LET.
   c. RBE.
   d. fractionation.
4 The relative biologic effectiveness (RBE)
   a. is a numeric description of the resistance of biologic tissue to radiation damage.
   b. increases as x-ray energy increases.
   c. is equal to 1.0 for orthovoltage x rays.
   d. is equal to 3.0 for diagnostic x rays.
5 The law of Bergonié and Tribondeau relates to which of the following?
   a. radiosensitivity and cellular differentiation
   b. radiocurability and tumor size
   c. radiosensitivity and oxygenation
   d. radioresistance and cell lethality
6 Relative biologic effectiveness
   a. is a ratio of effects needed to produce a given dose.
   b. is a ratio of effects produced at a given dose.
   c. has a value of 1 to 100.
   d. is higher for high LET radiation than for low LET radiation.
7 Linear energy transfer is measured in
   a. rad.
   b. keV/rad.
   c. keV/μm.
   d. gray.
8 Which of the following has the highest LET?
   a. alpha particles
   b. cobalt 60 gamma rays
   c. protons
   d. neutrons
9 The maximum value of RBE is about
   a. 0.5.   c. 2.
   b. 1.   d. 3.

10 Dose fractionation is less effective than a single dose because
   a. recovery occurs between doses.
   b. fractionated doses are lower.
   c. dose fractionation has a low LET.
   d. dose fractionation has a low oxygen enhancement ratio (OER).

11 The OER
   a. is independent of LET.
   b. is highest for low LET radiation.
   c. is higher for protons than for photons.
   d. has a maximum value of about 10.

12 Linear energy transfer is useful for expressing radiation
   a. dose.   c. quality.
   b. response.   d. quantity.

13 Linear energy transfer is to radiobiology what _____ is to radiation protection.
   a. dose   c. quality factor
   b. response   d. quantity factor

14 Which of the following has the lowest LET?
   a. cobalt 60 gamma rays
   b. diagnostic x rays
   c. alpha particles
   d. fast neutrons

15 The difference between dose fractionation and protraction is
   a. dose.
   b. dose rate.
   c. dose integration.
   d. dose accumulation.

16 Which of the following is considered a physical dose-modifying factor?
   a. age   c. protraction
   b. recovery   d. oxygen

17 Which of the following is considered a biologic dose-modifying factor?
   a. linear energy transfer
   b. the oxygen effect
   c. dose per fraction
   d. geometry

18 Dose fractionation is less effective than an equal single dose because of
   a. reduced LET.
   b. reduced OER.
   c. recovery and repair.
   d. oxygenation and proliferation.

19 Which of the following does **not** describe a purpose for radiation dose-response relationships?
   a. to predict the therapeutic value of a radiation dose
   b. to predict the value of a radiologic examination
   c. to predict the harmful effects of radiation after an accidental exposure
   d. to establish risk estimates after diagnostic exposures

20 Since different types of radiation produce different degrees of effect for the same dose,
   a. the varying degrees of effect can be measured quantitatively by the OER.
   b. the quantitative value is determined by dividing the dose of standard radiation necessary to produce the same effect by the dose of test radiation.
   c. generally speaking, low LET radiation produces more damage per unit dose than high LET radiation.
   d. the value of this measure of effect is about 10 keV/µm for diagnostic x rays.

Name _____

Date _____

Fundamental Principles of Radiobiology

BIOLOGIC FACTORS AFFECTING RADIOSENSITIVITY
....
RADIATION DOSE-RESPONSE RELATIONSHIPS
....

Biologic material that is irradiated in the presence of oxygen (aerobic) has a higher degree of response to a given dose of radiation than that irradiated under reduced levels or absence of oxygen (hypoxic, anoxic, or anaerobic). The magnitude of this difference in response is called the **oxygen enhancement ratio (OER)** and is defined as follows:

$$OER = \frac{\text{Radiation dose necessary to produce an effect under anaerobic conditions}}{\text{Radiation dose necessary to produce same effect under aerobic conditions}}$$

Radiobiology is the science of investigation into the action of ionizing radiation on living cells and tissues. Most radiobiologic investigations are designed to establish the nature of radiation dose-response relationships. Such relationships can generally be classified as either **linear** or **nonlinear** and **threshold** or **nonthreshold**. Knowledge of the precise nature of the radiation dose-response relationship allows one to predict the extent of human response following a given dose of radiation. Conversely, after accidental exposure, the radiation dose may be estimated by the degree of response.

EXERCISES

1 Radiation-induced damage in biologic tissue
   a. is greater in the presence of oxygen.
   b. is irreversible.
   c. is caused by basic interaction at tissue level.
   d. generally results in only latent effects.

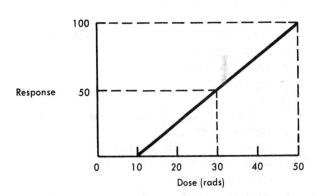

2 When one considers the biologic modifying factors to radiation response,
   a. age is not a factor.
   b. oxygen tension is not a factor.
   c. pharmaceutical agents are capable of only sensitization.
   d. pharmaceutical agents are capable of both sensitization and protection.

3 Given the graph above on radiation dose and effect, what is the value of the threshold dose?
   a. 0 rad   **c.** 30 rad
   b. 10 rad   **d.** 50 rad

4 The least sensitive time in life to radiation is in
   a. utero.   **c.** adulthood.
   b. childhood.   **d.** old age.

5 Which of the following effects should exhibit a threshold type of dose-response relationship?
   a. lung cancer   **c.** thyroid cancer
   b. leukemia   **d.** cataracts

6 When a dose-response relationship intercepts the response axis at a positive value,
   a. the radiation has a high LET.
   b. the response at the intercept is not related to radiation.
   c. the relationship is linear.
   d. the relationship is nonlinear.

7 Which of the following effects should follow a sigmoid type of dose-response relationship?
   a. leukemia
   b. life-shortening
   c. tissue atrophy
   d. death

8 Radiation protection guides are based on which type of dose-response relationship?
   a. linear, threshold
   b. linear, nonthreshold
   c. nonlinear, nonthreshold
   d. linear, quadratic

9 The late effects of diagnostic x rays probably follow which type of dose-response relationship?
   a. linear, threshold
   b. linear, nonthreshold
   c. nonlinear, nonthreshold
   d. linear, quadratic

10 A wide error bar on a data point indicates
   a. great confidence.
   b. little confidence.
   c. high LET.
   d. low LET.

11 The linear, quadratic dose-response relationship
   a. applies to high LET radiation.
   b. holds for high RBE radiation.
   c. suggests a higher response at low doses than the linear, nonthreshold model.
   d. suggests a lower response at low doses than the linear, nonthreshold model.

12 The OER, RBE, and LET are interrelated. Therefore which of the following statements is true?
   a. Diagnostic x rays have an LET of about 2.5 keV/μm and an OER of 3.
   b. Diagnostic x rays have a lower LET than cobalt 60 gamma rays.
   c. High LET radiations have low RBE.
   d. High RBE radiations have high OER.

13 Which of the following factors has no influence on response to radiation exposure?
   a. dose protraction   c. sex
   b. age   d. occupation

14 Which of the following has the highest OER?
   a. cobalt 60 gamma rays
   b. diagnostic x rays
   c. neutrons
   d. alpha particles

15 Humans are most sensitive to radiation
   a. preconception.   c. during childhood.
   b. in utero.   d. during old age.

16 When an irradiated cell dies before the next mitosis, it is called _____.
   a. cytogenetic death   c. interphase death
   b. clonal death   d. mitotic death

17 Which of the following is a radiation sensitizer?
   a. cysteine   c. water
   b. sulfhydryls   d. vitamin K

18 A linear, nonthreshold dose-response relationship
   a. suggests that even the smallest dose may be risky.
   b. states that there is a range of very low doses that are totally safe.
   c. is shaped like an S.
   d. has a maximum response followed by a minimum.

19 A sigmoid radiation dose-response relationship can be
   a. linear.   c. linear, nonthreshold.
   b. threshold.   d. linear, threshold.

20 When a linear, nonthreshold dose-response relationship intersects the response axis at zero dose, that means
   a. it is not really linear.
   b. it is not really nonthreshold.
   c. recovery and repair have occurred.
   d. there is a natural incidence of the response.

WORKSHEET 99

Molecular and Cellular Radiobiology

IRRADIATION OF MACROMOLECULES
....
RADIOLYSIS OF WATER
....
DIRECT AND INDIRECT EFFECT
....

When irradiated in vitro, that is, outside the body, molecules are relatively insensitive to radiation damage. However, when irradiated in vivo, that is, inside the body, even relatively minor molecular damage can produce visible and sometimes significant effects at the whole body level. Irradiation of macromolecules results in main-chain scission, cross-linking, or point lesions. The macromolecules of principal importance in vivo are DNA and proteins.

The irradiation of water produces free radicals, hydrogen peroxide (H_2O_2), and the hydroperoxyl radical (HO_2), each of which is considered a harmful molecular by-product.

If the radiation interacts with a macromolecule of importance, the subsequent effect is said to be **direct.** On the other hand, if the radiation interacts with water and thus creates one of the harmful by-products, which then diffuses through the cell to the macromolecule, the subsequent effect is said to be **indirect.**

EXERCISES

1 Of the various macromolecules sensitive to radiation damage, _____ is (are) considered the most sensitive.
   a. proteins   **c.** DNA
   b. free radicals   **d.** RNA

2 After a low radiation dose, most cellular radiation damage that results in a late total body effect occurs because of
   a. cross-linking.   **c.** point lesions.
   b. reduced viscosity.   **d.** in vitro effects.

3 The biologically reactive molecular by-products formed during the radiolysis of water are thought to be
   a. O_2 and H_2.   **c.** H* and OH*.
   b. H_2O.   **d.** SH compounds.

4 Usually, radiation interacts with DNA
   a. directly.   **c.** and causes cell death.
   b. indirectly.   **d.** and causes irreversible damage.

5 Free radical ions are associated with biologic injury induced by which of the following types of radiation?
   a. diagnostic x-ray   **c.** microwave radiation
   b. ultrasound   **d.** laser radiation

6 Chromosome aberrations can
   I. lead to cell death.
   II. result in abnormal metabolic activity.
   III. occur in a genetic cell.
   a. I and II   **c.** II and III
   b. II   **d.** I, II, and III

7 Which of the following statements is true about target theory?
   I. A key sensitive molecule exists.
   II. A hit is a microphysical event.
   III. Radiation interaction with targets is random.
   a. I and II   **c.** II and III
   b. II   **d.** I, II, and III

8 When water is irradiated, products of the initial interaction are
   a. OH* and H*.   **c.** H_2O and e^-.
   b. OH* and e^-.   **d.** HOH+ and e^-.

9 Which of the following is an example of anabolism?
   a. the radiolysis of water   **c.** protein synthesis
   b. main-chain scission   **d.** transfer RNA

10 An atom or molecule having an unpaired electron in its outer shell is called
   a. a bremsstrahlung atom.
   b. a free radical.
   c. a recoil proton.
   d. an ion pair.

11 The genetic code of DNA
   a. is transcribed by mRNA.
   b. consists of sets of five base pairs.
   c. is duplicated during G_2 phase.
   d. consists of codons only at S phase.
12 Of the following types of damage to DNA, which is not considered sructural?
   a. severance of one side rail
   b. severance of both side rails
   c. change of a base
   d. separation of bases
13 A comparison of the G_2 with G_1 phase indicates that
   a. they both require the same time.
   b. there is twice the DNA in G_1 as in G_2.
   c. there is twice the DNA in G_2 as in G_1.
   d. G_2 is twice as long as G_1.
14 Radiation-induced changes in DNA that result in genetic damage follow which type of dose-response relationship?
   a. linear, threshold
   b. linear, nonthreshold
   c. nonlinear, nonthreshold
   d. nonlinear, threshold
15 Which of the following is a free radical?
   a. e^- c. H_2O_2
   b. HOH^- d. HO_2*
16 When molecules are irradiated
   a. inside the cell or body, they are irradiated in vitro.
   b. in suspension in a tube, they are irradiated in vivo.
   c. in suspension, they are irradiated in solution.
   d. in solution in vitro, they are in free radicals.
17 DNA synthesis occurs during
   a. metaphase.   c. the S phase.
   b. the G_2 phase.   d. the G phase.
18 When pure DNA molecules are irradiated in vivo, the types of damage produced include
   I.   main-chain scission.
   II. free radical formation.
   III. point lesions.
   a. I and II   c. I and III
   b. II and III   d. I, II, and III
19 Which of the following effects are due to irradiation of chromosomes?
   I.   free radical formation
   II. cytogenetic damage
   III. genetic damage
   a. I and II   c. I and III
   b. II and III   d. I, II, and III
20 When water is irradiated, which of the following can occur?
   I.   It can become ionized.
   II. Ion pairs can form.
   III. An OH* radical can form.
   a. I and II   c. I and III
   b. II and III   d. I, II, and III

21 Radiation effects at the total body level occur mainly because of
   a. irradiation in vitro.
   b. indirect effect.
   c. alterations in viscosity.
   d. direct effect.
22 The effect of irradiating molecular DNA may be
   a. to induce radioactivity.
   b. cross-linking.
   c. increased viscosity.
   d. free radical formation.
23 Which of the following will occur in DNA molecules as a result of irradiation?
   I.   hydrogen-bond breakage
   II. H_2O_2 formation
   III. a single- or double-strand break
   a. I and II   c. II and III
   b. I and III   d. I, II, and III
24 Radiation may interfere with DNA synthesis by
   a. G_1 effect: failure to commence DNA synthesis because of damage during G_1 period.
   b. S effect: interference with mitosis in progress.
   c. G_2 effect: failure to initiate DNA synthesis because of blocking of preceding mitosis.
   d. causing cells to omit some phases of the cell cycle.
25 At low radiation dose _____ may result in late radiation effects.
   a. cross-linking   c. point mutations
   b. transmutation   d. double strand breaks

Ionization of water will yield the following:

$$H_2O \xrightarrow{\text{Energy}} H_2O^+ + e^-$$

H_2O^+ is unstable and instantly produces two subunits as follows:

H_2O^+	$H^+ + OH*$
(A)	(B) (C)

and

$H_2O + e^-$	H_2O^-
(D) (E)	(F)

followed by

H_2O^-	$H* + OH^-$
(G)	(H) (I)

Match the ionization products given above (labeled A through I) with the descriptions below:
26 Hydrogen ion   _____
27 Hydroxyl free radical   _____
28 Positive ionized water   _____
29 Hydroxyl ion   _____
30 Hydrogen free radical   _____

WORKSHEET 100

Molecular and Cellular Radiobiology

TARGET THEORY
....
CELL SURVIVAL KINETICS
....
LET, RBE, AND OER
....

Radiation effects at the total body level, whether somatic or genetic, occur because of radiation damage to cells. Cellular damage, in turn, occurs because of molecular responses to radiation. It is thought that certain critical molecules constitute sensitive targets within the cell, each of which must be inactivated to produce the ultimate response—cell lethality. Such a statement is the result of a body of theoretic considerations and experimental data known as the **target theory.** In its simplest form, the target theory states that certain discrete intracellular targets, presumably portions of the DNA, must be inactivated for the cell to die.

The radiation dose-response relationship for cell lethality is **nonlinear** and **nonthreshold.** Depending on the type of cell and the conditions of irradiation, cell survival will follow either the single-target, single-hit model or the multitarget, single-hit model of radiation-induced lethality. These models are the consequence of target theory and incorporate parameters useful for measuring the efficiency of various conditions of irradiation and the sensitivity of different types of cells.

D_{37} = Radiation dose following which 37% of the cells will survive, while, conversely, 63% will die

D_0 = Mean lethal dose; similar to D_{37} but applicable only to the straight-line portion of the multitarget, single-hit model

n = Extrapolation number

D_Q = Threshold dose or shoulder dose

The intersection between the extrapolated straight-line portion of the cell survival curve and the ordinate (y axis) is sometimes referred to as the target number rather than the extrapolation number. D_Q is the intersection between the extrapolated straight-line portion of the cell survival curve and 100% survival. D_Q is a measure of the ability of the cell to sustain sublethal damage and recover. D_{37} and D_0 are measures of the cell's sensitivity to radiation.

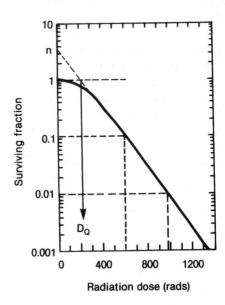

EXERCISES

1 If undifferentiated cells are irradiated in vivo, such cells are
   a. resistant to radiation. **c.** easy to replace.
   b. sensitive to radiation. **d.** difficult to replace.
2 Which of the following phases of the cell cycle is considered most resistant?
   a. M phase   **c.** early S phase
   b. G_1 phase   **d.** late S phase

3 Using cell survival curves, the measure of cell radiosensitivity is

a. n. **c.** the slope of the curve.
b. D_Q. **d.** RBE.

4 For the cell survival curve shown in the graph on p. 219, the extrapolation number is closest to

a. 0. **c.** 2.
b. 1. **d.** 4.

5 To explain radiation effects on living cells, the target theory states that

a. only one target exists within the cell.
b. a target can receive a hit by direct or indirect effect.
c. not all targets must be hit for cell death.
d. there is only one kind of target.

6 The probability of human cell death can be computed

a. if only D_0 is known. **c.** if only n is known.
b. if only D_Q is known. **d.** using the Poisson distribution.

7 If a dose equal to D_{37} were **uniformly** distributed, what percentage of cells would survive?

a. 0% **c.** 63%
b. 37% **d.** 100%

8 If a dose equal to D_{37} were **randomly** distributed, what percentage of cells would die?

a. 0% **c.** 63%
b. 37% **d.** 100%

9 The multitarget, single-hit model

a. is not a part of target theory.
b. presumes a threshold.
c. is characterized by D_{37}.
d. contains D_0, the threshold dose.

10 The difference in generation time among different types of cells is due mainly to the length of the

a. phase. **c.** S phase.
b. G_1 phase. **d.** G_2 phase.

11 Which of the following factors does **not** influence the radiation response of mammalian cells?

a. LET **c.** the presence of
b. the stage of the cell oxygen
in its cycle **d.** the sex of the cell

12 In cellular radiobiology

a. in vitro studies employ cells grown and irradiated in the body.
b. single cells are sometimes allowed to grow into colonies.
c. a cell colony is considered to exist following the first cell division.
d. only cells irradiated inside the body can be used.

13 According to the multitarget model of cell lethality,

a. cells have more than one critical target, each of which has to be inactivated for cell death.
b. the critical target is considered to be the RNA.
c. the cell can accumulate radiation dose.
d. only cell death can be measured with accuracy.

14 In the graph above showing two cell survival curves,

a. both curves have the same D_Q.
b. both curves have the same mean lethal dose.
c. both curves have the same D_{37}.
d. curve A could represent oxygenated cells if curve B represented anoxic cells.

15 According to target theory,

a. a hit can occur only by direct effect.
b. a hit can occur only by indirect effect.
c. there is no favoritism between radiation and the target molecule.
d. radiation interacts uniformly.

16 In the presence of oxygen, the _____ effect is amplified with _____ LET radiation.

a. direct, low **c.** indirect, low
b. direct, high **d.** indirect, high

17 When irradiated with x rays, human cells follow the

a. single-target, single-hit model.
b. single-target, multihit model.
c. multitarget, single-hit model.
d. multitarget, multihit model.

18 When irradiated with high LET radiation, human cells follow the

a. single-target, single-hit model.
b. single target, multihit model.
c. multitarget, single-hit model.
d. multitarget, multihit model.

19 The factor _____ is termed the mean lethal dose.

a. D_0 **c.** D_{37}
b. D_Q **d.** Dn

Early Effects of Radiation

ACUTE RADIATION LETHALITY
....

LOCAL TISSUE DAMAGE
....

Radiation is harmful to human beings. The degree of harm is related to the radiation dose by a dose-response relationship, the form of which depends on the type of response observed. These conclusions are drawn from experimentation with animals and from observations of humans irradiated both accidentally and intentionally.

Those effects of radiation exposure at the total body level that occur within weeks of exposure are termed the **acute,** or **early,** effects of radiation exposure. These effects include radiation lethality and radiation effects on local tissues. They are generally due to the death of many cells in the tissue. Any tissue of the body, if it receives a sufficient dose of radiation, will be affected. Observation of such responses has led to a classification of the relative radiosensitivity of various cells and tissues of the body.

EXERCISES

1 The $LD_{50/30}$ for humans is closest to
 a. 100 rad.
 b. 200 rad.
 c. 300 rad.
 d. 500 rad.

2 A whole-body dose equivalent of 3000 rem (30 Sv) would probably cause death in 4 to 10 days by which of the following mechanisms?
 a. hematopoietic death
 b. gastrointestinal death
 c. central nervous system death
 d. hiccups

3 Concerning radiation exposure of mammalian gonads,
 a. the spermatocyte is the most sensitive stage in the male.
 b. germ cell depression has been measured as low as 10 rad.
 c. effects are apparently independent of LET.
 d. a linear, nonthreshold dose-response relationship prevails for sterility.

4 The minimum testicular dose for transient infertility is approximately _____, whereas that for permanent sterility is approximately _____.
 a. 5 rad, 50 rad   **c.** 500 rad, 1000 rad
 b. 200 rad, 500 rad   **d.** 1000 rad, 1500 rad

5 The $LD_{50/30}$ means a
 a. lovely dance for half the people under 30 years of age.
 b. lethal dose of total body radiation for 30% to 50% of the people so exposed.
 c. lethal dose of total body radiation for 30% of the people so exposed in 50 days.
 d. lethal dose of total body radiation for 50% of the people so exposed in 30 days.

6 Which of the following is considered an early response to radiation exposure?
 a. leukemia   **c.** cytogenetic damage
 b. genetic damage   **d.** shortened life span

7 The $LD_{50/30}$ represents the dose
 a. required to kill 30% of the cells in 50 days.
 b. required to kill 50% of the cells in 30 days.
 c. equivalent to 37% cell survival (D_{37}).
 d. that will kill half the people in 30 days.

8 Human radiation lethality follows a _____ dose-response relationship.
 a. nonlinear, threshold
 b. linear, threshold
 c. nonlinear, nonthreshold
 d. linear, nonthreshold

9 Which dose range, applied to both ovaries, is needed to induce permanent sterility?
  a. 100 to 200 rad   **c.** 900 to 1100 rad
  b. 300 to 800 rad   **d.** above 1200 rad

10 The _____ syndrome has a mean survival time that is independent of dose.
  a. prodromal   **c.** gastrointestinal
  b. hematologic   **d.** central nervous system

11 The dose of x rays necessary to produce an erythema in half those exposed is about
  a. 100 rad.   **c.** 600 rad.
  b. 300 rad.   **d.** over 1000 rad.

12 The acute radiation syndrome consists of all **except** the
  a. hematologic syndrome.
  b. gastrointestinal syndrome.
  c. latent injury syndrome.
  d. central nervous syndrome.

13 Which of the following is **not** an early response to radiation exposure?
  a. intestinal distress occurring 1 week after exposure
  b. skin erythema occurring 2 weeks after exposure
  c. chromosome aberrations
  d. breast cancer

14 Which of the following is **not** an acute local tissue effect?
  a. skin erythema
  b. cataracts
  c. transient sterility
  d. epilation

15 Three days after receiving a dose of 1000 rad (10 Gy), physiologic alterations occurring in the small intestine include
  a. leakage of proteins from the intestinal lumen.
  b. loss of electrolytes and water.
  c. diarrhea.
  d. all of the above.

16 The acute radiation syndrome
  a. can occur after high doses administered over either a short period of time or over several months' duration.
  b. includes the most sensitive of the syndromes, the gastrointestinal syndrome.
  c. includes the gastrointestinal syndrome, which occurs after doses of approximately 5000 to 10,000 rad.
  d. if accompanied by gastrointestinal death indicates a mean survival time of about 4 to 10 days.

17 The mean survival time for mammals after a single whole-body dose of radiation is
  a. independent of dose.
  b. dependent on dose between approximately 200 and 1000 rad.
  c. independent of the type of death.
  d. the same for all species.

18 Death caused by a single dose of total body irradiation primarily involves damage to the
  a. bone marrow.   **c.** skeletal system.
  b. skin.   **d.** respiratory system.

19 The mean survival time following a lethal radiation dose is constant
  a. between 200 and 1000 rad.
  b. for hematologic death.
  c. for gastrointestinal death.
  d. with increasing dose above 5000 rad.

20 Whole-body radiation affects humans in which of the following ways?
  a. The survival time of the organism can be lengthened.
  b. The immediate lethal action, dependent on dose, can be ascribed to failure of a vital organ system.
  c. The order of increasing sensitivity of organ systems is gastrointestinal system, hemopoietic system, and central nervous system.
  d. none of the above

Name _____

Date _____

Early Effects of Radiation

HEMATOLOGIC EFFECTS
....
CYTOGENETIC EFFECTS
....

All of the acute radiation effects observed at the total body level have been thoroughly studied in experimental animals. Most have been observed in human population groups, such as the atomic bomb survivors, radiation accident victims, and radiation oncology patients.

One body tissue, blood, has received considerable attention as a biologic in vivo radiation dosimeter. Because of the relatively high radiosensitivity of blood and its ease of sampling, it is often used to predict the likely outcome of an unknown radiation exposure. Cell counts and cytogenetic analysis of lymphocytes are conducted on all radiation accident victims, such as those at Chernobyl, to determine how vigorous the course of supportive therapy should be and to help guide the management of the patient.

EXERCISES

1 Which of the following cell types will be depressed most severely by radiation?
   a. erythrocytes   **c.** granulocytes
   b. lymphocytes   **d.** megakaryocytes
2 In the normal human karyotype, there are
   a. 23 chromosomes.
   b. 44 autosomes.
   c. 46 autosomes.
   d. none of the above.
3 Of the following chromosome aberrations, which requires a karyotype for analysis?
   a. isochromatid fragments
   b. dicentric chromosome
   c. ring chromosome
   d. reciprocal translocation

4 Which of the following blood observations is most appropriate when monitoring for radiation damage?
   a. hematocrit   **c.** thrombocyte count
   b. erythrocyte count   **d.** lymphocyte count
5 If a whole-body radiation dose of 25 rad were received, which of the following would most likely be observed?
   a. skin erythema
   b. erythrocyte depression
   c. cytogenetic damage
   d. depletion of oogonia
6 Which of the following is **not** a principal type of mature blood cell?
   a. granulocyte   **c.** erythrocyte
   b. lymphocyte   **d.** cytocyte
7 Radiation effects on the hematologic system
   a. are measurable at whole-body doses as low as 5 rad.
   b. are first observed as a leukocyte depression.
   c. are permanent.
   d. suggest that routine blood analysis of radiation workers be performed.
8 Which of the following blood observations is most appropriate for routine monitoring of radiation workers?
   a. erythrocyte count   **c.** lymphocyte count
   b. thrombocyte count   **d.** none of the above
9 Which of the following types of chromosome aberrations obeys a linear, nonthreshold dose-response relationship?
   a. ring chromosome   **c.** dicentric
   b. chromatid break   **d.** tricentric
10 The _____ are involved in human immune response.
   a. lymphocytes   **c.** thrombocytes
   b. granulocytes   **d.** erythrocytes
11 The _____ are most sensitive to radiation.
   a. lymphocytes   **c.** thrombocytes
   b. granulocytes   **d.** erythrocytes

12 Which of the following types of chromosome aberrations exhibits a threshold response?
a. ring chromosomes   c. dicentrics
b. chromatid breaks   d. none of the above

13 The_____ is the precursor to thrombocytes (platelets).
a. lymphocyte   c. megakaryoblast
b. myeloblast   d. reticulocyte

14 The _____ and the _____ are the most radiosensitive cells in the body.
a. granulocytes, lymphocytes
b. granulocytes, oogonia
c. spermatogonia, oogonia
d. spermatogonia, lymphocytes

15 Human cells that are most often used for cytogenetic analysis are
a. spermatogonia.   c. thrombocytes.
b. skin cells.   d. lymphocytes.

16 Chromosome aberrations in peripheral blood cells usually appear _____ after exposure.
a. within hours   c. years
b. months   d. anytime

17 The principal response of the blood to radiation exposure is
a. rearrangement of chromosomes.
b. fragmentation of chromosomes.
c. a decrease in cell number.
d. a stimulation of cell proliferation.

18 Following radiation exposure the first blood cells to respond are the
a. lymphocytes.   c. thrombocytes.
b. granulocytes.   d. erythrocytes.

19 A chromosomal karyotype is
a. unrestrained growth of chromosomes.
b. an orderly map of all of the chromosomes.
c. an analysis of chromosome fragments.
d. a description of the radiation response.

20 Which of the following types of chromosome aberrations is considered most significant?
a. chromatid deletion
b. dicentric
c. chromatid break
d. point mutation

WORKSHEET 103

Late Effects of Radiation

LOCAL TISSUE EFFECTS
....
LIFE SPAN SHORTENING
....
RISK ESTIMATES
....

Delayed or late responses to radiation exposure include genetic effects and those somatic effects that require months, and even years, to develop. Considerable evidence is available from observations on experimental animals for all of the late effects. It is unfortunate that observations of late somatic effects of radiation on humans are meager. Consequently, radiation scientists rely heavily either on extrapolation of observations following high radiation doses or on large-scale epidemiologic studies.

These late effects generally follow low doses of radiation exposure. Thus most of the evidence at the human level is of an epidemiologic nature. Precise dose-response relationships are seldom possible to determine; therefore radiation scientists resort to various estimates of risk. Such estimates require observations on extremely large numbers of individuals. If the dose to which the population is exposed is known, an **absolute risk** with the units of **incidence/10⁶/rad/yr** can be described. If the radiation dose is unknown, the best that can be done is to express the **relative risk,** the ratio of observed to expected cases, or the **excess risk,** which is the number of cases above those expected. The principal late effects of concern are the induction of malignant disease and genetic effects. Each of these is presumed to follow a linear, nonthreshold dose-response relationship. Late local tissue effects are for the most part threshold in nature.

EXERCISES

1 Which of the following is an example of a linear, nonthreshold dose-response relationship?
   a. lethality   **c.** leukemia
   b. CNS syndrome   **d.** cataracts
2 Which of the following statements is most appropriate regarding radiation-induced cataracts after a multifilm tomographic examination of the head?
   a. Cataracts are possible because there is no threshold.
   b. The probability of cataracts is high.
   c. The dose is probably in the neighborhood of the threshold for such an effect.
   d. The dose is certainly below the threshold for such an effect.
3 If radiation-induced life-span shortening occurs, the best estimate for such an effect is a reduction of _____ for every rad.
   a. 10 hours   **c.** 24 hours
   b. 10 days   **d.** 24 days

4 Which of the following statements is true concerning radiation-induced life-span shortening?
   a. Best estimates of reduced life span are 1 day per rad exposure.
   b. American and British radiologists have experienced premature aging and death.
   c. Radiation causes nonspecific aging.
   d. The dose-response relationship is apparently a threshold phenomenon.

5 It has been determined that diagnostic x rays will produce
   a. organ atrophy.
   b. shortening of life.
   c. cataracts.
   d. none of the above.

6 Which of the following is **not** a possible result of exposure to ionizing radiation?
   a. cataract formation
   b. shortening of life
   c. induction of carcinoma
   d. increased resistance to infection

7 At least _____ people are necessary in order to establish that a 10 rad dose caused leukemia in that population.
   a. 10^3
   b. 10^4
   c. 10^5
   d. 10^6

8 If the incidence of cancer is 1 case in 5000, what is the relative risk if an irradiated population shows an incidence of 4 cases in 10,000?
   a. 2
   b. 4
   c. 1000
   d. 4000

9 Which of the following groups has **not** suffered radiation damage?
   a. atomic bomb survivors
   b. radiologic technologists
   c. radium watch-dial painters
   d. diagnostic x-ray patients

10 Radiation-induced cataracts
   a. follow a nonlinear, threshold type of dose-response relationship.
   b. follow a linear, nonthreshold type of dose-response relationship.
   c. exhibit a threshold to x rays of approximately 10 rad.
   d. have a latent period of approximately 1 year.

11 Given 1 million Americans, approximately how many will die of malignant disease from natural causes?
   a. less than 5%
   b. 10%
   c. 20%
   d. 40%

12 Significant gonadal radiation exposure occurs
   a. in whole-body MRI.
   b. only when no collimator is used.
   c. when the gonads are in the primary beam.
   d. when radiation is scattered from other parts of the body.

13 Epidemiology is the study of
   a. radiation.
   b. statistics.
   c. populations.
   d. late effects.

14 Radiation-induced chromosome aberrations are
   a. considered to be only early effects.
   b. considered to be only late effects.
   c. considered to be early or late effects.
   d. present only following whole-body irradiation.

15 The average latent period for radiation-induced cataracts is _____ years.
   a. 5
   b. 15
   c. 30
   d. 50

16 To produce nearly 100% incidence of cataracts, an x-ray dose of approximately _____ will be required.
   a. 1 Gy
   b. 10 Gy
   c. 100 Gy
   d. 1000 Gy

17 When engaged in a busy fluoroscopy schedule, _____ need wear protective lens shields.
   a. only radiologists
   b. only technologists
   c. both radiologists and technologists
   d. neither radiologists nor technologists

18 Which of the following carries the greatest loss of life expectancy?
   a. cancer
   b. radiation
   c. all accidents
   d. being male

19 Protective lens shields for patients should be used
   a. always.
   b. whenever the lens is in the primary beam.
   c. when such use does not interfere with the examination.
   d. never.

20 Breast cancer is observed in 30 out of 450 patients. If the normal incidence is 2 cases per 1000, what is the approximate relative risk to these patients?
   a. 10
   b. 30
   c. 100
   d. 300

WORSHEET **104**

Late Effects of Radiation

RADIATION-INDUCED MALIGNANCY
....
TOTAL RISK OF MALIGNANCY
....
RADIATION AND PREGNANCY
....

Without doubt, humans are most sensitive to the harmful effects of radiation while in utero. Further, the fetus is most sensitive early in pregnancy. Considerable evidence is available from observations on experimental animals to describe these effects of radiation in utero, both quantitatively and qualitatively. The effects include prenatal and postnatal mortality, congenital abnormalities, and development of latent malignant disease. Some limited data also suggest genetic effects in the offspring of animals irradiated in utero. Nearly all of these observations, however, have followed exceedingly high doses—in excess of 50 rad (0.5 Gy).

No such observations have been made on humans except for a small number of atomic bomb survivors who were in utero at the time of the bomb and whose fetal dose exceeded 100 rad (1 Gy). The effects observed in such individuals were central nervous system disorders such as microcephaly and mental retardation.

After low dose irradiation, for example, less than 10 rad (0.1 Gy), no such effects have been observed in humans. Only epidemiologic studies such as the Oxford Survey have suggested that there is an increased relative risk of latent malignant disease after low dose, in utero irradiation. The generally accepted relative risk for such situations is 1.5.

No direct evidence exists at the human level for radiation-induced genetic effects. Observations on flies and mice, however, have shown the following:

1. Radiation-induced genetic mutations follow a linear, nonthreshold dose-response relationship.

2. With time, some recovery occurs from the genetic effects of radiation.

3. Radiation does not induce specific genetic mutations but rather increases the incidence of those that already exist.

4. Radiation-induced genetic mutations are usually recessive.

5. For humans the doubling dose is estimated to be between 20 rad and 200 rad. Fifty rad is usually assumed correct.

EXERCISES

1 The relative risk for the development of leukemia after irradiation at low but unknown dose levels is considered to be approximately
   a. 0.5.   **c.** 3.5.
   b. 1.5.   **d.** 5.0.
2 The generally accepted absolute risk factor for radiation-induced breast cancer is _____ cases/10^6/rad/yr.
   a. 0.06   **c.** 6
   b. 0.6   **d.** 60
3 Radiation-induced leukemia
   a. apparently follows a linear, threshold dose-response relationship.
   b. probably does not occur at doses less than about 25 rad.
   c. has been demonstrated in both animals and humans.
   d. apparently does not occur after long-term, low level radiation exposure.
4 Which of the following dose-response relationships best describes radiation-induced lung cancer?
   a. linear, nonthreshold
   b. nonlinear, nonthreshold
   c. linear, threshold
   d. nonlinear, threshold
5 Which of the following numbers approximates the total cases of leukemia observed in atomic bomb survivors?
   a. 50   **c.** 500
   b. 150   **d.** 1500

6 It has been claimed that radiation-induced liver cancer developed in Thorotrast patients.

   a. The findings are positive and statistically significant.

   b. The findings are positive but not statistically significant.

   c. The findings are negative.

   d. The suspected principal radiation dose comes from beta emission.

7 For which of the following organs or tissues has radiation-induced malignancy been identified in humans?

   a. scalp   **c.** tongue

   b. bone   **d.** gonads

8 The latent period of radiation-induced leukemia is considered to be

   a. 1 year.   **c.** 4 to 7 years.

   b. 1 to 3 years.   **d.** over 10 years.

9 Analysis of the survivors of the atomic bomb shows that the induction of leukemia

   a. does not exist.

   b. suggests a threshold at 300 rad.

   c. supports a linear, nonthreshold dose-response relationship.

   d. peaked 10 years after the bomb.

10 All of the following populations have shown an increased incidence of leukemia following radiation exposure except

   a. atomic bomb survivors.

   b. American radiologists.

   c. American radiologic technologists.

   d. radiotherapy patients.

11 Which of the following types of cancer has (have) been demonstrated in humans following irradiation?

   a. lung   **c.** skin

   b. breast   **d.** all of the above

12 Which type of radiation-induced cancer apparently exhibits a threshold dose-response relationship?

   a. liver   **c.** bone

   b. skin   **d.** breast

13 Which of the following has **not** shown a positive relationship between radiation exposure and leukemia?

   a. the atomic bomb survivors

   b. children irradiated for thymic enlargement

   c. American radiologists

   d. patients irradiated therapeutically for ankylosing spondylitis

14 All except _____ leukemia have been implicated as radiation induced.

   a. acute myelocytic

   b. chronic myelocytic

   c. acute lymphocytic

   d. chronic lymphocytic

15 Which of the following responses after irradiation in utero is most likely to occur if the radiation is delivered during the organogenesis stage?

   a. prenatal death

   b. neonatal death

   c. congenital abnormalities

   d. latent malignancy

16 Concerning radiation-induced genetic mutations,

   a. the most frequent types are dominant.

   b. the dose-response relationship is threshold.

   c. the doubling dose is approximately 50 to 250 rad.

   d. the male is more sensitive than the female.

17 The data and conclusions of the Oxford Survey

   a. suggest shortening of the life span by 10 days/rad.

   b. show a 100% incidence of effects after exposure of 200 rad.

   c. suggest a threshold for cataracts of approximately 200 rad.

   d. suggest a relative risk of approximately 8:1 during the first trimester of pregnancy.

18 The relative risk for the development of leukemia after irradiation in utero

   a. would equal 1.0 if there were no risk.

   b. would equal 100 if there were no risk.

   c. is estimated to be 50.

   d. is estimated to be 100.

19 The radiation dose-response relationship for genetic mutations is

   a. linear.

   b. exponential.

   c. independent of dose.

   d. threshold.

20 Following a dose of 10 rad at 6 weeks' gestation, the increase in congenital abnormalities will be approximately

   a. 0.1%.   **c.** 10%.

   b. 1%.   **d.** 50%.

Name _____

Date _____

Health Physics

CARDINAL PRINCIPLES OF RADIATION PROTECTION
....
MAXIMUM PERMISSIBLE DOSE
....

Over the years a body of rules, regulations, and recommendations has developed, which constitute the principles of radiation protection. Exposure levels considered to be safe have been established, and these have been supplemented by the concept of **ALARA** (as low as reasonably achievable). Procedures and techniques have been developed for maintaining occupational exposures below established limits and ensuring that all exposures are ALARA.

The **maximum permissible dose** (MPD) is that dose which, if received each year during a 50-year occupational span, would result in a completely acceptable risk of latent injury. The value of the basic MPD is 5000 mrem/yr (50 mSv/yr). A number of other dose-limiting recommendations are derived from this.

Among the principles of radiation control are three known as the cardinal principles:
1. Maintain the time of radiation exposure as short as possible.
2. Increase the distance from the source.
3. Place shielding between the source and the individual being shielded.

Application of these cardinal principles of radiation protection is essential. Nearly all of the protective procedures and devices that are employed in diagnostic radiology incorporate some aspect of these principles.

EXERCISES

1 Half-value layer (HVL) is related to which of the following principles of radiation protection?
  a. time   **c.** shielding
  b. distance   **d.** monitoring

2 If all other factors remain constant, radiation dose is related to x-ray beam-on time
  a. directly.   **c.** by the inverse square.
  b. inversely.   **d.** exponentially.

3 If all other factors remain constant, radiation dose is related to source-to-object distance (SOD)
  a. directly.   **c.** by the inverse square.
  b. proportionately.   **d.** exponentially.

4 If all other factors remain constant, radiation dose is related to shielding
  a. directly.   **c.** by the inverse square.
  b. inversely.   **d.** exponentially.

5 One tenth-value layer (TVL) is defined as
  a. 10 times the HVL.
  b. 1/10 the initial dose.
  c. 1/10 the initial shielding.
  d. the shielding thickness necessary to reduce the exposure to 1/10.

6 One TVL is equal to how many HVLs?
  a. 2.0   **c.** 3.3
  b. 2.2   **d.** 10.0

7 During radiography an acceptable position for the technologist is
  a. in the room and next to the patient.
  b. in the room and as far from the patient as practical.
  c. holding the patient.
  d. behind the control booth.

8 During fluoroscopy an acceptable position for the technologist is
  a. in the room and next to the patient.
  b. in the room and as far from the patient as practical.
  c. holding the patient.
  d. in the darkroom.

9 The HVL for 70 kVp is greater
  a. than that for 90 kVp.
  b. than the TVL for 70 kVp.
  c. with single-phase than with three-phase power.
  d. with high total filtration than with low total filtration.

10 The exposure rate from a point source is 100 mR/hr (26 μC/kg-hr) at 120 cm. If a technologist moves to within 30 cm of the source of radiation, how many HVLs would be needed to reduce the exposure rate to 100 mR/hr?
  a. one   c. four
  b. two   d. eight

11 If a survey meter reads 25 mR/hr (6.5 μC/kg-hr), how long can a person stay at that location before receiving an exposure of 100 mR?
  a. 1 hr   c. 4 hr
  b. 2 hr   d. 8 hr

12 If the exposure rate 1 m from a source is 9000 mR/hr (2.3 mC/kg-hr), what will the exposure rate be 3 m from the source?
  a. 100 mR/hr   c. 1000 mR/hr
  b. 900 mR/hr   d. 3000 mR/hr

13 The exposure rate alongside a fluoroscopic table (distance = 60 cm from the source) is 400 mR/hr (103 μC/kg-hr). Therefore, if the technologist
  a. completed a procedure requiring 10 minutes, the exposure would be 40 mR.
  b. is engaged in 10 fluoroscopic examinations at the 120 cm distance, each averaging 4 minutes of beam-on time, the total exposure would be 67 mR.
  c. moved 60 cm further from the table, the exposure rate would be increased.
  d. moved 60 cm further from the table, the exposure rate would be 200 mR/hr.

14 The MPD for a technologist is
  a. 5000 mrem/yr.
  b. 5000 mrem/9 mo.
  c. 500 mrem/yr.
  d. 500 mrem/9 mo.

15 You are a 17-year-old student technologist. How much occupational exposure are you allowed?
  a. 100 mrem/yr   c. 500 mrem/yr
  b. 100 mrem/9 mo   d. 500 mrem/9 mo

16 During fluoroscopy a survey meter shows the exposure rate at the technologist's position to be 350 mR/hr (90 μC/kg-hr). How much x-ray beam-on time before the technologist reaches a weekly MPD?
  a. 8 min   c. 35 min
  b. 17 min   d. 1 hr

17 The cumulative MPD can be computed from
  a. 10 mSv × N.   c. 5N − 18.
  b. 50 mSv × N.   d. 5 − 18N.

18 A protective apron is equivalent to 2 HVLs. How much more time will that allow the technologist to remain during fluroscopy than without the apron?
  a. twice as much time
  b. four times as much
  c. eight times as much
  d. not enough information

19 For which of the following is the MPD 15 rem/yr?
  a. whole-body occupational radiation
  b. whole-body nonoccupational radiation
  c. forearm radiation
  d. skin radiation

20 The MPD for the hands is
  a. 30 mSv/yr.   c. 750 mSv/yr.
  b. 300 mSv/yr.   d. 7.5 Sv/yr.

21 Under the 1987 NCRP guidelines, the cumulative MPD for a 30-year-old radiologic technologist is _____ rem (×10 mSv).
  a. 5   c. 60
  b. 30   d. 150

22 According to the 1987 NCRP MPD guidelines, which of the following body parts is **not** allowed a dose of 50 rem (0.5 Sv) per year?
  a. skin   c. gonads
  b. breast   d. eye lens

23 The 1987 NCRP guidelines specify the annual MPD for the hands to be _____ rem (×10 mSv).
  a. 15   c. 50
  b. 30   d. 75

24 Under the 1987 NCRP guidelines, the MPD for a developing fetus for the entire gestational period is _____ rem (×10 mSv).
  a. 0.1   c. 1.0
  b. 0.5   d. 5.0

25 In 1987 the NCRP recommended that the MPD for the _____ should be 15 rem (×10 mSv) per year.
  a. gonads
  b. forearms
  c. skin
  d. eye lens

Health Physics

X-RAYS AND PREGNANCY
....

The exposure that individuals experience in diagnostic radiology, whether as a patient or a technologist, is extremely low. No individual need be at all concerned regarding such routine exposures he or she may receive. The only exception is during pregnancy, and even then the risk is exceedingly low. Nevertheless, because of the increased sensitivity of the fetus to radiation, some extra effort is required in administering a radiation safety program.

Patients who are pregnant or suspect pregnancy should be handled according to the **10-day rule.** This can be done by elective booking or by simply posting information in the waiting area. Pregnant technologists should be assigned to activities that do not include fluoroscopy and portable radiography. Under some circumstances a second personnel radiation monitor might be issued to the pregnant technologist, with instructions that it be worn under the protective apron at waist level.

If, after a radiologic examination, a radiology patient is found to be pregnant, several things should be done. The extent of the examination should be reviewed, the fetal dose should be estimated, and the time of gestation at which the dose was delivered should be determined. **Rarely will termination of pregnancy be indicated.** However, should the fetal dose exceed 10 rad, serious consideration should be given to such termination.

The pregnant technologist should inform her supervisor as soon as she knows of her condition. If her previous radiation exposure history indicates that a second monitor is required, an estimate of the abdominal exposure during the period between conception and discovery of the pregnancy should be made.

EXERCISES

1 If an AP examination of the pelvis results in a skin exposure of 300 mR, the approximate fetal dose would be
 a. 50 mrad.   **c.** 200 mrad.
 b. 100 mrad.   **d.** 300 mrad.

2 It is sometimes necessary to calculate the dose received by a fetus during a radiographic procedure. Which of the following is needed for such a calculation?
 a. fetal sex   **c.** gestation period
 b. grid ratio   **d.** x-ray output

3 To reduce the radiation dose to the fetus of a pregnant patient, a technologist could
 a. use specific area shields if appropriate.
 b. use screens with slower speeds.
 c. increase the SID and mAs.
 d. decrease kVp and increase mAs.

4 A patient is to have a radiographic examination because of low back pain. As she is being positioned, she asks whether this will affect her current pregnancy. What should the technologist do?
 a. Reassure her and proceed with the examination.
 b. Refuse to do the examination.
 c. Seek advice from the radiologist before proceeding with the examination.
 d. Use a high kVp technique and gonad shield.

5 Which of the following techniques would result in the lowest exposure to the fetus?
 a. 85 kVp, 200 ms, 300 mA
 b. 100 kVp, 200 ms, 100 mA
 c. 60 kVp, 80 ms, 100 mA
 d. 120 kVp, 100 ms, 100 mA

6 After a skull series, a brain scan, a barium enema, and an intravenous pyelogram (IVP), it is discovered that the patient is pregnant. What should be done?
 a. Terminate the pregnancy.
 b. Do nothing.
 c. Estimate the fetal dose.
 d. Perform a hysterosalpingogram.

7 Radiation dose to the fetus from diagnostic radiographic procedures is usually
   a. less than 1 rad.
   b. between 2 and 4 rad.
   c. between 5 and 10 rad.
   d. between 10 and 20 rad.

8 If a woman is pregnant when a diagnostic radiographic study is carried out, which of the following enters into the decision of whether to terminate the pregnancy?
   a. the radiation dose
   b. the time of gestation
   c. the hazard of the pregnancy to the mother
   d. all of the above

9 A patient who is 2 months' pregnant is to receive an intravenous pyelogram. Which of the following is correct?
   a. The possibility of spontaneous abortion is high.
   b. No more than two radiographs should be made.
   c. Normal precautions are adequate, since fetal damage is least likely during this period of gestation.
   d. The examination should be delayed if possible.

10 The 10-day rule states that
   a. appropriate x-ray examinations should be scheduled within the 10 days after the onset of menstruation.
   b. appropriate x-ray examinations should be scheduled during the 10 days preceding the onset of menstruation.
   c. all x-ray examinations should be scheduled in the 10-day interval after the completion of menstruation.
   d. only fluoroscopic examinations should be selectively scheduled.

11 The greatest nonlethal radiation hazard to an embryo or fetus occurs during
   a. the first 2 weeks of gestation.
   b. the first trimester.
   c. the second trimester.
   d. the third trimester.

12 An elective booking procedure designed to protect against exposure of the fetus recommends that
   a. diagnostic x-ray exposures of the pelvis should be avoided only if pregnancy is confirmed.
   b. exposure of fertile women to **all** diagnostic x rays should occur only during the first 10 days after the onset of menstruation.
   c. no restriction is required if the fetal dose per view is less than 1 rad.
   d. none of the above be done.

13 The National Council on Radiation Protection recommends a therapeutic abortion if the fetal dose exceeds
   a. 5 rad.
   b. 10 rad.
   c. 25 rad.
   d. no recommendation is made.

14 In pelvic radiography a dose to the shielded female gonads is primarily due to which one of the following?
   a. leakage radiation and air scatter
   b. secondary electrons scattered out of the x-ray field
   c. characteristic x rays released by high atomic number atoms in the pelvis
   d. scattered x rays from surrounding irradiated tissue

15 When a technologist becomes pregnant, she should be
   a. fired.
   b. given a temporary leave of absence.
   c. given an additional lead apron.
   d. counciled on proper radiation safety.

16 **Reasonable** radiation protection practice when dealing with a pregnant technologist includes
   a. assignment to a low exposure job.
   b. no fluoroscopy.
   c. providing two personnel monitors.
   d. all of the above.

17 Elements of a radiation protection program dealing with a pregnant technologist include
   a. assignment to a low exposure job.
   b. no fluoroscopy.
   c. providing two personnel monitors.
   d. reviewing radiation safety procedures.

18 When a second radiation monitor is provided to a pregnant technologist
   a. she should alternate wearing the two
   b. she should wear both under the apron at waist level.
   c. it should be worn under the apron at waist level.
   d. it should be worn outside the apron at waist level.

19 The fetal dose above which termination of pregnancy should be considered is
   a. 1 rad.
   b. 10 rad.
   c. 20 rad.
   d. 50 rad.

Design of Radiologic Imaging Facilities

THE X-RAY DEPARTMENT

········

Many hospitals and clinics provide inadequate attention to the details of a most important patient service: imaging. Special consideration is required for diagnostic ultrasound, nuclear medicine, and magnetic resonance imaging; however, the bulk of medical imaging remains x-ray.

A design team with input from a radiologist, a medical physicist, the technical director, and an architect should be chaired by an administrator. Decisions regarding size and location should be made first. Arrangement of the various department functions should then be designed. Finally, equipment specification and arrangement should be determined.

EXERCISES

1 Who should be included on the design team for an x-ray imaging facility?
 I. hospital administrator
 II. radiologist
 III. medical physicist
 IV. staff technologist
 a. I and III
 b. II and IV
 c. I, II, and III
 d. I, II, III, and IV

2 What would be the most likely reason to position the x-ray tube so that it is directed to an outside wall on the 15th floor?
 a. It reduces the cost of construction.
 b. X-ray photons help to reduce air pollution.
 c. Radiation helps to keep pigeon population low.
 d. It improves radio reception.

3 When planning a radiographic/fluoroscopic room, what is the approximate minimum size?
 a. 100 ft^2 **c.** 500 ft^2
 b. 300 ft^2 **d.** 700 ft^2

4 Ten percent of the total space required for an x-ray department is approximately equal to the
 a. percentage of additional radiologic technologists needed each year.
 b. number of radiologic technologists needed.
 c. estimated growth per year.
 d. estimated growth in the next 5 years.

5 The ideal x-ray examination room should have which of the following.
 a. as much space as possible
 b. as much equipment as possible
 c. as much lead as possible
 d. multiple toilets

6 The necessary information on facility work load, flow patterns, and anticipated future requirements is provided by the
 a. medical physicist
 b. hospital administrator
 c. architect
 d. radiologist and director of radiology

7 If a hospital does 9000 examinations per year, approximately how many x-ray rooms are needed?
 a. one   **c.** three
 b. two   **d.** four

8 Where should the x-ray department be located?
 a. in the basement
 b. on the ground floor
 c. on the top floor
 d. near the emergency center

9 The estimated number of examinations per day that a general purpose x-ray room can easily accommodate is
 a. 10.   **c.** 30.
 b. 20.   **d.** 50.

10 Why are some x-ray rooms on the ground floor?
   a. because the ground is used to absorb x rays
   b. because of the added expense to get the equipment to the second floor
   c. because patients are in too much pain to get to the second floor
   d. because most clinics only have one floor

11 Radiologists spend most of their clinical time
   a. looking up pathologic conditions to match the patient's condition.
   b. in the examining room, reading room, or consultation area.
   c. making sure the technologist has prepared the patient properly.
   d. on a golf course.

12 Who is the principal member of the design team?
   a. hospital administrator
   b. radiology nurse
   c. radiologist
   d. director of radiology

13 Which is the most important consideration when designing an x-ray room?
   a. width of corridor
   b. wall color
   c. location
   d. ceiling height

14 If there are four x-ray rooms, what is the minimum space that the department should have?
   a. 2000 ft^2
   b. 4000 ft^2
   c. 6000 ft^2
   d. 8000 ft^2

15 A new hospital anticipates doing 19,000 x-ray examinations the first year it is open. How many x-ray rooms should be planned?
   a. 1   c. 3
   b. 2   d. 4

16 The most common x-ray examination is
   a. chest.
   b. abdomen.
   c. extremities.
   d. head and neck.

17 Approximately what fraction of x-rays are taken in hospitals?
   a. ¼   c. ⅔
   b. ½   d. ¾

18 An acceptable location for the x-ray department in a hospital is near the
   a. outpatient, emergency, and surgery areas.
   b. top floor.
   c. cafeteria.
   d. administrative offices.

19 A hospital does 10,000 examinations this year. How many would you project for next year?
   a. 10,000   c. 15,000
   b. 11,000   d. none (The hospital will be bankrupt.)

20 A new hospital anticipates doing 45,000 x-ray examinations. How much space should be allocated to the radiology department?
   a. 10,000 ft^2
   b. 20,000 ft^2
   c. 30,000 ft^2
   d. 40,000 ft^2

Designing for Radiation Protection

DESIGN OF X-RAY APPARATUS
·····················

DESIGN OF PROTECTIVE BARRIERS
·····················

Considerable care and attention are given to the design of x-ray facilities and equipment, and much of this attention results from the need for radiation protection.

X-ray machines have filters, collimators, shields, and additional special design features for the reduction of radiation exposure to patients and personnel. Attention is given to proper design and calibration of kVp, mA,

and timer circuits so that techniques can be accurately and consistently employed. This accuracy reduces the number of reexaminations required, which in turn reduces human exposure. For this reason periodic radiation control surveys and calibrations of x-ray apparatus are recommended.

Nearly all diagnostic x-ray rooms have lead in the walls. Sometimes floor and ceiling barriers are also required. Barriers in radiotherapy facilities usually incorporate rather large thicknesses of concrete. However, examination rooms for nuclear medicine do not normally require shielding. The required barrier thickness is determined by first calculating:

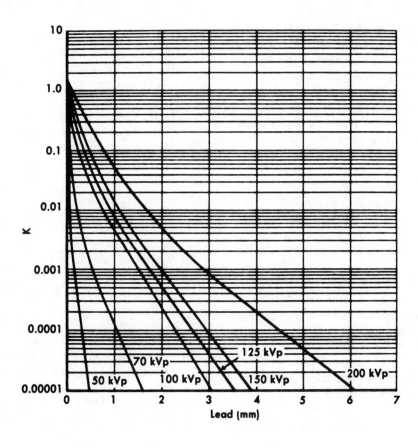

$$K = \frac{Pd^2}{WUT}$$

where

P = MPD in R/wk

d = distance from tube to barrier in meters

W = work load

U = use factor

T = time of occupancy factor

The value of K, obtained by this calculation is then used with the accompanying graph to determine the required thickness of lead.

EXERCISES

1 Every diagnostic x-ray tube housing must be sufficiently shielded to limit the level of exposure 1 m from the housing to
   a. 10 mR/hr.
   b. 100 mR/hr.
   c. 1000 mR/hr.
   d. a factor that varies according to kVp.

2 During mammography, at tube potentials less than 50 kVp, the minimum acceptable filtration is
   a. 0.1 mm Al.   c. 1.0 mm Al.
   b. 0.5 mm Al.   d. 2.5 mm Al.

3 The minimum permissible filtration for general purpose radiographic or fluoroscopic tubes is
   a. 0.5 mm Al.   c. 2.5 mm Al.
   b. 1.5 mm Al.   d. 3.5 mm Al.

4 The fluoroscopic tube should not be positioned closer than 38 cm to the tabletop because the
   a. geometric unsharpness would increase.
   b. patient dose would be excessive.
   c. heat load on the tube would increase.
   d. resulting magnification would be objectionable.

5 A controlled area is defined as one in which _____ is controlled.
   a. public access   c. x-ray operation
   b. radiation exposure d. patient flow

6 Radiographic work load (W) has units of
   a. R/mA min/wk.   c. R/wk.
   b. mA min/wk.   d. mR/mAs.

7 An estimate of radiographic workload in a busy room is
   a. 10 mA min/wk.   c. 500 mA min/wk.
   b. 100 mA min/wk.   d. 5000 mA min/wk.

8 Which of the following locations in a hospital should have the highest occupancy factor?
   a. the waiting room   c. a laboratory
   b. the restroom   d. an elevator

9 The maximum thickness of lead required for a primary protective barrier should not exceed
   a. 4 lb/ft^2.   c. 1/16 in.
   b. 1.6 mm.   d. all of the above.

10 Which of the following is usually considered to be a secondary protective barrier?
   a. floor   c. chest wall
   b. lateral wall   d. control booth barrier

11 Fluoroscopic x-ray units must
   a. have at least 1.5 mm Al filtration.
   b. never exceed 10 R/min at the tabletop.
   c. limit leakage radiation to 1000 mR/hr at 1 m from the tube.
   d. be image intensified.

12 Which of the following contributes to the exposure of personnel?
   a. remnant x rays   c. off-focus radiation
   b. useful beam   d. scatter radiation

13 The design limit for exposure of occupants in controlled areas is
   a. 1 mR/wk.   c. 100 mR/wk.
   b. 10 mR/wk.   d. 1000 mR/wk.

14 The use factor (U)
   a. describes the use of the x-ray tube.
   b. is always 1 for secondary barriers.
   c. takes on values from 0 to 10.
   d. applies only to radiography, not fluoroscopy.

15 All fluoroscopes have a 5-min reset timer
   a. to protect the x-ray tube.
   b. to permit a tube cool-down period.
   c. to protect the patient.
   d. because no patient shall ever receive more than 5 minutes of x-ray beam-on time.

16 When assessing adequate filtration of an x-ray tube, one considers
   I. only inherent filtration.
   II. only added filtration.
   III. filtration contributed by the light-localizing collimator.
   a. I   c. I and II
   b. II   d. I, II, and III

17 A test to assure that radiation intensity is doubled when mA is doubled is called a test for
   a. reproducibility.   c. coincidence.
   b. linearity.   d. alignment.

18 A reduction in _____ occurs when the fluoroscopic tube is mounted farther under the table.
   a. patient dose   c. filtration
   b. scatter radiation d. beam alignment

19 Which of the following would definitely be a secondary barrier?
   a. the chest wall in an R & F room
   b. the door
   c. the floor
   d. any wall in a CT room.

20 What is the weekly work load if 20 patients are examined each day at an average 78 kVp/60 mAs per view and 3.4 views per patient?
   a. 68 mA min/wk   c. 442 mA min/wk
   b. 340 mA min/wk   d. over 500 mA min/wk

Name _____

Date _____

Designing for Radiation Protection

RADIATION DETECTION AND MEASUREMENT

....

The existence of x rays was first discovered because of the unexpected blackening of a photographic emulsion. For many years thereafter, film was the only type of detector available to indicate the presence of radiation. As a radiation detector, the photographic emulsion has many advantages but also many disadvantages. Its advantages continue to quality it as today's principal method for personnel radiation monitoring—the film badge. Newer methods of radiation detection and measurement are now available, some of which are more sensitive, more accurate, and more applicable for certain situations. Among the newer types of radiation detection and measuring devices having application in diagnostic radiology are the gas-filled detector, the thermoluminescence dosimeter (TLD), and the scintillation detector.

Gas-filled detectors are used for x-ray output calibration and radiation monitoring of areas for exposure levels. Thermoluminescent dosimeters are used for personnel monitoring and patient dose estimation. Scintillation detectors find principal application in nuclear medicine imaging apparatus such as the gamma camera. None of these detection and measurement devices is restricted to those just enumerated. Instruments incorporating nearly all of these methods can be designed for many different uses. To apply the best possible instrumentation to a given situation, one must understand the basic operating principles of each method and the associated characteristics of sensitivity, accuracy, range, and type of radiation detected.

EXERCISES

1 Which of the following is characteristic of the cutie pie?
   a. wide range, 0 to 1000 mR/hr
   b. narrow range, 0 to 50 mR/hr
   c. highly sensitive, 0.01 mR/hr
   d. a Geiger-Muller counter

2 Gas-filled radiation detectors are used
   a. for contamination surveys in nuclear medicine laboratories.
   b. as a proportional counter to measure the output of an x-ray machine.
   c. as an integration type of ionization chamber.
   d. in the Geiger region to map the radiation exposure levels in fluoroscopy.

3 If each stage of a photomultiplier tube has a gain of approximately 4, a 10-stage photomultiplier tube will have a gain of approximately
   a. 40.
   b. 10^4.
   c. 4^9.
   d. 4^{10}.

4 Which of the following is used in thermoluminescent dosimetry?
   a. calcium tungstate
   b. polyester
   c. lithium fluoride
   d. barium fluorochloride

5 Which of the following detectors can be used to identify an unknown gamma emitter?
   a. lithium fluoride
   b. photographic emulsion
   c. Geiger-Muller counter
   d. multichannel crystal spectrometer

6 Which of the following normally operates in the rate mode?
   a. a Geiger-Muller counter
   b. a thermoluminescence dosimeter (TLD)
   c. photographic emulsion
   d. an ion chamber

7 Operation in which region of a gas-filled chamber results in the lowest output?
   a. Geiger-Muller region
   b. ionization
   c. recombination
   d. continuous discharge

8 The resolving time of a radiation detector is the time required
  a. for the meter to respond.
  b. to identify different types of radiation.
  c. to read the meter.
  d. to detect sequential ionizations.

9 The amount of light emitted by a scintillation phosphor is proportional to the _____ photon energy.
  a. incident   **c.** transmitted
  b. scattered   **d.** absorbed

10 In thermoluminescence dosimetry, a plot of output intensity versus temperature is called a
  a. pulse-height analysis.
  b. glow curve.
  c. pulse-height spectrum.
  d. glow worm.

11 Which of the following statements correctly applies to the voltage-response plot for the ideal gas-filled detector?
  a. The proportional region occurs at a higher voltage than the Geiger-Muller region.
  b. Instrument sensitivity is highest in the Geiger region.
  c. The lowest voltage of operation corresponds to the Geiger-Muller detector.
  d. There are three distinct regions to this curve.

12 Which of the following is a gas-filled detector?
  a. Geiger-Muller counter
  b. scintillation counter
  c. thermoluminescent dosimeter
  d. film badge

13 When making a measurement of radiation exposure in air, a(n) _____ should be used.
  a. film badge   **c.** TLD
  b. scintillation detector **d.** ionization chamber

14 Which of the following is characteristic of a Geiger-Muller counter?
  a. measures integrated radioactivity
  b. for laboratory use only
  c. wide range (1 to 10^4 mR/hr)
  d. measures counts per minute

15 Which of the following is characteristic of scintillation monitors that are sometimes used as survey instruments?
  a. very low detection efficiency
  b. independent of energy
  c. can detect individual ionizations
  d. need extremely high voltage

16 Sodium iodide is a good gamma-ray detector because
  a. it has a high Z.
  b. it has an energy resolution of about 1%.
  c. photoelectrons are easily collected for charge measurement.
  d. it is gas filled.

17 Scintillation counters _____ than Geiger-Muller counters.
  a. are more sensitive to gamma rays
  b. are less sensitive to beta rays
  c. will count longer
  d. have a lower background counting rate

18 Which of the following can be used to detect gamma radiation?
  a. lithium fluoride
  b. photographic emulsion
  c. Geiger-Muller counter
  d. all of the above

19 The active element of a gas-filled radiation detector is the
  a. planchet.
  b. central electrode.
  c. ionization region.
  d. scintillation crystal.

20 A hermetic seal is used to
  a. shield against radiation.
  b. keep light out.
  c. keep moisture out.
  d. maintain a vacuum.

Name _____

Date _____

Radiation Protection Procedures

OCCUPATIONAL EXPOSURE
....

PATIENT DOSE
....

The biologic effects of radiation are influenced by a number of factors, the most important of which is the radiation dose. Radiation control procedures in diagnostic radiology are designed to maintain occupational exposures and patient dose **ALARA** while producing quality images. This requires estimation and measurement of patient dose.

There are three ways to express patient dose. The first, entrance exposure, or **skin dose,** can be easily measured. One can directly measure the output intensity of an x-ray unit at the source-to-skin distance (SSD), or one can position dosimeters such as those used in thermoluminescence dosimetry (TLD) on the skin of the patient for direct measurement during examination. Entrance exposure is usually expressed in units of mR; however, conversion to skin dose in mrad is not difficult.

The second method of expressing patient dose is to state the radiation dose to the bone marrow. This dose, of course, cannot be measured directly but must be computed from phantom exposures and skin measurements. The marrow dose is used to estimate the population **mean marrow dose,** which is considered to be an indication of the leukemogenic radiation hazard.

A third method of expressing patient dose relates to organ dose and specifically to gonad dose. Gonad dose can be directly measured in males but can only be estimated in females. This is an important patient dose quantity because from it is estimated the **genetically significant dose (GSD).** The GSD is that dose of radiation which, if received by the entire population, would result in the same dose to the gene pool that is actually received by those irradiated.

EXERCISES

1 To protect a patient from soft radiation, one should use
   a. a high speed screen.
   b. a cone.
   c. a small focal spot.
   d. an aluminum filter.
2 In radiography of the lumbar spine, which technique would provide the **least** radiation exposure?
   a. 84 kVp, 100 mAs
   b. 90 kVp, 100 mAs
   c. 100 kVp, 50 mAs
   d. 120 kVp, 25 mAs
3 Which of the following units is most appropriate when expressing patient dose?
   a. roentgen
   b. coulomb/kilogram
   c. rem
   d. gray
4 All of the following procedures help to reduce patient dose during x-ray examination **except** using
   a. cones.   **c.** fast screens.
   b. filtration.   **d.** grids.
5 When producing an acceptable radiograph, patient dose increases as _____ increases.
   a. film speed   **c.** kVp
   b. grid ratio   **d.** SID

"It took us a helluva lot of x rays but we've diagnosed your problem. You've been exposed to too much radiation."

6 Which of the following is **most** important in determining patient dose during radiography?
  a. size of the field exposed
  b. grid ratio
  c. size of the focal spot
  d. single-phase or three-phase power

7 Which of the following procedures might result in skin dose exceeding 10 rad?
  a. intravenous pyelogram (IVP)
  b. 5 minutes of fluoroscopy
  c. mammogram
  d. sonogram

8 A multidirectional tomographic examination of the orbit may cause
  a. a gonad dose as high as 1 rad.
  b. a lens dose as high as 20 rad.
  c. the probability of cataract induction to be approximately 10%.
  d. leukemia.

9 The genetically significant dose (GSD) is
  a. a radiation dose that will produce chromosome aberrations.
  b. the radiation dose considered to be the threshold for genetic mutations.
  c. an index of radiation received by the gene pool.
  d. used to predict the level of genetic damage.

10 The mean marrow dose is
  a. greater than the gonad dose for examinations of the abdomen and pelvis.
  b. considered an important indicator of somatic radiation hazard.
  c. approximately 200 mrad/yr.
  d. that which results in leukemia.

11 The current U.S. level of GSD from medical radiation is approximately
  a. 2 mrad/yr.   **c.** 200 mrad/yr.
  b. 20 mrad/yr.   **d.** 2000 mrad/yr.

12 The average annual occupational exposure received by a radiologic technologist is approximately
  a. 10 to 50 mrem.   **c.** 500 to 800 mrem.
  b. 100 to 300 mrem.   **d.** 1000 to 5000 mrem.

13 If a KUB (radiography of the kidneys, ureters, and bladder) examination of a 26-year-old female is conducted, which will be highest?
  a. skin dose   **c.** mean marrow dose
  b. bone marrow dose **d.** gonad dose

14 Which of the following examinations will probably result in the highest skin dose?
  a. lateral skull   **c.** lumbar spine
  b. cervical spine   **d.** abdomen

15 If the skin dose from a single CT scan is compared to that from multiple scans, the
  a. single scan dose will be slightly higher.
  b. dose will be the same for both.
  c. multiple scan dose will be slightly higher.
  d. multiple scan dose will be proportionally higher in relation to the number of scans.

16 Which of the following is **not** a beam-restricting device designed for patient protection purposes?
  a. a dental pointer cone with an integral diaphragm
  b. 2.5 mm Al added filtration
  c. fluoroscopic shutters
  d. a positive beam-limiting (PBL) system

17 At 70 kVp, 10 mAs, the patient dose is 50 mrad. What is it at 86 kVp, 5 mAs?
  a. 25 mrad
  b. 31 mrad
  c. 38 mrad
  d. 151 mrad

18 The exposure to a patient undergoing a radiographic examination can be reduced by all **except**
  a. using the smallest possible field size.
  b. increasing the filtration of the x-ray beam.
  c. using a high speed screen.
  d. using a grid.

19 The GSD from diagnostic radiology is influenced by all **except** the
  a. age of patient.
  b. sex of patient.
  c. occupation of patient.
  d. fraction of population examined.

20 The GSD from medical radiation exposure depends on
  I. the number of persons examined in any given year.
  II. the future childbearing expectancy of the population in any given year.
  III. the average gonad dose per examination.
  a. I   **c.** I and II
  b. II   **d.** I, II, and III

Radiation Protection Procedures

REDUCTION OF OCCUPATIONAL EXPOSURE

....

REDUCTION OF UNNECESSARY PATIENT DOSE

....

The maximum permissible dose (MPD) applies only to occupationally exposed persons, not to patients. It is the dose of radiation below which the probability of harmful somatic or genetic effects is vanishingly small, even when the MPD is received each year of a working career. Some currently recommended MPDs are as follows:

Whole body	5000 mrem/yr (50 mSv/yr)
Cumulative whole body	1000 mrem × age (10 mSv × age)
Lens of eye	15,000 mrem/yr (150 mSv/yr)
Other organs	50,000 mrem/yr (500 mSv/yr)

Personnel monitoring is a program designed to measure the occupational exposure of workers. The quantity measured is the dose equivalent (DE), and the unit of dose equivalent is the rem (sievert).

Nearly all occupational radiation exposure received by radiologic technologists occurs during fluoroscopy and portable radiography. Consequently, it is during these procedures that maximum care with attention to good radiation safety practices should be observed. Without doubt the greatest influence on accurate estimation of personnel radiation exposure is the position at which the radiation monitoring device is worn. Although there is no uniform code regarding the positioning of the personnel radiation monitor, most would agree that during fluoroscopy and portable radiography, when a protective apron is worn, the monitor should be positioned above the apron on the collar region.

EXERCISES

1 Which of the following is **not** helpful in a personnel radiation monitoring program?
   a. film badges
   b. routine blood examinations
   c. pocket ionization chambers
   d. thermoluminescence dosimeter (TLD)

2 Pocket ionization chambers are not normally employed in a radiology personnel monitoring program because they
   a. require daily attention and recording.
   b. are not sufficiently sensitive.
   c. must be worn for at least 2 weeks.
   d. are heat and humidity sensitive.

3 To reduce occupational exposure during portable x-ray examination, the
   a. technologist should wear a personnel monitor.
   b. technologist should wear a protective apron.
   c. radiographic tube head should have PBL.
   d. patient should be given a film badge.

4 In evaluating a personnel monitoring report,
   a. the skin dose is considered the sum of the whole body dose and the extremity dose.
   b. beta radiation is considered to contribute to the whole body dose.
   c. the column for unused permissible dose applies to employees under 18 years of age.
   d. it is recommended that the cumulative quarterly dose should not exceed 1250 mrem.

5 Which of the following is required on the personnel monitoring report?
   a. occupational position
   b. birthdate
   c. cumulative annual skin exposure
   d. activity in millicuries

6 Recommendations proposed for portable x-ray machines state that the exposure cord should be at least _____ long.

a. 1 m   c. 1.8 m
b. 1.5 m   d. 3 m

7 Personnel monitoring is required

a. for all radiology employees.
b. only for technologists and radiologists.
c. when it is likely that one will receive 1/10 the MPD.
d. when it is likely that one will receive ¼ the MPD.

8 Which of the following is **not** normally used as a personnel monitor?

a. Geiger-Muller tube   c. film badge
b. pocket ion chamber   d. TLD

9 Which of the following personnel monitors can be worn the longest?

a. Geiger-Muller tube
b. pocket ionization chamber
c. film badge
d. TLD

10 During fluoroscopy the personnel radiation monitor should be worn

a. on the collar.   c. at the waist.
b. on the chest.   d. anywhere; it really does not matter.

11 The longest time interval allowed for personnel monitoring is

a. every 2 weeks.   c. every 2 months.
b. monthly.   d. quarterly.

12 A 0.25 mm Pb equivalent apron will attenuate a 75 kVp x-ray beam by approximately

a. 10%.   c. 70%.
b. 30%.   d. 90%.

13 Which of the following persons is the most appropriate choice to hold a patient during a radiologic examination?

a. radiologic technologist   c. nurse
b. radiology secretary   d. relative

14 Which of the following statements is true regarding the use of protective apparel?

a. It is unnecessary during portable radiography.
b. During pregnancy, two aprons should be worn.
c. Gloves should be worn by all who hold patients.
d. Aprons are required even when behind the control booth barrier.

15 Which of the following personnel radiation monitors is most sensitive?

a. Geiger-Muller tube
b. pocket ionization chamber
c. film badge
d. TLD

16 Which of the following is an advantage of film over TLD for personnel monitoring?

a. can be used for longer periods of time
b. is less energy dependent in the diagnostic range
c. is cheaper
d. is less sensitive to heat and humidity

17 Personnel monitoring of the extremities should be required

a. when the dose to the hands may exceed 5000 mrem/yr.
b. during special fluoroscopic procedures where the hand may be in or near the useful beam.
c. during contrast injections.
d. during portable radiography.

18 Filters are used in film badges to

a. discriminate between different radiation energies.
b. discriminate between different directions of radiation.
c. correct for film fog.
d. increase the sensitivity.

19 Protective lead aprons are **not** required when the technologist remains in the examination room

a. during fluoroscopy.
b. while holding a patient.
c. during mammography.
d. during overhead radiography.

20 Which of the following screening examinations is recommended?

a. an annual mammogram for women over 50 years of age
b. a chest x-ray on hospital admission
c. a preemployment lumbar spine x-ray
d. a chest x-ray for the general population

CROSSWORD PUZZLES

ACROSS

1. Rate of change of velocity with time
3. X-ray procedure that allows radiologist to view a moving, dynamic image
4. Removal of an electron from an atom
5. Rate of doing work
7. Removal of low-energy photons from the useful beam
8. Unit of occupational exposure
10. Rate of change of position with time
12. Newton's first law; often called the law of _____
13. Force on a body caused by pull of gravity on the body

DOWN

2. Restriction of the x-ray beam to the area of interest
5. Energy based on ability to do work by virtue of position
6. Mass × Acceleration = _____
9. Energy of motion
11. Unit of heat

ANSWERS ON P. 381

ACROSS

1. Bergonié and Tribondeau state that when metabolic activity is high, _____ is also high.
6. A radiation dose delivered continuously but at a lower dose rate is said to be _____.
8. The most _____ portion of the cell cycle occurs in the late S-phase.
9. Fuel for cell metabolism in the body is the chief function of _____ in the body.
10. The reduction division process by germ cells is called

_____.
11. The principal action of radiation on humans is through the _____ effect.

DOWN

2. The dose-response relationship, which expects a response to any dose, regardless of dose size, is called

_____.
3. As LET _____, the ability of ionizing radiation to produce a biologic response increases.
4. _____ molecules are life supporting and contain carbon.
5. A free _____ is an uncharged molecule containing a single, unpaired electron in the outermost shell.
7. In the DNA molecule one possible base-bonding combination is adenines to _____.

ANSWERS ON P. 382

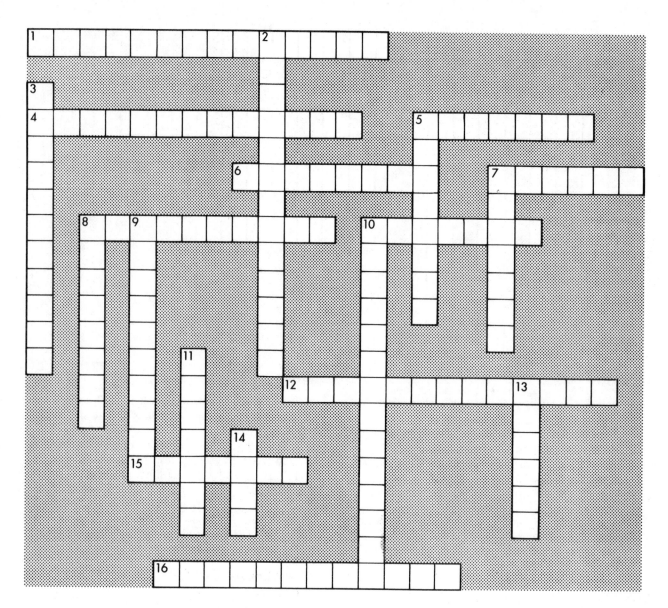

ACROSS

1. X-ray production at discrete energy levels
4. Method of converting AC to DC
5. Type of energy most electron energy is converted to at anode
6. Unit of measure for ionizations in air
7. _____ induction is possible only with AC and is the way transformers work.
8. Level of voltage above which mA is solely a function of filament temperature
10. The author of my favorite rad tech physics book!
12. X-ray production interaction based on absorption in the diagnostic energy range
15. The negative diode of the x-ray tube
16. On graduation and successful completion of the boards every rad tech student deserves to be called a "Radiologic _____ "

DOWN

2. X-rays emitted in all directions
3. Device used to alter intensity of voltage and current
5. Common anode material
7. Wavelength associated with maximum photon energy
8. The filament transformer is _____ transformer.
9. _____ emission denotes electron release by a material when heated to sufficient temperature.
10. Also known as "braking" x-ray production
11. X-ray interaction that dominates at higher energy levels in the diagnostic range
13. Dashes on spin top image, half-wave rectified, single-phase equipment, 0.5 second
14. Number of diodes required for full-wave rectification

ANSWERS ON P. 383

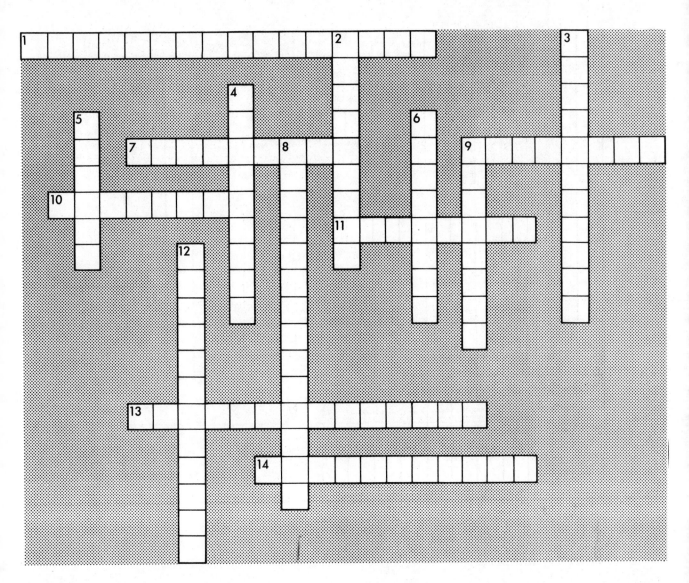

ACROSS

1. During processing, silver atoms are attracted to and concentrate at this location.
7. Reducing agent that acts rapidly and controls lighter shades of gray
9. _____ quality refers to the permanence of the radiograph.
10. If replenishment rate is too low, a significant _____ in contrast will occur.
11. Higher speed film has thicker _____
13. Hardener included in developer
14. Device that controls the replenishment rate of processing chemistry

DOWN

2. Most commonly used radiographic film base today
3. Film designed to be exposed to ultraviolet light through an exposed radiograph
4. Curved metal lip that assists film around turns in bottom of a transport rack
5. Invisible image on film after exposure but before processing
6. Developer is an _____ solution.
8. Another name for green-sensitive film
9. Irregular-density on radiograph *not* caused by shadowing of object by primary beam
12. Reducing agent that acts slowly and is responsible for very blackest shades of radiograph

ANSWERS ON P. 384

ACROSS

4. Period of apparent well-being following the initial radiation sickness.
5. Radiation protection guidelines are based on a linear, _____ dose-response relationship.
6. All cells of the hemopoietic system develop from the _____ stem cells.
8. A commonly used angiographic contrast medium from 1925 to 1945 that has since been proven to cause cancer
9. Loss of hair

DOWN

1. Acute radiation syndrome that typically occurs following doses of approximately 1000 to 5000 rad
2. LD$_{50/30}$ is the radiation dose that will result in _____ within 30 days to 50% of the subjects so irradiated.
3. Ulceration and denudation of the skin
4. The _____ and the spermatogoni are considered the most radiosensitive cells in the body.
6. Nausea, vomiting, diarrhea, and/or white cell count reduction immediately following a dose of about 100 rad; the _____ syndrome
7. Sunburnlike reddening of the skin

ANSWERS ON P. 385

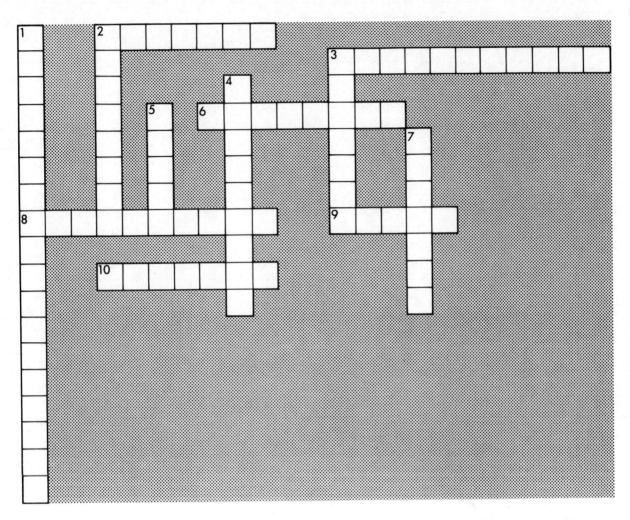

ACROSS

2. _____ radiation is the useful diagnostic x-ray beam.
3. Annual occupational exposure that would not be expected to produce radiation effects; the maximum _____ dose
6. Dose to an individual is _____ related to the duration of exposure.
8. Largest source of unnecessary patient dose: x-ray examination(s)
9. _____ filtration of diagnostic beam operated above 70 kVp must be at lease 2.5 mm Al.
10. Protective housing of an x-ray tube must reduce radiation to less than 100 mR/hr at 1 m.

DOWN

1. _____ dosimeter is most often used to measure skin dose.
2. _____ x-ray equipment must have an exposure cord at least 1.8 m long.
3. Most important scattering object in radiology
4. _____ personnel monitoring device is to be worn for no longer than 1 month.
5. While wearing a protective apron in fluoroscopy, the radiologic technologist should wear the personnel monitor _____ the apron on the collar.
7. _____ shielding should be used for all patients who are potentially reproductive when it does not interfere with the diagnosis.

ANSWERS ON P. 386

EXPERIMENT SECTION

Inverse Square Law

OBJECT

To demonstrate the effect that distance from the x-ray source has on x-ray intensity.

DISCUSSION

X rays are emitted isotropically (i.e., with equal intensity in all directions) from the target of the x-ray tube. The anode and diagnostic housing prevent x rays from exiting in any direction other than through the window of the tube and port of the housing. The collimator or other beam-restricting devices further define the useful x-ray beam. The intensity of the x-ray beam decreases as the square of the distance from the source. If the distance from the source is doubled, the intensity will be reduced to one fourth its former value. This relationship, known as the **inverse square law,** is based solely on geometry. It has nothing to do with x-ray absorption. The x-ray intensity (I_1) passing through a unit area at some distance (r_1) from the target will be

$$I_1 = \frac{I_0}{4\pi r_1^2}$$

where I_0 is the total number of x rays emitted from the target. The intensity (I_2) at any other distance (r_2) from the target will similarly be as follows:

$$I_1 = \frac{I_0}{4\pi r_2^2}$$

Combining these equations:

$$\frac{I_1}{I_2} = \frac{\dfrac{I_0}{4\pi r_1^2}}{\dfrac{I_0}{4\pi r_2^2}} \quad \text{and} \quad \frac{I_2}{I_2} = \frac{\dfrac{I_0}{r_1^2}}{\dfrac{I_0}{r_2^2}}$$

results in

$$\frac{I_1}{I_2} = \frac{r_2^2}{r_1^2} = \left(\frac{r_2^2}{r_1^2}\right)$$

MATERIALS REQUIRED

Radiographic x-ray unit
Ionization chamber
Tape measure

PROCEDURE

1. The x-ray machine may be used as it is normally filtered. Record the total filtration present if known.
2. Set the tube potential to 70 kVp. This will remain constant throughout the experiment.
3. Locate the position of the source (the target) of x rays. Many tube housings are marked at the position of the target; if not, assume the target position to be at the middle of the tube housing.
4. Position the ionization chamber on the central ray of the useful beam and as close to the source as possible.
5. Record this distance on the data sheet provided and take three readings of intensity. If possible, the mA and exposure time should remain constant throughout this experiment. However, if the response range of the ionization chamber will not accommodate such measurements, either or both may require adjustment.
6. Repeat these measurements at approximately 25 cm intervals to a distance of 200 cm from the source.
7. Express the radiation intensity as exposure rate (mR/mAs) at each distance by use of the following expression:

Exposure rate (mR/mAs) =

$$\frac{\text{Exposure (mR)}}{\text{Tube current (mA) exposure time(s)}}$$

RESULTS

Plot exposure rate (mR/mAs) as a function of distance from the source (cm) on the semilog graph paper provided.

EXERCISES

1 What was the shape of the curve obtained? Why?
2 Calculate the quantity $1\sqrt{mR/mAs}$, and plot this as a function of distance from the target on the linear graph paper provided. What is the appearance of this curve and why? Where does the curve intersect the x axis (distance axis), and where should it have intersected?

3 If the output intensity of an x-ray tube is 2.5 mR/mAs (0.65 μC/kg-mAs) at 100 cm source-to-image receptor distance (SID), what would the intensity be at 150 cm SID?
4 The output intensity is shown to be 150 mR/mAs (3.87×10^{-5} C/kg-mAs) at 100 cm SID. At what SID will the intensity be 100 mR/mAs?

DATA SHEET
Laboratory experiment 1

| Source to ionization chamber distance (cm) | Exposure (mR) | | | | Tube current (mA) | Exposure time(s) | mAs | mR/mAs | $\frac{1}{\sqrt{mR/mAs}}$ |
	First measurement	Second measurement	Third measurement	Average					

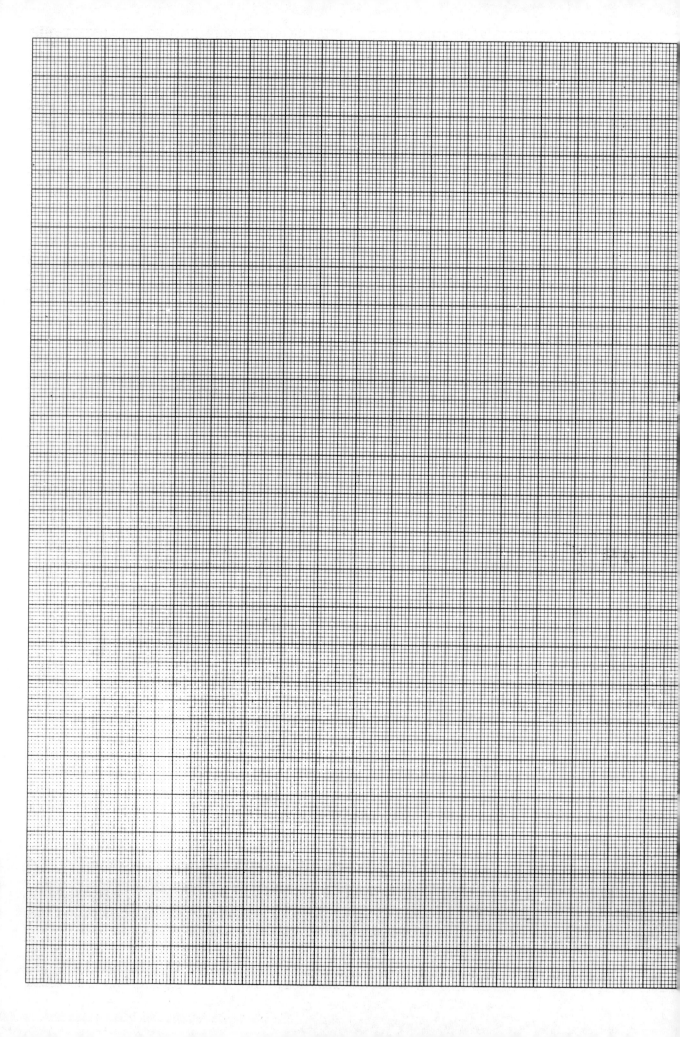

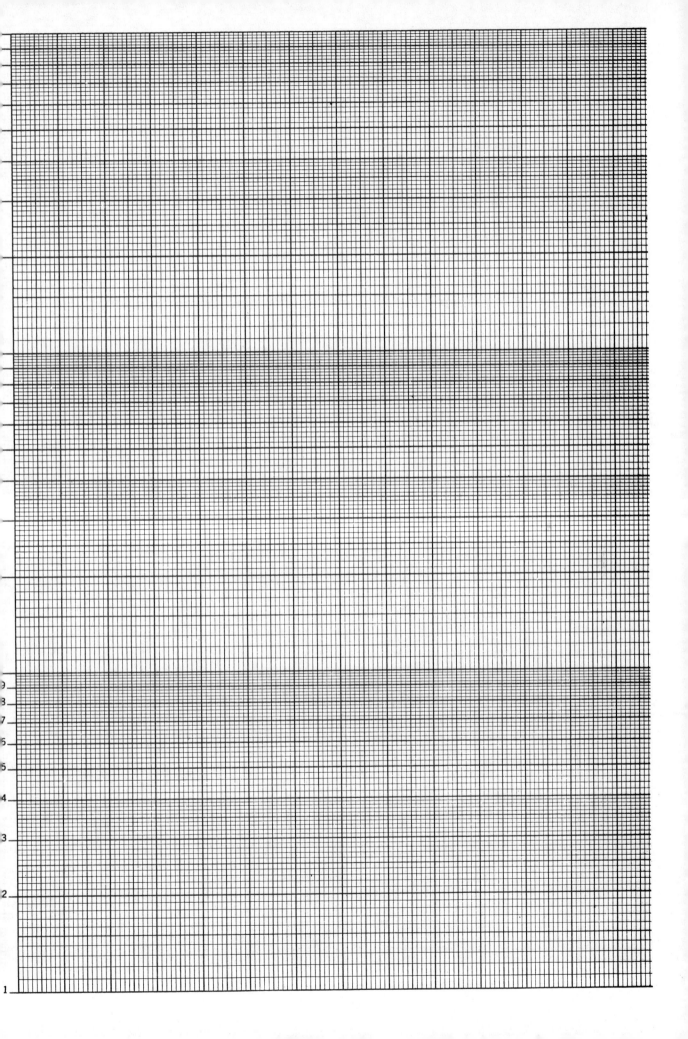

Name _____

Date _____

Effect of Source-To-Image Receptor Distance on Optical Density

OBJECT

To demonstrate the effect of changing the source-to-image receptor distance (SID) on the optical density (OD) of the image.

DISCUSSION

As demonstrated in experiment 1, an adjustment in SID changes radiation intensity is inversely proportional in proportion to the inverse square of the distance. The intensity of the x-ray beam directly controls the OD of the film; consequently film responds according to the same law. To maintain a given OD when changing SID, technique must be compensated according to a "square law." For example, if the distance were reduced to one half, the mAs should be cut to one quarter (one half squared). If this adjustment were not made to compensate for the change in distance, then the resulting radiograph would be four times darker according to the inverse square law.

MATERIALS REQUIRED

Radiographic x-ray machine
Step-wedge penetrometer
X-ray film processor
200-speed 14 in × 17 in (35 cm × 42 cm) screen film cassette
Leaded rubber sheets
Rectangular sponge approximately 4 inches thick
Tape measure
Lead numbers
View box
Densitometer
Calculator

PROCEDURE

1. Warm up the processor if needed, and run a couple of "scrap" films through it to stabilize temperature and circulation.
2. Load and place the cassette on the tabletop. Three exposures will be taken on one film. Collimate the light field to a 5 in × 10 in area crosswise at one end of the film. Use the leaded sheets to mask the adjacent film area.
3. Place the thick, flat sponge over the light-field area. This creates a large object-to-film distance, which must be kept constant on all exposures.
4. Place the step-wedge penetrometer crosswise on the sponge, centered to the light field.
5. Number each exposure with a lead marker on the cassette. Take three exposures using the following techniques or alternate techniques to accommodate your equipment.

Exposure 1	Carefully set the SID at 100 cm to the tabletop.
	Technique: 100 mA, 0.1 s (1/10 s; 100 ms), 50 kVp.
Exposure 2	Carefully set the SID at 50 cm to the tabletop. Be sure to collimate the light field, opening it up to include the entire step wedge if possible.
	Technique: 100 mA, 0.025 s (1/40 s; 2.5 ms), 50 kVp.
Exposure 3	Place the cassette on the floor with the sponge and step wedge over the last third of the film. Carefully measure and set the SID to 180 cm from the cassette. Collimate the light field.
	Technique: 100 mA, 0.35 s (3/10 s; 350 ms), 50 kVp.

6. Process the film.
7. On the resulting images, select a step on the step

251

TABLE E2–1

	Total mAs	SID	OD
Exposure 1			
Exposure 2			
Exposure 3			

wedge from which to take OD measurements. On exposure 1, the selected step must have a medium OD, between 1.0 and 2.0. Using the densitometer, determine the optical density at this step for each exposure.

RESULTS

In Table E2-1, record for each exposure the total mAs used at each SID and the measured OD.

EXERCISES

1 Compute the relative change in OD for exposures 2 and 3 by dividing the OD for 1 into that for 2 and by dividing the OD for 1 into 3, and record here:

2/1:_____ 3/1:_____

2 Compute the average OD change by summing these two ratios and then dividing by two:

Average density change ratio:_____

3 OD change ratio of 1.0 would indicate that the ODs produced by the different techniques are exactly the same. Is your computed average change within 15% of the original; that is, does it fall between 0.85 and 1.15?

4 Visually compare exposure 2 to exposure 1. In 2 the SID was reduced to one half of the original, and, using the square law, the mAs was reduced to one fourth. Did the "square law" for the technique reasonably maintain image OD in this case?

5 On exposure 2, if the mAs had not been adjusted, how dark would the exposure have turned out compared to 1?

6 If the SID were doubled, what change in mAs would be required to maintain OD?

7 Restate your answer to 5 in terms of sets of doubling mAs. For example, would you double the original mAs once, twice, three times, or four times to compensate?

8 Now consider a change in SID from 100 cm to 150 cm. This can be thought of as going halfway to doubling the distance. In light of your answer to 6, how many doublings of mAs would be required at 150 cm to maintain a constant OD?

9 Visually compare 3 with 1. The SID for exposure 3 was 180 cm, roughly halfway between 150 cm and 200 cm. Was OD reasonably maintained? By what ratio was the mAs increased for exposure 3?

10 As a rule of thumb, by what factor must mAs be changed to compensate for adjusting the SID from 100 cm to 180 cm?

EXPERIMENT 3

Effect of Source-To-Image Receptor Distance on Image Blur

OBJECT

To demonstrate the effect of changing the source-to-image receptor distance (SID) on the degree of blurring of an image.

DISCUSSION

In addition to optical density (OD), distance affects two geometric properties of an image. The amount of focal spot blurring in an image is inversely proportional to the SID. Long SIDs result in less blur and increased sharpness. The magnification of the image is reduced with a long SID. Usually blur and magnification are undesirable; therefore as a rule the longest practical SID should be used.

MATERIALS REQUIRED

Radiographic x-ray machine
Small dry bone such as a phalanx (or other small object)
Line pairs per millimeter (lp/mm) resolution test pattern
X-ray film processor
200-speed 14 in × 17 in (35 cm × 42 cm) screen film cassette
Leaded rubber sheets
Rectangular sponge approximately 4 inches thick
Tape measure
Lead numbers
View box
Calculator

PROCEDURE

1. Warm up processor if needed, and run a couple of "scrap" films through it to stabilize temperature and circulation.
2. Load and place the cassette on the tabletop. Two exposures will be taken on one film. Collimate the light field to a 5 in × 10 in area crosswise at one end of the film. Use the leaded sheets to mask the adjacent film area.
3. Place the thick, flat sponge over the light-field area to create a large object-to-film distance, which must be kept constant on all exposures.
4. Place the resolution template crosswise on the sponge with the small bone alongside. Pay close attention to the position in which the bone is laid, since you must lay it precisely the same way on subsequent exposures.
5. Number each exposure with a lead marker on the cassette. Take two exposures using the following techniques or alternate techniques to accommodate available equipment.

Exposure 1	Carefully set the SID to 50 cm. Open the light field to include the resolution template and the bone. Technique: 50 mA, 0.008 s (1/120 s; 8 ms), 60 kVp.
Exposure 2	Place the cassette on the floor with the sponge, resolution template and bone over the other half of the film. Carefully measure and set the SID at 180 cm. Technique: 50 mA, 0.1 s (1/10 s; 100 ms), 60 kVp.

6. Process the film.

RESULTS

On the images of the resolution test pattern, scan across the black and white line pairs from thickest to thinnest, and determine the first position where they are so blurred that you cannot distinguish separate lines from one another. Note this value of lp/mm. Refer to the test pattern itself or to the table provided by your instructor.

	SID	Resolution in lp/mm	Bone image length
Exposure 1			
Exposure 2			

Actual bone length: _____

The unit "line pairs per millimeter" (lp/mm) is a direct measurement of spatial resolution or image blur. The greater the number of lp/mm resolved, the better the resolution of the system and the less blur there is in the image. In the table below, record each SID and the lp/mm resolved.

When you have completed this, obtain a millimeter ruler and measure the length of the bone images on both exposures. Then, taking care to hold the bone as it was placed on the cassette and lining the ruler up precisely to the same points as you did on the radiographs, measure the length of the actual dry bone. Record these measurements also in Table E3-1.

EXERCISES

1 Visually examine the marrow portion of the bone images for fine trabecular details. At which SID is more detail resolved? At which SID does the image appear to have sharper edges, less blur, and better spatial resolution?

2 Refer to Table E3-1. Which SID resolved the greater number of line pairs per millimeter? Does this agree with your visual observations in exercise 1?

3 What general rule of thumb can you make for SID to consistently produce radiographs with minimum image blur (best resolution)?

4 From Table E3-1 compute the magnification factor (MF) for the two exposures, using the formula below:

$$MF = \frac{\text{Imaged bone length}}{\text{Actual bone length}}$$

Exposure 1 magnification:_____

Exposure 2 magnification:_____

5 Convert the above MFs to percentages by subtracting 1.0 from the ratio and then multiplying the result by 100. (For example, a ratio of $1.33 - 1.0 = 0.33 \times 100 = 33$. This would be 33% magnification.) Record your answers below:

Exposure 1 percent magnification:_____
Exposure 2 percent magnification:_____

6 Which SID caused the greater percent magnification?

7 What general rule of thumb can you make for SID to consistently produce radiographs with minimum magnification?

EXPERIMENT 4

Effect of mAs on X-ray Quantity

OBJECT

To measure the effect on radiation intensity of mAs.

DISCUSSION

The product of x-ray tube current (mA) and exposure time(s) controls the radiation intensity (mR) emitted by the x-ray tube directly. That is, as the mAs is increased, the radiation intensity increases proportionally. Selection of a certain mA station (e.g., 50, 100, 200 mA) causes a precise current to flow through the filament of the x-ray tube cathode. This change in filament current alters the heating of the filament and changes the tube current accordingly. The x-ray tube current is the number of electrons accelerated across the tube from cathode to anode per second. When multiplied by exposure time(s), the product (mAs) represents the total number of electrons used for that exposure. As these electrons strike the target of the anode, x rays are produced. The number of x rays produced is the x-ray output intensity or x-ray quantity.

By following this logic further, one can see that if the number of electrons is increased, the quantity of x rays is increased proportionally. Tube current is controlled by selecting an appropriate mA station. When energized for a certain exposure time, the total mAs obtained determines the x-ray quantity (mR).

MATERIALS REQUIRED

Radiographic x-ray machine
Tape measure
Ionization chamber

PROCEDURE

1. Position the ionization chamber 100 cm from the x-ray source.
2. The x-ray machine may be used as it is normally filtered. Record the amount of total filtration present if possible.
3. Adjust the tube potential to 70 kVp. If, as you change mA stations, the kVp drifts, readjust it to 70 kVp so that it will remain constant throughout the experiment.
4. Select the lowest mA station and, using the data sheet provided, record three readings of radiation intensity.
5. The exposure time selected should be held constant throughout these measurements in case there is a timer error. However, the response range of the ionization chamber may require that exposure time be reduced as mA is increased. If this occurs, note it on the data sheet.
6. Repeat these measurements for at least four additional mA stations, including the small and the large focal spots. The highest possible mA should be one of these five.
7. Determine the average intensity (mR) at each mAs.
8. Express the x-ray intensity as exposure rate in mR/mAs. The following relationship may be used:

$$\text{Exposure rate (mR/mAs)} = \frac{\text{Exposure (mR)}}{\text{mAs}}$$

RESULTS

Plot exposure rate (mR/mAs) vs. mAs on the linear graph paper provided.

EXERCISES

1 What was the shape of the curve obtained? Why?
2 What effect was observed when focal spot size was changed? In a properly designed x-ray machine, what should you expect?
3 Calculate the quantity mR/s at each mA station. If these data were graphed, what would be the shape of the curve?
4 If 200 mA, 0.5 s results in an exposure of 50 mR $(1.29 \times 10^{-5}$ C/kg-mAs), what exposure would 100 mA, 1 s produce?
5 An x-ray machine produces an output intensity of 4.5 mR/mAs $(1.2 \times 10^{-6}$ C/kg-mAs). What radiation

exposure would result from the following conditions?
a. 50 mA, 200 ms
b. 300 mA, 1.5 s
c. 800 mA, 16 ms

Constant factors
70 kVp

Total filtration _____ mm Al
100 cm source-to-detector distance

DATA SHEET
Laboratory experiment 4

Tube current (mA)	Exposure time (s)	Exposure (mR)			Average exposure (mR)	Exposure rate	
		First	Second	Third		mR/mAs	mR/s
Small focal spot							
1							
2							
3							
4							
5							
6							
7							
8							
9							
10							
Large focal spot							
1							
2							
3							
4							
5							
6							
7							
8							
9							
10							

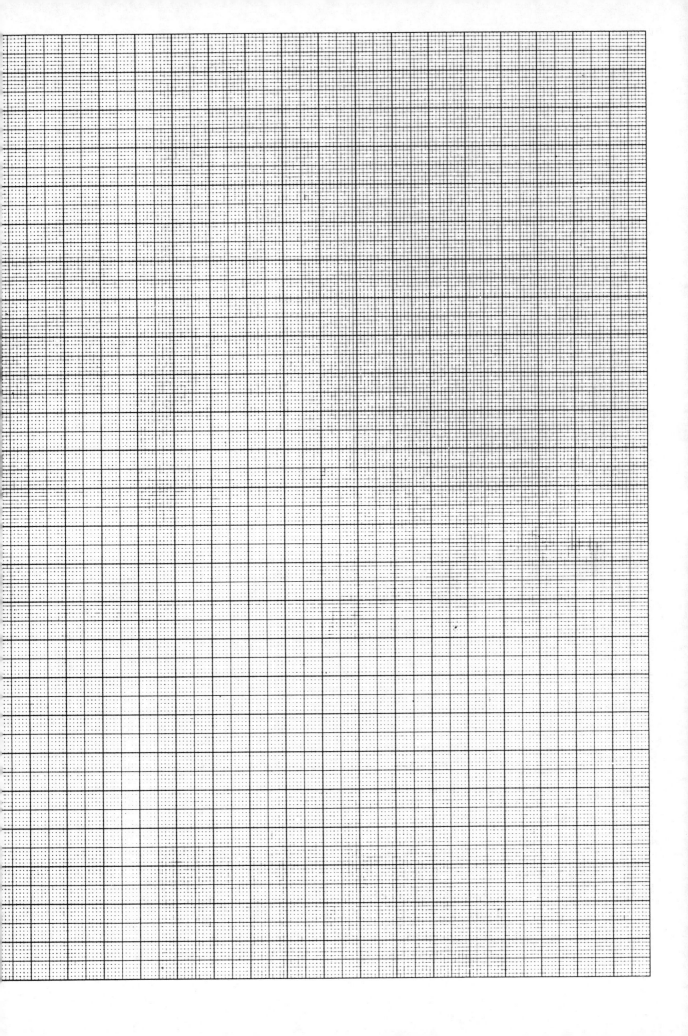

Effect of mAs on Optical Density

OBJECT

To demonstrate the relationship among mA, exposure time, and total mAs and their combined effect on radiographic optical density (OD).

DISCUSSION

When the radiographic unit is properly calibrated, the radiation intensity will be directly proportional to the mA and to the exposure time selected at the console. For example, a doubling of either mA or exposure time will result in twice as much radiation intensity for a particular exposure. The radiographic film normally responds proportionally to exposure; that is, twice the radiation will result in a radiograph twice as dark.

The total mAs is the product of the selected mA station and the exposure time. OD is directly proportional to mAs. To maintain constant OD when the mA is doubled, the exposure time should be cut to one half. Conversely, if the mA is cut to one third its original value, the exposure time should be tripled to maintain constant OD. In other words, mA and exposure time are **inversely** related to each other when maintaining constant mAs and therefore constant OD.

MATERIALS REQUIRED

Radiographic x-ray machine
Step-wedge penetrometer
Leaded rubber sheets
X-ray film processor
200-speed 14 in × 17 in (35 cm × 42 cm) screen film cassette
Lead numbers
View box
Densitometer
Calculator

GENERAL PROCEDURE

1. Set 50 kVp. This will remain constant throughout the experiment. If the kVp drifts when changing mA stations, adjust it to remain constant at 50 kVp.
2. Warm up the processor if needed, and run a couple of "scrap" films through it to stabilize temperature and circulation.
3. Position the x-ray tube 100 cm from the tabletop.

PART II PROCEDURE

1. Load and place the cassette faceup on the tabletop. Place the step-wedge penetrometer crosswise at one end of the cassette. Four exposures will be taken on one film. It is important to use one film so that processing conditions will be constant.
2. Collimate the light field to a 4 in × 10 in area, and center over the step wedge. Use the leaded sheets to mask the adjacent film area to prevent scatter fogging.
3. Number each exposure with a lead marker on the cassette. Take four exposures using the techniques listed below or recording alternate techniques you use. Begin with a very low mA and an exposure time of 0.025 s (1/40 s; 25 ms) or less that can be exactly doubled at least twice. After the first exposure, move the step wedge to the next quarter of the film, double the time as shown in technique 2 below, and so on. For the fourth exposure, double the mA station instead of the time. Always use leaded sheets to mask the cassette adjacent to either side of the exposure area.

Exposure 1	50 mA, 0.05 s (1/20 s; 50 ms)
Exposure 2	50 mA, 0.1 s (1/10 s; 100 ms)
Exposure 3	50 mA, 0.2 s (1/5 s; 200 ms)
Exposure 4	100 mA, 0.2 s (1/5 s; 200 ms)

4. Process the film.
5. On the resulting images, select a step on which to make OD measurements. The step selected must have a measured OD of less than 0.3 on exposure 1, yet it should be visibly darker on exposure 2. This will be an extremely light OD on exposure 1. Using the densitometer, determine the OD for each exposure, taking care to measure the same step each time.

TABLE E5–1

	mA	Time	Total mAs	OD
Exposure 1				
Exposure 2				
Exposure 3				
Exposure 4				

RESULTS

In Table E5-1, record for each exposure the mA and exposure time used, the total resulting mAs, and the measured OD.

EXERCISES

1 Compute the relative OD change for each increase in technique by dividing the density for 2 by that for 1, 3 by that for 2, and 4 by that for 3, and record the results below. You will note that these relative changes vary somewhat because x-ray machines are not perfectly calibrated.

2/1:_____   3/2:_____   4/3:_____

2 Compute an average OD change by summing these three numbers and then dividing by 3:

Average density change:_____

Does this change fall within 15% of a doubling; that is, does it fall between 1.7 and 2.3?

3 If the relationship between total mAs and OD were plotted on linear paper, what would be the appearance of the graph?
4 What term best describes this relationship?
5 In terms of the resulting OD, is there any difference between doubling the mA and doubling the exposure time?

PART II PROCEDURE

1. Load and place the cassette faceup on the tabletop. Place the step-wedge penetrometer crosswise at one end of the cassette. Three exposures will be taken on one film. It is important to use one film so that processing conditions will be constant.
2. Collimate the light field to a 4 in × 10 in area and center over the step wedge. Use the leaded sheets to mask the adjacent film area to prevent scatter fogging.
3. Number each exposure with a lead marker on the cassette. Take three exposures using the techniques listed below or recording alternate techniques you

TABLE E5–2

	mA	Time	total mAs	OD
Exposure 1				
Exposure 2				
Exposure 3				

use. After the first exposure, move the step wedge to the next third of the film. Double the mA station, but cut the exposure time to exactly one half of the original so that the same total mAs results. For exposure 3, double the mA and halve the exposure time again. Always use leaded sheets to mask the cassette adjacent to either side of the exposure area.

Exposure 1   50 mA, 0.2 s (1/5 s; 200 ms)
Exposure 2   100 mA, 0.1 s (1/10 s; 100 ms)
Exposure 3   200 mA, 0.05 s (1/20 s; 50 ms)

4. Process the film.
5. On the resulting images, select a step on which to make OD measurements; the step selected must have a medium-gray OD between 0.5 and 1.5 as measured on the densitometer. Determine the OD for each exposure, taking care to measure the same step each time.

RESULTS

In Table E5-2, record for each exposure the mA and exposure time used, the total resulting mAs, and the measured OD.

EXERCISES

1 Compute the relative OD changes between these techniques by dividing the density for 2 by that for 1, 3 divided by 2, and 3 divided by 1, and record here:

2/1:_____   3/2:_____   3/1:_____

2 Compute the average OD change by summing these three numbers and then dividing by 3:

Average OD change:_____

An OD change ratio of 1.0 would indicate that the ODs produced by the different techniques are exactly the same. Is your computed average change close to 1.0?

3 Visually examine the three images. Is there a substantial difference in OD among them?
4 As long as the total mAs is the same, does the particular mA station or exposure time make any difference in terms of overall OD?
5 In maintaining a given OD, what term would describe the relationship between milliamperage and exposure time?
6 Why should you generally choose short exposure times with high mA station?
7 When would you choose a very long exposure time with a low mA station?

Name _____

Date _____

X-ray Beam Penetration

OBJECT

To demonstrate the relationships among kVp, x-ray beam penetration, and the resulting gray scale of the radiographic image.

DISCUSSION

To produce useful optical densities (ODs) on the radiograph, x rays must first penetrate through each tissue of interest and interact with the film. If the x-ray beam does not have enough energy to penetrate a tissue, an inadequate image will result regardless of how many x rays are used. Therefore no amount of mAs, which controls only x-ray quantity, will ever compensate for insufficient kVp.

As kVp is increased, more different types of tissue are penetrated and recorded on the film. Thus more ODs are present in the image. The image has a longer **gray scale.** Tissues that are not penetrated result in white areas on the radiograph. Such areas have no information recorded and therefore are diagnostically useless.

Adequate penetration is essential to the production of a useful radiograph. Penetration is also directly related to the number of different gray shades produced on the image. The penetrating ability of the x-ray beam, often termed **radiation quality,** is controlled by kVp.

MATERIALS REQUIRED

Radiographic x-ray machine
Pelvis phantom or other large phantom such as a skull
X-ray film processor
200-speed 10 in × 12 in (24 cm × 30 cm) screen film
   cassette
Lead numbers
View box
Densitometer

PROCEDURE

1. Warm up the processor if needed, and run a couple of "scrap" films through it to stabilize temperature and circulation.
2. Position the x-ray tube 100 cm from the tabletop.
3. Load and place a cassette lengthwise in the Bucky tray. Place the pelvis phantom on the table in supine position.
4. Collimate the light field to the film size and center.
5. Number each exposure with a lead marker on the cassette. Take four exposures on separate films using the techniques listed here or alternate techniques to accommodate your equipment.

Exposure 1	200 mA, 0.1 s (1/10 s;100 ms), 84 kVp
Exposure 2	200 mA, 0.2 s (1/5 s; 200 ms), 50 kVp
Exposure 3	200 mA, 0.5 s (½ s; 500 ms), 50 kVp
Exposure 4	200 mA, 1.0 s (1 s; 1000 ms), 50 kVp

6. Process the films.

RESULTS

For comparison purposes, exposure 1 must be of good average OD. If it is not, change the mA station used, but keep the mA constant throughout the experiment.

Visually examine each radiograph in comparison with exposure 1 to determine the amount of diagnostic information present and the number of different shades of gray produced.

EXERCISES

1 For each succeeding exposures 2, 3, and 4, the total mAs was approximately doubled each time, but a very low kVp was used. Note that for exposure 4 the total mAs is 10 times the mAs used for exposure 1. Has a satisfactory OD been achieved on exposure 2, 3, or 4?

2 Would a satisfactory OD be achieved at 40 kVp if the total mAs were increased to 1000 mAs?

3 Explain why this is so in terms of x-ray intensity and beam penetration.

4 Restate your answer from 3 in terms of mAs and kVp.

5 Count the number of different ODs, or shades of gray, on exposure 1 and 2, and record them here:

Exposure 1:_____ Exposure 2:_____

6 Which of these two radiographs displays the longest gray scale?

7 Explain why this is so.

Effect of kVp on X-ray Quantity

OBJECT

To measure the effect of varying x-ray tube potential (kVp) on radiation intensity.

DISCUSSION

Experiment 4 demonstrated that x-ray quantity is directly related to mAs. X-ray quantity varies more rapidly with changes in kVp. The output intensity of an x-ray unit increases approximately as the square of the increase in kVp according to the relationship

$$\frac{I_1}{I_2} = \left(\frac{kVp_1}{kVp_2}\right)^2$$

where I_1 and I_2 are the x-ray intensities at kVp_1 and kVp_2, respectively. The exponent 2 is a reasonable approximation. Experimentally it has been shown to range from 1.5 to 3, depending on the x-ray tube design.

The number of electrons accelerated from cathode to anode is measured by the mAs. The number of accelerated electrons does not change with increasing tube potential (kVp). However, as kVp is increased, each electron possesses increased kinetic energy, which is transformed into more heat and x rays. As kVp is increased, each electron has a higher probability of multiple interactions with target atoms, thereby producing more x rays. Further, each x ray so produced will average a higher energy and therefore be more penetrating.

Changing kVp changes x-ray quantity and quality; changing mAs affects only x-ray quantity.

MATERIALS REQUIRED

Radiographic x-ray unit   Tape measure
Ionization chamber

PROCEDURE

1. Position the ionization chamber 100 cm from the x-ray tube target.

2. The x-ray machine may be used as it is normally filtered. Record the amount of total filtration present if known.
3. Select a low mA station (i.e., less than 100 mA) so that a number of repeat exposures will be possible at all kVp settings without overheating the tube.
4. Beginning at 40 kVp and increasing in 20 kVp increments, record the measured radiation intensity on the data sheet provided. Three measurements should be recorded at each kVp and the average value calculated. In addition to constant mA, the exposure time should remain fixed if the response range of the detector will allow; otherwise, the exposure time will have to be reduced with increasing kVp.
5. Determine the average exposure (mR or C/kg) at each kVp setting.
6. Express the x-ray output intensity as exposure rate in mR/s (C/kg-s). The following relationship may be used:

$$\text{Exposure rate (mR/s)} = \frac{\text{Exposure (mR)}}{\text{Exposure time (s)}}$$

RESULTS

Plot exposure rate (mR/s or C/kg-s) vs. tube potential (kVp) on the linear graph paper provided.

EXERCISES

1 What was the shape of the curve obtained? Why?
2 Calculate the quantity mR/mAs (C/kg-mAs) at each kVp selected. If these data were graphed, what would be the shape of the curve?
3 From the data recorded, estimate the actual value of n for this machine in the following expression:

$$\frac{I_1}{I_2} = \left(\frac{kVp_1}{kVp_2}\right)^n$$

4 From the data obtained, estimate the x-ray quantity resulting from the following factors:
  a. 55 kVp, 100 mA, 50 ms
  b. 73 kVp, 200 mA, 0.25 s
  c. 96 kVp, 50 mA, 750 ms
  d. 124 kVp, 300 mA, 16 ms
  e. 114 kVp, 300 mA, 16 ms

5 A useful rule of thumb states that a 15% increase in kVp accompanied by a 50% reduction of mA will result in the same density on the film and reduced patient exposure. Can this be confirmed by your data? Begin with 70 kVp/50 mAs.

DATA SHEET
Laboratory experiment 7

Constant factors
100 cm source-to-detector distance
mA _____
Filtration _____ mm Al

kVp	Exposure time (s)	Exposure (mR)			Average exposure (mR)	Exposure rate	
		First	Second	Third		mR/s	mR/mAs
1							
2							
3							
4							
5							
6							
7							
8							
9							
10							

265

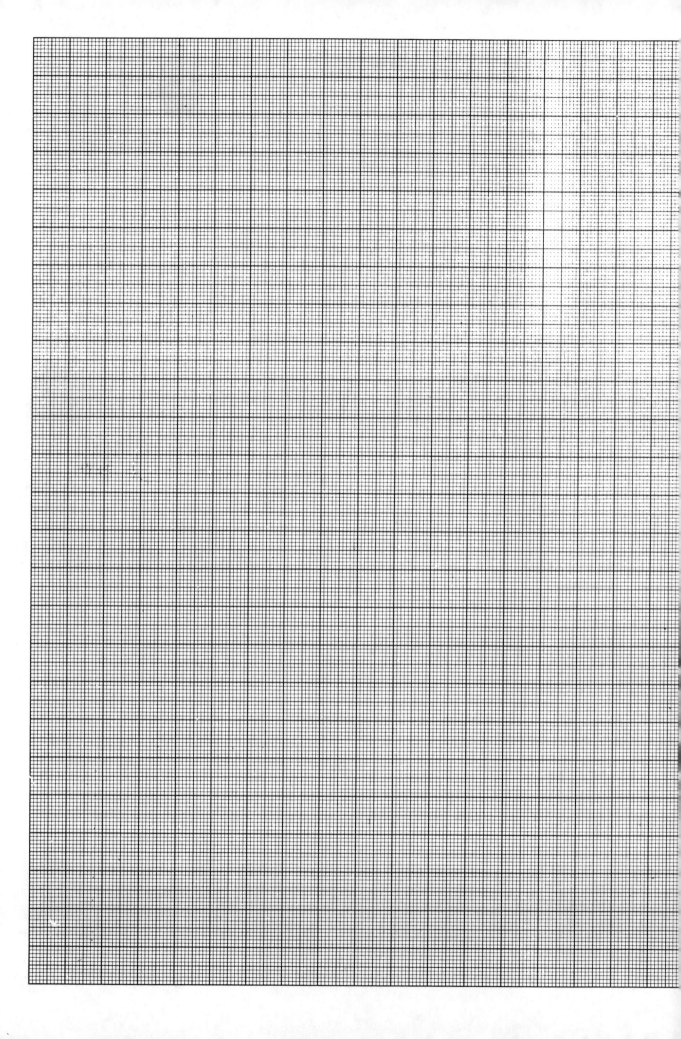

Name _____

Date _____

Effect of kVp on Optical Density

OBJECT

To demonstrate how kVp influences optical density (OD; the 15% rule).

DISCUSSION

Peak kilovoltage controls the energy level of the x-ray beam. This property of the x-ray beam is also called **penetrability,** or x-ray beam quality. At higher energy levels, a greater percentage of the x rays penetrates through the anatomy and reaches the film, thus contributing to OD. Also, at higher kVp the x-ray tube emits more x rays. When this higher radiation intensity is added to the increased penetration, the resulting image becomes much darker. That is, a small change in kVp causes a big change in OD.

When kVp is changed, it is not easy to predict exactly how much OD will change because it depends on two different processes: changing beam intensity and changing beam penetration. However, a rule of thumb traditionally used by radiologic technologists has proved very useful. The **15% rule** states that if the kVp is changed by 15%, the resulting OD will change roughly by a factor of two. Therefore a 15% increase in kVp should be accompanied by a 50% reduction in mAs to maintain constant OD.

MATERIALS REQUIRED

Radiographic x-ray machine
Skull phantom, other large phantom, or large step wedge
X-ray film processor
200-speed 10 in × 12 in (24 cm × 30 cm) screen film cassette
Lead numbers
Positioning sponges
View box
Densitometer
Calculator

PROCEDURE

1. Warm up the processor if needed, and run a couple of "scrap" films through it to stabilize temperature and circulation.
2. Position the x-ray tube 100 cm from the tabletop.
3. Load and place a cassette crosswise on the tabletop. Place the anatomic phantom on the cassette in lateral position, using sponges as needed to balance it.
4. Collimate the light field to the film size, and center to the anatomic phantom.
5. Number each exposure with a lead marker on the cassette. Take four exposures on separate films using the techniques listed here or alternate techniques to accommodate your equipment. If possible, use the same mA station for all exposures. Kilovoltage increases are made in 15% increments. Beginning with exposure 3, these changes are compensated by cutting the exposure time in half each time.

Exposure 1   50 mA, 0.1 s (1/10 s; 100 ms), 70 kVp
Exposure 2   50 mA, 0.1 s (1/10 s; 100 ms), 80 kVp
Exposure 3   50 mA, 0.05 s (1/20 s; 50 ms), 80 kVp
Exposure 4   50 mA, 0.025 s (1/40 s; 25 ms), 92 kVp

6. Process the films.
7. On the resulting images, select an area within the bony anatomy that shows a smooth medium gray OD on exposure 1. Circle this area, and, using the densitometer, determine the OD in this same area for each exposure.

RESULTS

In Table E8-1, record for each exposure the total mAs and kVp used and the measured OD.

EXERCISES

1 Compute the relative OD change for exposure 2 by dividing the OD for 1 into that for 2, and record here:

2/1:_____

TABLE E8–1

	mAs	kVp	OD
Exposure 1			
Exposure 2			
Exposure 3			
Exposure 4			

2 Visually compare exposure 2 to exposure 1. When kVp is increased without adjusting any other factors, what happens to overall OD?

3 According to your preceding calculation, how much darker is exposure 2 compared with exposure 1?

4 Compute the relative OD changes for the adjustments in technique made in the subsequent exposures by dividing the OD for 3 by that for 1, and the OD for 4 by 3, and record here:

    3/1:_____   4/3:_____

5 Compute an average OD change by summing these two numbers and then dividing by 2:

    Average OD change:_____

6 An OD change ratio of 1.0 would indicate that the ODs produced by the different techniques are exactly the same. Is your computed average change within 15% of the original; that is, does it fall between 0.85 and 1.15?

7 In exposures 3 and 4, a 15% increase in kVp was accompanied by halving the mAs. Does the 15% rule of thumb work in approximately maintaining overall OD when changing kVp?

Name _____

Date _____

Effect of kVp on Image Contrast

OBJECT

To demonstrate how image contrast changes when kVp is changed.

DISCUSSION

Kilovoltage also affects image contrast for two important reasons. First, at higher energies, the x rays penetrate more tissues and thus lengthen the gray scale recorded. Gray scale is the opposite of contrast. Second, at higher x-ray beam energies, very few photoelectric interactions occur in the tissues. The fogging of the image from Compton interactions then becomes more apparent. Combining the effects of a longer gray scale with more visible fog, contrast is reduced. Conversely, using low kVp's will restore higher image contrast.

MATERIALS REQUIRED

Radiographic x-ray machine
Skull phantom, other large phantom, or large step wedge
X-ray film processor
Two-speed 10 in × 12 in (24 cm × 30 cm) screen film cassette
Lead number
Positioning sponges
View box
Densitometer
Calculator

PROCEDURE

1. Warm up the processor if needed, and run a couple of "scrap" films through it to stabilize temperature and circulation.
2. Position the x-ray tube 100 cm from the tabletop.
3. Load and place a cassette crosswise on the tabletop. Place the anatomic phantom on the cassette in lateral position, using sponges as needed to balance it.
4. Collimate the light field to the film size, and center to the anatomic phantom.

5. Number each exposure with a lead marker on the cassette. Take two exposures on separate films using the techniques listed below or alternate techniques to accommodate your equipment. If possible, use the same mA station for both exposures.

Exposure 1	50 mA, 0.1 s (1/10 s; 100 ms), 70 kVp
Exposure 2	50 mA, 0.025 s (1/40 s; 25 ms), 92 kVp

6. Process the films.
7. On the resulting images, select an area within the bony anatomy that shows a uniform light gray OD on exposure 1 and a uniform medium gray OD on exposure 2. Circle these areas, and using the densitometer, determine the OD in each area for each exposure.

RESULTS

In Table E9-1, record for each exposure the kVp used and the measured OD in area A and area B.

EXERCISES

1 Compute the contrast for each exposure by subtracting the area A OD by the area B OD, and record here:

   Exposure 1 contrast (A-B):_____
   Exposure 2 contrast (A-B):_____

2 Compare the computed contrast levels. Even though mAs was compensated for kVp to maintain OD, what

TABLE E9–1

	kVP	Area A OD	Area B OD
Exposure 1			
Exposure 2			

happened to the measured contrast for exposure 2 when a much higher kVp was used?

3 Visually compare exposure 2 to exposure 1. When using a much higher kVp, is the change in contrast visible?

4 The difference between exposure 1 and exposure 2 is 22 kVp. Would a difference in contrast be visible for a much smaller change, such as an increase of 4 kVp?

5 Briefly explain why this contrast change occurs at high kVp levels.

EXPERIMENT **10**

Half-value Layer

OBJECT

To determine the half-value layer (HVL) of an x-ray beam under three conditions of kVp.

DISCUSSION

HVL is defined as that thickness of an absorbing material required to reduce the intensity of the x-ray beam to one half its original value. HVL is the single most appropriate unit of measure for beam quality. Total filtration, effective energy, and kVp are also useful for describing beam quality. The absorbing material most often used to determine the HVL of diagnostic x-ray machines is aluminum.

MATERIALS REQUIRED

Radiographic x-ray machine
Ionization chamber
Aluminum absorbers
Ring stand and clamps

PROCEDURE

1. Position the ionization chamber 100 cm from the x-ray source. Place aluminum absorbers approximately midway between the ionization chamber and the x-ray tube target.
2. The x-ray machine may be used as it is normally filtered. Record the amount of total filtration if possible.
3. Using the light localizer, collimate to just cover the area of the ionization chamber.
4. Adjust the tube potential to 60 kVp.
5. Select a technique of mAs that will provide a reading that is nearly full scale on the ionization chamber.
6. Expose the ionization chamber sequentially three times, and record each measurement on the data sheet provided.

7. Insert 0.5 mm Al filtration midway between the target and detector, and record three additional measurements.
8. Repeat this process with added aluminum filtration thicknesses of 1.0, 2.0, 3.0, 4.0, 6.0, and 8.0 mm. If an increase in mA, exposure time, or both is required at greater thicknesses of aluminum filtration, record these changes.
9. Repeat steps 4 through 8 at 90 kVp and again at 120 kVp.
10. Calculate the average intensity (mR) for each level of filtration at each kVp. Express the x-ray intensity in mR/mAs as follows:

X-ray intensity (mR/mAs) =
$$\frac{\text{Average intensity (mR)}}{\text{Tube current (mA)} \times \text{Exposure time (s)}}$$

RESULTS

Plot the x-ray intensity vs. mm Al added filtration for each kVp on the linear and semilog graph paper provided. Estimate the HVL for each curve.

EXERCISES

1 Complete Table E10-1.
2 On the linear graph paper provided, plot HVL vs. kVp. From the extrapolation of this curve, what would be the estimated HVL at 40 kVp? At 140 kVp?

TABLE E10–1

kVp	HVL (mm Al)
60	
90	
120	

3 Given the data obtained at 90 kVp, if an additional 1 mm Al were added to the existing total filtration, what would the HVL be?

4 The homogeneity coefficient is defined as the ratio of the first HVL to the second HVL. From the data collected at 60 and 120 kVp, estimate the homogeneity coefficient for each condition.

DATA SHEET

Laboratory experiment 10

Constant factors
100 cm source-to-ionization chamber distance
Total filtration _____ mm Al

kVp	Added filtration (mm Al)	Tube current (mA)	Exposure time (s)	Exposure (mR)			Average exposure (mR)	mR/mAs
				First	Second	Third		
60	0							
60	0.5							
60	1.0							
60	2.0							
60	3.0							
60	4.0							
60	6.0							
60	8.0							
90	0							
90	5.0							
90	1.0							
90	2.0							
90	3.0							
90	4.0							
90	6.0							
90	8.0							
120	0							
120	0.5							
120	1.0							
120	2.0							
120	3.0							
120	4.0							
120	6.0							
120	8.0							

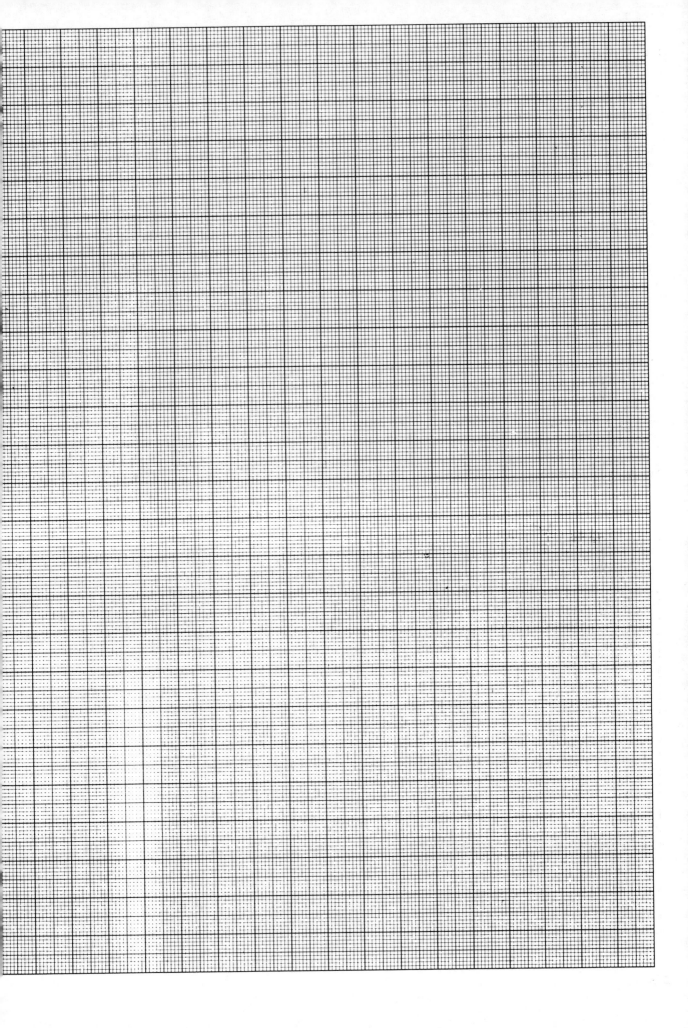

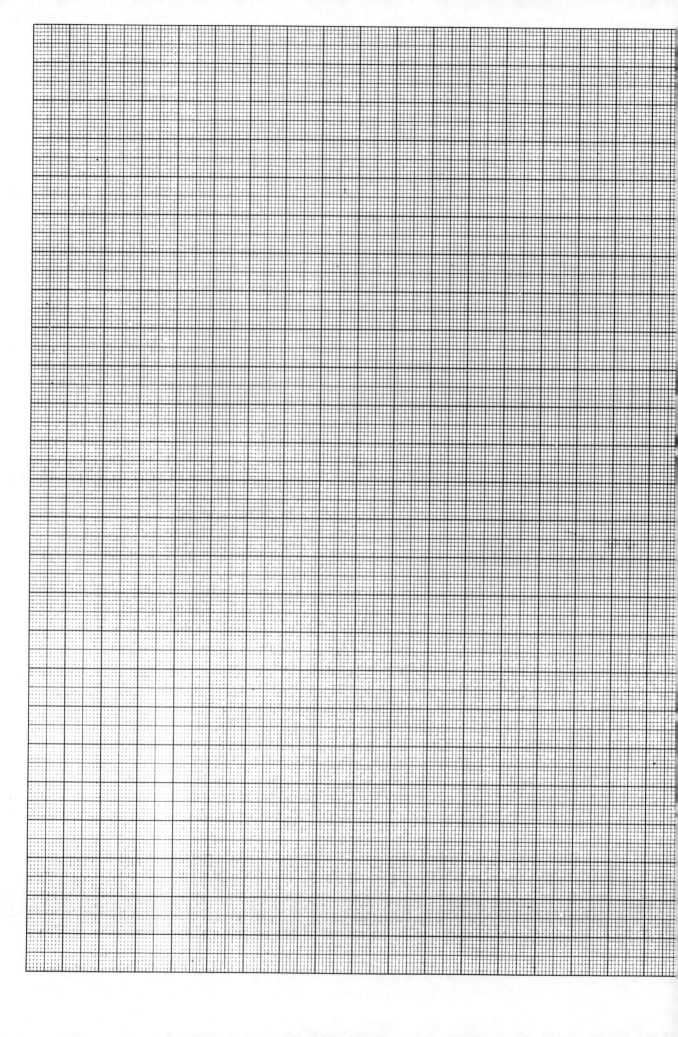

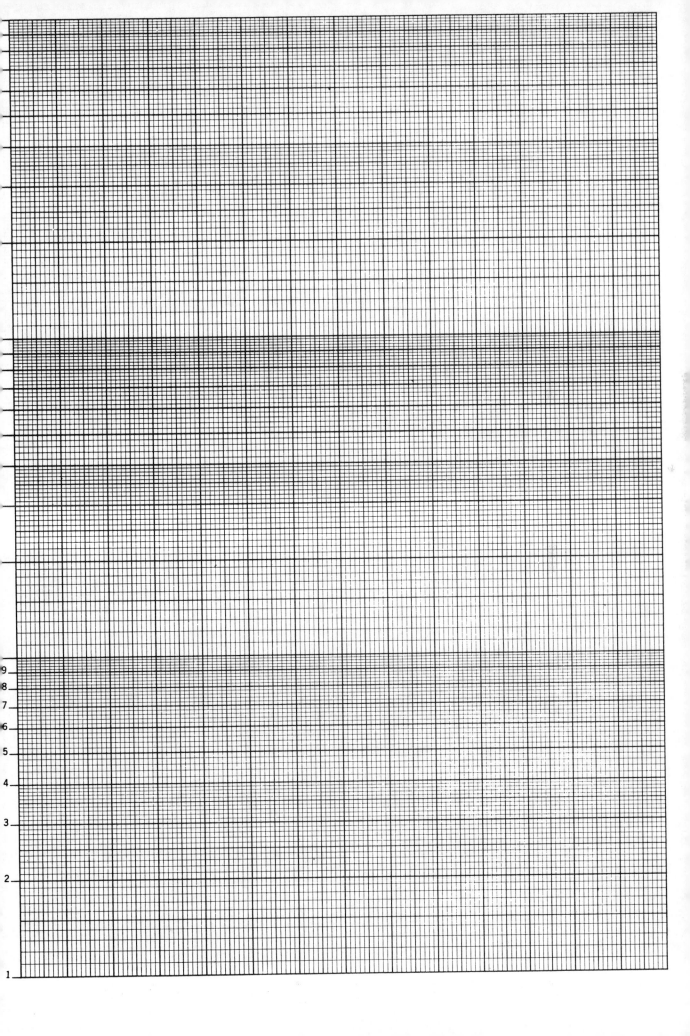

EXPERIMENT 11

Field Size

OBJECT

To demonstrate the effects of field size limitation (collimation) on image optical density (OD) and contrast.

DISCUSSION

When the size of the x-ray field is reduced, a smaller volume of tissue is exposed to radiation. The volume of tissue exposed determines the amount of scatter radiation produced and thus affects the amount of fog density of the radiograph. By collimating the x-ray field to a smaller size, less fog density is produced on the final image, which will therefore demonstrate higher contrast.

The total image OD is contributed to both by primary x rays penetrating to the film and by secondary scatter x rays produced within tissues. In reducing scatter radiation by collimation of the x-ray field to a smaller size one also produces an image with lower OD (lighter).

MATERIALS REQUIRED

Radiographic x-ray machine
Pelvis phantom or other phantom large enough to generate substantial scatter radiation
X-ray film processor
200-speed screen film cassettes, one 14 in × 17 in (35 cm × 42 cm) and one 10 in × 12 in (24 cm × 30 cm) or smaller
Sponges, sandbags, or positioning clamps
Lead numbers
View box
Densitometer
Calculator

PROCEDURE

1. Warm up the processor if needed, and run a couple of "scrap" films through it to stabilize temperature and circulation.

2. Set 86 kVp, 100 mA, and 0.1 s (1/10 s; 100 ms) exposure time. These will remain constant throughout the experiment.
3. Position the x-ray tube 100 cm from the tabletop.
4. Have sponges and sandbags, or clamps, at hand to hold the pelvis phantom in a **lateral** position. If using another test object, position it with the thickest dimension vertical.
5. Number each film with a lead marker on the cassette. Take two exposures on separate films, using the techniques listed here or alternate techniques used to accommodate your equipment.

| Exposure 1 | Load and place the large cassette lengthwise on the tabletop. Place the pelvis phantom in lateral position on the film. Open the field size to 14 in × 17 in, and center over the lumbar vertebrae. Expose the film. |
| Exposure 2 | Load and place the small cassette lengthwise on the tabletop. Place the pelvis phantom in lateral position on the film. Collimate the field size to a 5 in × 5 in square, and center over the lumbar vertebrae. Expose the film using the same technique. |

6. Process the films.
7. On exposure 2, select and circle two uniform OD areas within the anatomy to take densitometer measurements as follows: area A must show a medium dark gray soft tissue density. Area B must show a light gray bony density. Now circle the same two smooth density areas on exposure 1. Using the densitometer, determine the OD in these two areas for each exposure, and record below.

RESULTS

In Table E11-1, record for each exposure the field size used and the measured OD in areas A and B.

TABLE E11–1

	Field size	Area A OD	Area B OD
Exposure 1			
Exposure 2			

EXERCISES

1 In Table E11-1, what happened to the OD in area A when the field size was reduced? Can you visually see the difference in area A between the two films?
2 Why does this effect occur when reducing field size?
3 Compute the radiographic technique change that would be required to maintain OD when field size is reduced in this case as follows: divide area A OD for exposure 2 into that for exposure 1. This is the factor by which mAs must be changed in order to maintain constant OD:

$$\frac{\text{Exposure 1, area A}}{\text{Exposure 2, area A}} = \underline{\hspace{2cm}} =$$

4 Change the above answer into a percentage as follows: from this ratio, subtract 1.0 and then multiply the remaining decimal number by 100:

$$\underline{\hspace{2cm}} - 1.0 = \underline{\hspace{2cm}} \times 100 = \underline{\hspace{2cm}}\%$$

This is the percentage by which mAs must be changed to compensate. When collimating down to the smaller 5 in square field, should mAs be increased or decreased by this percentage to maintain OD?
5 Compute the contrast for each exposure as follows: subtract the area A OD by the area B OD, and record here:

  Exposure 1 contrast (A-B):_____
  Exposure 2 contrast (A-B):_____

6 Compare the computed contrast levels. What happened to the measured contrast for exposure 2 when a much smaller field size was used?
7 Visually compare exposure 2 to exposure 1. When using a much higher kVp, would the change in contrast be visible?
8 Briefly explain why this contrast change occurs with smaller field sizes.

EXPERIMENT 12

Effect of Radiographic Grids on Optical Density and Contrast

OBJECT

To demonstrate the effects of radiographic grids on optical density (OD) and contrast.

DISCUSSION

When radiographing thick body parts, the quality of the image will be reduced by the scatter radiation produced. Radiographic grids should be used in such cases to improve image contrast. The narrow slits of the grid allow most of the primary x rays to pass through while absorbing much of the scattered x rays. The effectiveness of a grid can be measured by comparing the image contrast produced with the grid to that produced without the grid.

It is unfortunate that this reduction in scatter radiation, along with the absorption of some of the primary beam, results in a loss of OD. To restore proper OD, radiographic technique must be increased. This leads to an increase in patient dose, but this increase is necessary for adequate image quality. The higher the grid ratio, the more the radiographic technique must be increased to maintain OD.

MATERIALS REQUIRED

Radiographic x-ray machine
Pelvis phantom or other phantom large enough to generate substantial scatter radiation
X-ray film processor
Wafer grids, (clamp-on or tape-on type) of different ratios as available; 10 in × 12 in size preferred
200-speed screen film cassettes of the same size as the wafer grids available
Sponges, sandbags, or positioning clamps
Leaded rubber sheets
Lead numbers
View box
Densitometer
Calculator

PROCEDURE

1. Warm up the processor if needed, and run a couple of "scrap" films through it to stabilize temperature and circulation.
2. Position the x-ray tube 100 cm from the tabletop.
3. Position sponges, sandbags, or clamps to hold the pelvis phantom in a lateral position. If using another phantom, position it with the thickest dimension vertical.
4. Set 86 kVp. This will remain constant throughout the experiment.
5. Number each film with a lead marker on the cassette. Take exposures on separate films using the techniques listed here or record the alternate techniques you use.

Exposure 1	No grid: Place the cassette on the tabletop. Collimate to a 14 in × 17 in lengthwise field, regardless of the film size used. Technique: 200 mA, 0.05 s (1/20 s; 50 ms), 10 mAs. NOTE: Process and check this film. It should be of medium overall density yet appear quite gray with low contrast. If it is very light or very dark, adjust the mAs and repeat. Record this alternate technique: _____ Alternate technique: _____
Additional exposures	Wafer grid: Place the film on the tabletop with the grid centered on the top of the film. Precisely center the light field to the grid. Then arrange the phantom in lateral position on top of the grid. Do not change collimation. Technique: Find the grid ratio labelled or embossed on one side of the grid. Refer to Table E12-1, and multiply the mAs used

TABLE E12-1

Grid ratio	Multiply nongrid mAs by:
5:1 or 6:1	2
8:1	3
10:1 or 12:1	4
15:1 or 16:1	5

TABLE E12-2

	Grid ratio	Area A OD	Area B OD
Exposure 1			
Exposure 2			
Exposure 3			
Exposure 4			

in the first exposure by the factor listed. (NOTE: The new mAs only needs to be approximate. Do *not* change the mA station unless there is no other way to approximate the needed mAs.) Record each ratio and the mAs used:

	Grid ratio	mAs
Exposure 2:	_____	_____
Exposure 3:	_____	_____
Exposure 4:	_____	_____

1. Process the films.
2. On the first exposure, select and circle two uniform OD areas within the anatomy to take densitometer measurements. Area A must show a dark gray soft tissue density but must not be black. Area B must show a medium gray bony density. Now circle the same two uniform optical density areas on all other exposures. Using the densitometer, determine the OD in these two areas for each exposure, and record in Table E12-2.

RESULTS

In Table E12-2, record for each exposure the grid ratio used and the measured OD in areas A and B.

EXERCISES

1 Consider only the ODs for area A. Compute the relative OD change for exposures 2, 3, and 4 by dividing the area A OD for 1 into each of them, and record here:

2/1:_____   3/1:_____   4/1:_____

2 An OD change of 1.0 would indicate that the ODs produced by the different techniques are exactly the same. Consider the value above the exposure 2: Is your computed average change within 20% of the original; that is, does it fall between 0.8 and 1.2? Did the value for the other grids also fall within this range? If not, list below the factors you would use in place of those from the table.
3 Visually compare exposures 2, 3, and 4 to exposure 1. Did the technique factors from the table reasonably maintain OD when changing from nongrid to grid exposures?
4 If these technique adjustments were not made, how would these radiographs have appeared? Why?
5 Compute the contrast for each exposure as follows: subtract the area A optical density by the area B optical density, and record here:

	Grid ratio	Contrast (A-B)
Exposure 1	_____	_____
Exposure 2	_____	_____
Exposure 3	_____	_____
Exposure 4	_____	_____

6 Compare the computed contrast levels for exposures 2, 3, and 4 to the contrast when a grid is used.
7 How do grids accomplish this change in contrast?

Effect of Radiographic Grids and Grid Cutoff

OBJECT

To demonstrate grid cutoff.

DISCUSSION

Grid cutoff, a massive loss of optical density (OD), can be caused by laterally off-centering the grid in relation to the central ray, by laterally angling the grid to the central ray so that they are not perpendicular to each other, by placing the grid at an improper distance from the x-ray tube (outside of the grid radius), or by placing the grid upside down. The pattern of grid cutoff can often be used to determine which of these errors caused it.

MATERIALS REQUIRED

Radiographic x-ray machine
Pelvis phantom or other phantom large enough to generate substantial scatter radiation
X-ray film processor
Wafer grids (clamp-on or tape-on type) of different ratios as available; 10 in × 12 in size preferred (Bucky may be used if you can determine the ratio of the grid in it.)
200-speed screen film cassettes of the same size as the wafer grids available
Sponges, sandbags, or positioning clamps
Leaded rubber sheets
Lead numbers
View box
Densitometer
Calculator

PROCEDURE

1. Warm up the processor if needed, and run a couple of "scrap" films through it to stabilize temperature and circulation.
2. Position the x-ray tube 100 cm from the tabletop.
3. Set 50 mA and 0.05 s (1/20 s; 50 ms). This will remain constant throughout the experiment except on the last exposure.
4. No phantom or test object is used for this experiment. Use the highest ratio 10 in × 12 in wafer grid available to you, placing it over each film and exposing it directly to the x-ray beam.
5. Open the light field in 10 in × 12 in, and leave it at this position throughout the experiment.
6. Number each film with a lead marker on the cassette. Take exposures on separate films, following the directions below. Different angles and kVp levels are required at different grid ratios for the experiment. Instructions are listed for an 8:1 grid and for a 12:1 grid. Use those closest to the grid you have.

		If using 8:1 GRID	If using 12:1 GRID
Exposure 1:	Angle beam parallel to grid strips and center	30-degree angle, 70 kVp	25-degree angle, 80 kVp
Exposure 2:	Angle beam perpendicular to grid strips and center	30-degree angle, 70 kVp	25-degree angle, 80 kVp
Exposure 3:	Off-center a perpendicular beam across grid strips by 3 inches	65 kVp	75 kVp

		If using 8:1 GRID	If using 12:1 GRID
Exposure 4:	Turn grid over and expose upside down using a perpendicular, centered beam	62 kVp	70 kVp
Exposure 5:	Use a perpendicular, centered beam, but change source-to-image receptor distance (SID) to 72 inches by placing the film and grid on the floor. NOTE: Change exposure time to 0.1 (1/10) s.	62 kVp	70 kVp

RESULTS

Visually observe the radiographs on a view box.

EXERCISES

1 Which of the preceding situations did not result in grid cutoff? Why?
2 Which of the preceding situations resulted in grid cutoff more severe toward one side of the film than the other?
3 Which of the preceding situations resulted in grid cutoff that is equal toward both sides of the film?
4 Which of the preceding situations caused the most severe grid cutoff overall?
5 If a higher ratio grid were used for this experiment, what change would you expect in all of the results? Why?

Intensifying Screens Effect on Optical Density and Image Contrast

OBJECT

To demonstrate how intensifying screens work and their effect on optical density (OD) and contrast.

DISCUSSION

Intensifying screens convert x rays into light, which in turn exposes the radiographic film. The principal result is a reduction in patient dose. They convert both the energy and the intensity of the x-ray beam into visible light that interacts with radiographic film more readily than x rays. Either an increase in kVp or an increase in mAs will result in the screen glowing brighter, resulting in a darker radiograph.

Intensifying screens can be made "faster" in several ways. Their absorption efficiency for x rays can be increased by using thicker emulsions. Their emission efficiency for light can be increased by improvements in phosphor composition. Their x ray to light conversion efficiency can be enhanced by using more effective phosphors, such as rare earth elements. To maintain OD, techniques must be reduced by specified amounts when employing faster screens.

Generally, intensifying screens increase contrast. This is not always measurable but is particularly pronounced when comparing screen exposures to non-screen direct exposures.

RECOMMENDED DEMONSTRATION

Open the different types of screens available, and lay them side by side on the tabletop. Open the light field to include portions of as many of the screens as possible. Turn off all lights in the examination room. Observe the different colors of light emitted by each screen when exposed using the following techniques:

1. 50 mA, 3 s, 50 kVp
2. 50 mA, 3 s, 90 kVp
3. 100 mA, 3 s, 50 kVp

At the same time compare the brightness of light emitted by each screen. Discuss the reasons for the different brightness levels with different types of screens and with different radiographic techniques.

MATERIALS REQUIRED

Radiographic x-ray machine
Hand phantom or similar thin phantom
Knee phantom or phantom of similar thickness
X-ray film processor
Direct exposure holder
100 speed screen cassette, preferably the same size as the direct exposure holder
400 screen cassette, preferably the same size as the direct exposure holder
Small, dry bone such as a phalanx
Rectangular sponge about 6 inches thick
Lead numbers
View box
Densitometer
Calculator

PROCEDURE

1. Warm up the processor if needed, and run a couple of "scrap" films through it to stabilize temperature and circulation.
2. Position the x-ray tube 100 cm from the tabletop.
3. Number each film with a lead marker on the cassette. Take exposures on separate films using the techniques listed here or recording alternate techniques you use.

Exposure 1 Load and place the high speed or rare earth screen cassette on the tabletop. Place the knee phantom on the cassette, using sponges as needed to balance it. Collimate to the film size.
Technique: 200 mA, 0.025 s (1/40 s; 25 ms), 5 mAs, 65 kVp.
NOTE: Process and check this film. It should be of medium OD. If it is very light or very dark, adjust the mAs and start over. Write your alternate technique here:
Alternate technique:_____

Exposure 2 Load and place the slow speed ("extremity" or "fine") or par speed screen cassette on the tabletop. Place the knee phantom on the cassette, in precisely the same position as you did for exposure 1. Do not change collimation from exposure 1.
Technique: Refer to Table E14-1, which gives technique factors for intensifying screens, and determine the mAs to be used as follows: Divide the factor listed for the new screen to be used by the factor listed for the screen used in exposure 1. Multiply the original mAs by your answer. (For example, if you used a rare earth medium, 200-speed screen on exposure 1 and are using a slow (50-speed) screen now, divide 2 by 1/2 = 4. Use four times as much mAs as in exposure 1.) Record the technique you use here:
Technique used:_____
Total mAs used:_____

Exposure 3 Again, use the slow speed ("extremity" or "fine") or par speed screen cassette on the tabletop. Collimate to the film size and center. Then place thick rectangular sponges on the film to create an OID of about 6 inches. Place the hand phantom on the sponges, with the resolution test pattern alongside it.
Technique: 50 mA, 0.025 s (1/40 s; 25 ms), 1.25 mAs, 54 kVp.
NOTE: Process and check this film. It should be of medium overall OD. If it is very light or very dark, adjust the mAs and start over. Write your alternate technique here:
Alternate technique:_____

Exposure 4 Load the direct exposure holder with the same type of film used in the cassettes, and place it on the tabletop. Center the light field first (do not change collimation from exposure 3). Place the 6 inches of sponge on the film, with the hand phantom and resolution template alongside it as before.

TABLE E14–1 Technique factors for intensifying screens

Type of screen	Technique factor
Direct exposure holder	
With screen film	80
With direct exposure film	30
50 speed	2
100 speed	1
400 speed	1/4

Technique: 250 to 300 mAs, 54 kVp. (This technique approximates the application of the factor for a direct exposure holder with screen film as listed in Table E14-1.)

4. Process the films.
5. On exposure 1, select and circle two smooth OD areas within the anatomy to take densitometer measurements as follows: area A must show a medium dark gray soft tissue density. Area B must show a light gray bony density. Now circle the same two smooth OD areas on exposure 2. Repeat this procedure with exposures 3 and 4, circling a dark soft tissue area for area A and a light bony area for area B. Using the densitometer, determine the OD in these two areas for each exposure, and record in Table E14-2.

RESULTS

In Table E14-2, record each type of screen used, the total mAs used, and the measured OD in areas A and B.

EXERCISES

1 On a view box, visually compare the overall ODs for exposures 1 and 2. Refer to Table E14-2. By what ratio was the mAs increased when changing from the higher speed screen to the slower screen?
2 Did this technique change reasonably maintain OD when changing screens? If not, what factor would you use in place of the one from Table E14-2?
3 If this change in screens were made without adjusting technique, what would happen to the resulting OD?
4 Compute the contrast for each exposure as follows: subtract the area A OD by the area B OD, and record here:

Exposure 1 contrast (A-B):_____
Exposure 2 contrast (A-B):_____
Exposure 3 contrast (A-B):_____
Exposure 4 contrast (A-B):_____

TABLE E14–2

	Type of screen	Total mAs used	Area A OD	Area B OD
Exposure 1				
Exposure 2				
Exposure 3				
Exposure 4				

5 Compare the computed contrast level for exposure 2 to the contrast on exposure 1. Is there any difference? If so, which of these two screen speeds produces the highest image contrast?

6 Now compare the computed contrast level for exposure 3 to the contrast on exposure 4. Which of these two methods of exposure produces the highest image contrast?

Intensifying Screens Effect on Image Blur

OBJECT

To demonstrate how intensifying screens work and their effect on image blur.

DISCUSSION

Intensifying screens convert x rays into light, which in turn exposes the radiographic film. The principal result is a reduction in patient dose. They convert both the energy and the intensity of the x-ray beam into visible light that interacts with radiographic film much easier than x rays. Either an increase in kVp or an increase in mAs will result in the screen glowing brighter, resulting in a darker radiograph.

The use of screens increases image blur when compared to direct exposure techniques. As the light passes from the screen to the film, it spreads, reducing the sharpness of the image. This property is called **screen blur.** This problem is not present with direct exposures, so they are much sharper.

MATERIALS REQUIRED

Radiographic x-ray machine
Hand phantom or similar thin phantom
Knee phantom or phantom of similar thickness
X-ray film processor
Direct exposure holder
100 speed screen cassette, preferably the same size as the direct exposure holder
400 screen cassette, preferably the same size as the direct exposure holder
Resolution test pattern (line pairs per millimeter [lp/mm])
Rectangular sponge about 6 inches thick
Lead numbers
View box
Densitometer
Calculator

PROCEDURE

1. Warm up the processor if needed, and run a couple of "scrap" films through it to stabilize temperature and circulation.
2. Position the x-ray tube 100 cm from the tabletop.
3. Number each film with a lead marker on the cassette. Take exposures on separate films using the techniques listed here or recording alternate techniques you use.

Exposure 1   Load and place the high speed or rare earth screen cassette on the tabletop. Place the resolution test pattern on the cassette. Collimate to the film size. Technique: 200 mA, 0.025 s (1/40 s; 25 ms), 5 mAs, 65 kVp.
NOTE: Process and check this film. It should be of medium overall optical density. If it is very light or very dark, adjust the mAs and start over. Write your alternate technique here:
Alternate technique:_____

Exposure 2   Load and place the slow speed ("extremity" or "fine") or par speed screen cassette on the tabletop. Place the resolution test pattern on the cassette. Do not change collimation from exposure 1.
Technique: Refer to Table E14-2 to determine the mAs to be used as described for that experiment.
Technique used:_____
Total mAs used:_____

Exposure 3   Again, use the slow speed ("extremity" or "fine") or par speed screen cassette on the tabletop. Collimate to the film size and center. Then place a thick rectangular sponge on the film to create an OID of about 6 inches. Place the resolution test pattern on the sponge. Technique: 50 mA, 0.025 s (1/40 s; 25 ms), 1.25 mAs, 54 kVp.

NOTE: Process and check this film. It should be of gray optical density. If it is very light or very dark, adjust the mAs and start over. Write your alternate technique here:

Alternate technique:_____

Exposure 4   Load the direct exposure holder with the same type of film used in the cassettes, and place it on the tabletop. Center the light field first (do not change collimation from exposure 3). Place the 6-in sponge on the film, with the resolution test pattern on it as before. Technique: 250 to 300 mAs, 54 kVp.

4. Process the films.

RESULTS

On the images of the resolution test pattern, scan downward across the black and white line pairs, from thickest to thinnest, and determine where they are blurred so that you cannot distinguish separate lines with clear edges. Note which line pair number this is. Refer to the resolution test pattern itself or to the table provided by your instructor to read off how many line pairs per millimeter correspond to this line pair number.

In Table E15-1, record each type of screen and the resolution in line pairs per millimeter.

TABLE E15–1

	Type of screen	Resolution (lp/mm)
Exposure 1		
Exposure 2		
Exposure 3		
Exposure 4		

EXERCISES

1 On a view box, visually compare only exposures 3 and 4. With which type of image receptor are more lines resolved? With which receptor do these lines appear to have sharper edges?

2 Refer to Table E15-1. Which receptor resolved the greatest number of line pairs per millimeter, the screen or the direct exposure holder? Does this agree with your visual observations in exercise 1?

3 Why does this effect occur when changing from screen to direct exposures?

4 Refer to Table E15-1. Which of the two screen speeds, the higher or the lower speed, resolved the greatest number of line pairs per millimeter?

Name _____

Date _____

Processor Quality Assurance

OBJECT

To demonstrate a quality assurance program for automatic film processors.

DISCUSSION

When a film is "too light" or "too dark," the most frequent cause is improper radiographic technique. However, the radiographic unit or automatic processor is occasionally at fault. By establishing a processor quality assurance program, problems with processors can be documented and sometimes corrected even before processing of patient films.

A processor control program is begun by reserving a box of film to be used exclusively for processor monitoring. The standard or control film is exposed with a sensitometer. The sensitometer is a device that has an accurately reproducible light intensity combined with optical filters to produce a step-wedge image. Each day before patient film processing a test film is made with the sensitometer. With a busy processor this test may be repeated several times each day. The test film is then compared with the standard film. No change should be observed, since the same lot of film, an identical exposure of film, and same processing are used. A variation between the standard film and the test film represents a change in the automatic film processor.

Since daily monitoring of a processor is not practical for a student laboratory exercise, perform the suggested monitoring weekly at the beginning of each laboratory period. You will maintain a record of each week's results and graph the data weekly during the course of the experiment. This data will be used to evaluate the stability of performance of one processor. During the final laboratory period, you will evaluate the uniformity of all of the processors within your department.

MATERIALS REQUIRED

Empty film box that can be resealed without light leaks
Sensitometer that produces steps discernible to the eye (i.e., approximately 15% exposure increase from one step to the next)
Film illuminator
25 sheets of 8 in × 10 in (20 cm × 25 cm) film from the same manufacturer's lot

PROCEDURE
First Week

1. Set aside 25 sheets of film from the same manufacturer's lot exclusively for this experiment in an empty box that can be restored to its light-tight condition.
2. Allow the sensitometer to warm up for 5 minutes to ensure stability of the light source.
3. Expose a film with the sensitometer.
4. Process the film in the automatic processor under investigation. Be careful to note the orientation of the transfer of the film from the sensitometer into the processor so that the procedure can be identical each week.
5. Record all the data registered on the data sheet.
6. Save the film, and label it as standard or control.

Each Successive Week

1. Repeat steps 2 to 5 of the instructions from the first week.
2. Label the film as Test Film Week No. _____, and date it.
3. Using the same area of the illuminator each week, visually match the images of the step wedges of the test film with the standard film. Each step represents a change of 15% in exposure. A variance of two steps or greater indicates that the processor requires attention.
4. Record the contrast comparison difference, developer temperature, and water temperature on the data sheet, and plot the data on the graph sheet provided.

Final Week

1. Expose the test film, and record the data as usual.
2. During this laboratory period, compare the response of this processor with four other processors in your

department. This can be done by using the sensitometer to expose films from the reserved package and processing them in the other processors in the same manner as all previous test films.

3. Identify the processor on each test film.
4. Compare the step-wedge images of these four processors with the test film from the processor monitored weekly, and record the results on the data sheet.

EXERCISES

1 Discuss the stability of the processor that was monitored.
2 If the contrast difference varies by more than two steps, what can the technologist check before requesting a service call?
3 How do the processors within your department compare in uniformity?

DATA SHEET

Laboratory experiment 16

Processor identification _____

Week no.	Contrast comparison	Developer temperature (°F or °C)	Water temperature (°F or °C)
1			
2			
3			
4			
5			
6			
7			
8			
9			
10			
11			
12			
13			
14			
15			
16			

	Processor				
	1*	2	3	4	5
Contrast comparison difference					

*Processor that has been monitored weekly

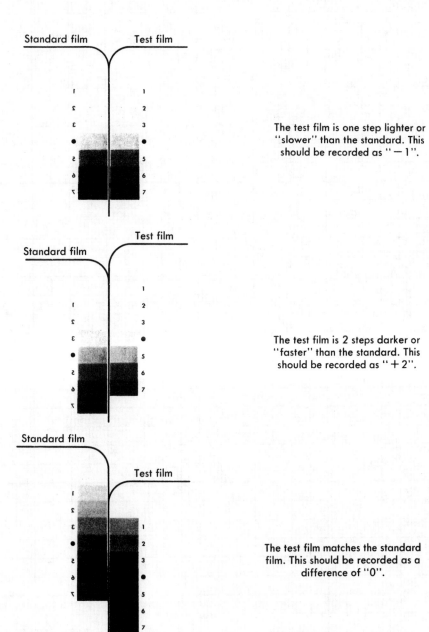

The test film is one step lighter or "slower" than the standard. This should be recorded as " − 1".

The test film is 2 steps darker or "faster" than the standard. This should be recorded as " + 2".

The test film matches the standard film. This should be recorded as a difference of "0".

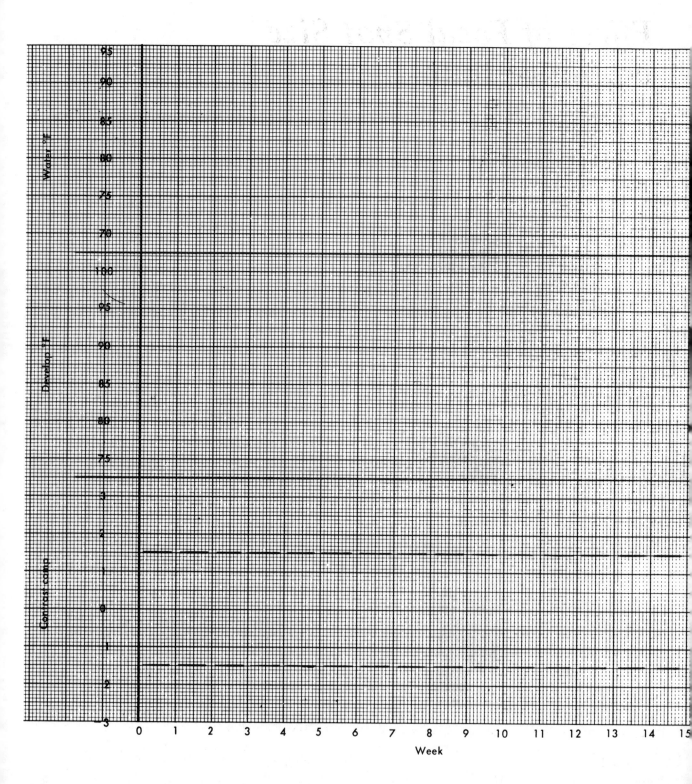

EXPERIMENT 17

Effect of Focal Spot Size on Image Blur

OBJECT

To demonstrate the effect that changing the focal spot size has on image blur.

DISCUSSION

The size of the focal spot is the only variable in radiography that affects image blur exclusively, without affecting any other image quality. It thus becomes the most important factor controlling the spatial resolution of the imaging system. The smaller the focal spot used, the less focal spot blur is transferred to the image.

Generally, small focal spots should be used for any anatomy that is small enough to be radiographed tabletop (without a Bucky) in order to maximize diagnostic image quality. Small focal spots are also used for cerebral angiography (small vessels), mammography (microcalcifications), and other examinations of small, high contrast structures.

MATERIALS REQUIRED

Radiographic x-ray machine
Small dry bone such as a phalanx (or other small object)
Resolution test pattern to measure line pairs per millimeter
X-ray film processor
200-speed screen film cassettes, 10 in × 12 in (24 cm × 30 cm)
Leaded rubber sheets
Rectangular sponge approximately 4 inches thick
Spherical object or head of a dry femur bone
Lead numbers
View box
Densitometer
Calculator
Magnifying glass

PROCEDURE

1. Warm up the processor if needed, and run a couple of "scrap" films through it to stabilize temperature and circulation.
2. Set 50 kVp. This will remain constant throughout the experiment.
3. Set the SID to 100 cm from the tabletop. This will remain constant.
4. Load and place the 10 in × 12 in cassette on the table. Two exposures will be taken on one film.
5. Collimate the light field to a 4 in × 8 in area crosswise at one end of the film. Use the leaded sheets to mask the other half of the film.
6. Place the thick (4-in) flat sponge on the film to create a large object-film distance, which must be kept constant on both exposures.
7. Place the resolution test pattern crosswise on one end of the sponge and the bone alongside it. Pay close attention to the position in which the bone is laid, because you must lay it precisely the same way on the second exposure. Both test objects must be within the light field.
8. Number each exposure with a lead marker on the cassette. Take two exposures, using the following techniques or any necessary alternate techniques.

   Exposure 1   50 mA, small focal spot, 0.035 s (1/30 s; 35 ms)
   Exposure 2   200 mA, large focal spot, 0.008 s (1/120 s; 8 ms)

9. Process the film.

RESULTS

On the images of the resolution test pattern, scan the black and white line pairs, from thickest to thinnest, and determine where they are blurred first so that you cannot distinguish separate lines with clear edges. Use the magnifying glass. Note which line pair number this is. Refer to the resolution test pattern itself or to the table provided by your instructor to read off how many line pairs per millimeter correspond to this line pair number.

The unit "line pairs per millimeter" is a direct measurement of spatial resolution. The greater the number of line pairs per millimeter resolved, the less the blur of the image. In Table E17-1, record each SID and the resolution in line pairs per millimeter.

When you have completed this, obtain a millimeter ruler and measure the length of the bone images for exposures 1 and 2. Then, taking care to hold the bone as it was placed on the cassette and lining the ruler up precisely to the same points as you did on the radiographs, measure the length of the actual dry bone. Record these measurements also in Table E17-1.

EXERCISES

1 Visually examine the marrow portion of the bone images for fine trabecular detail. With which focal spot size is more detail resolved? With which focal spot does this detail appear to have sharper edges?
2 Refer to Table E17-1. Which focal spot resolved the greater number of line pairs per millimeter? Does this agree with your visual observations in exercise 1?
3 What general rule of thumb can you make for focal spot size to consistently produce radiographs with maximum resolution?

TABLE E17–1

	Focal spot	Resolution (lp/mm)	Bone image size
Exposure 1	Small		
Exposure 2	Large		

Actual bone size: _____

4 From Table E17-1 compute the magnification factors for the two exposures using the formula below, and record:

$$\text{Magnification} = \frac{\text{Measured image length}}{\text{Actual bone length}}$$

Exposure 1 magnification:_____

Exposure 2 magnification:_____

5 Did one focal spot cause more magnification than the other? Does focal spot affect the gross size of the image?

EXPERIMENT 18

Effect of Object-to-Image Receptor Distance on Image Blur and Magnification

OBJECT

To demonstrate the effects of changing object-to-image receptor distance (OID) on image blur and magnification, the opposing relationship of OID and SID.

DISCUSSION

OID affects both image blur and magnification in the image. Ideally, the anatomic part being examined should be placed in direct contact with the image receptor so that the OID is minimized, but a substantial OID is often unavoidable. This increases focal spot blur and loss of image detail. It also results in image magnification. The only way to compensate for both of these problems is by increasing the SID as well.

MATERIALS REQUIRED

Radiographic x-ray machine
Small dry bone such as a phalanx (or other small object)
Resolution test pattern to measure line pairs per millimeter
X-ray film processor
200-speed screen film cassettes, 14 in × 17 in (35 cm × 42 cm)
Leaded rubber sheets
Rectangular sponge approximately 4 inches thick
Additional rectangular sponge approximately 2 inches thick (must be one half the thickness of the other sponge)
Spherical object or head of a dry femur bone
Lead numbers
View box

Densitometer
Calculator

PROCEDURE

1. Warm up the processor if needed, and run a couple of "scrap" films through it to stabilize temperatures and circulation.
2. Set 50 kVp. This will remain constant throughout the experiment.
3. Load and place the 14 in × 17 in cassette on the table. Three exposures will be taken on one film.
4. Collimate the light field to a 5 in × 8 in area crosswise at one end of the film. Use the leaded sheets to mask the adjacent film area. Both test objects must be within the light field.
5. Number each exposure with a lead marker on the cassette. Take three exposures, using the following techniques or necessary alternate techniques.

Exposure 1   Place the 2-in sponge on one end of the film. Place the resolution test pattern crosswise and the bone alongside it, resting on the sponge. Pay close attention to the position in which the bone is laid, because you must lay it precisely the same way on the second exposure. Set the SID precisely to 50 cm from the tabletop. Be sure to visually check the light field and open it up to include the test objects. Technique: 50 mA, 0.0083 s (1/120 s; 8 ms).

Exposure 2   Place the 4-in sponge in the middle of the film. Place the resolution test pattern crosswise on the sponge and

the bone alongside it exactly as you did for exposure 1. Keep the same SID. Check the light field to be sure the test objects are within it.
Technique: 50 mA, 0.0083 s (1/120 s; 8ms).

Exposure 3   Place the 4-in sponge at the remaining end of the film. Place the resolution template crosswise on the sponge and the bone alongside it exactly as you did for exposure 1. Keep the same SID. Collimate the light field down to the remaining cassette area.
Technique: 50 mA, 0.035 s (1/130 s; 35 ms).

6. Process the film.

RESULTS

On the images of the resolution test pattern, scan the black and white line pairs from thickest to thinnest, and determine where they are blurred first so that you cannot distinguish separate lines with clear edges. Note which line pair number this is. Refer to the resolution test pattern itself or to the table provided by your instructor to read off how many line pairs per millimeter correspond to this line pair number. In Table E18-1, record each SID, OID, and the resolution in line pairs per millimeter.

With a millimeter ruler, measure the length of the bone images for each exposure. Then, taking care to hold the bone as it was placed on the cassette and lining the ruler up precisely to the same points as you did on the radiographs, measure the length of the actual dry bone. Record these measurements also in Table E18-1.

EXERCISES

1 Visually examine the marrow portion of the bone images for fine trabecular detail. With which SID/OID combination is the detail most blurred?

2 Refer to Table E18-1, and compare exposures 1 and 2. At which OID were the greater number of line pairs per millimeter resolved?

TABLE E18–1

	SID	OID	Resolution (lp/mm)	Bone image size
Exposure 1				
Exposure 2				
Exposure 3				

Actual bone size_____

3 What general rule of thumb can you make for OID to consistently produce radiographs with maximum resolution?

4 Now compare from the table the line pairs resolved for exposure 3 and exposure 1. For exposure 3, both the SID and OID were doubled. Is the resolution different? Why or why not?

5 From Table E18-1 compute the magnification factor for the three exposures, using the following formula:

$$\text{Magnification} = \frac{\text{Measured image length}}{\text{Actual bone length}}$$

Exposure 1 magnification:_____

Exposure 2 magnification:_____

Exposure 3 magnification:_____

6 Compare the magnification for exposures 1 and 2. At which OID was magnification the greatest?

7 What general rule of thumb can you make for OID to consistently produce radiographs with minimum magnification?

8 Now compare the magnification for exposure 2 and exposure 3. For exposure 3, both the SID and the OID were doubled. Is the magnification different? Why or why not?

9 Based on your answers to exercises 4 and 8, in controlling magnification and resolution, what is the relationship between SID and OID?

Name _____

Date _____

Effect of Object Alignment on Image Distortion

OBJECT

To demonstrate the distorting effects of misalignment of the x-ray beam, object, and image receptor.

DISCUSSION

Misalignment problems include off-centering of the central ray from the anatomic part, angling the film or anatomic part so that one is not parallel to the other, and angling the central ray so that it is not perpendicular to either the anatomic part or the film. Generally, these conditions cause **distortion** of shape on the image of the anatomic part being radiographed. When the anatomic part and image receptor cannot be placed parallel to each other, shape distortion will be minimized by angling the central ray one half of the angle formed between the part and the film.

There are two types of shape distortion: **elongation** and **foreshortening** of the image. Distortion is always undesirable and should be minimized.

MATERIALS REQUIRED

Radiographic x-ray machine
X-ray film processor
200-speed screen film cassettes, 14 in × 17 in (35 cm × 42 cm)
Leaded rubber sheets
Rectangular sponge approximately 2 inches thick
45-degree angle sponge
Coin
Spherical object or head of a dry femur bone
Lead numbers
View box

PROCEDURE

1. Warm up the processor if needed, and run a couple of "scrap" films through it to stabilize temperatures and circulation.
2. Set 50 kVp. This will remain constant throughout the experiment.
3. Load and place the 14 in × 17 in cassette on the table. Six exposures will be taken on one film, dividing it into two rows of three exposures each.
4. Collimate the light field to a 5-in square area in one corner of the film. Use the leaded sheets to mask the adjacent film areas.
5. Place the 2-in flat sponge on the film to create an object-to-image receptor distance (OID). All views must be taken at the same OID.
6. Number each exposure with a lead marker on the cassette. Take six exposures using the following techniques.
7. Set 50 mA, 0.05 s (1/20 s; 50 ms), and 50 kVp.

Exposure 1	Place the spherical object or head of a femur on the sponge in the corner of the film. Pay close attention to how you place this object, because it must be placed exactly the same way on the next exposure. Center a 100 cm perpendicular beam to the sphere.
Exposure 2	Place the spherical object on the sponge in the same position as you did for exposure 1. Angle the x-ray beam 35 degrees, and maintain source-to-image receptor distance (SID) by reducing the tabletop-tube distance to 84 cm. Center to the sphere.
Exposure 3	Place the coin on the sponge lying parallel to the film. Center a 100 cm, perpendicular beam to the coin.

Exposure 4   Tape the coin to a 45-degree angle
              sponge at a spot that maintains exactly
              the same OID as the flat sponge in
              exposure 3. Angle the x-ray beam 45
              degrees so that the central ray is
              perpendicular to the coin, and maintain
              SID by reducing the tabletop-tube
              distance to 79 cm. Center to the coin.
Exposure 5   Keep the coin taped to the same spot on
              the 45-degree angle sponge as in
              exposure 4. Center a vertical beam
              perpendicular to the film. The SID should
              be 100 cm.
Exposure 6   Keep the coin taped to the same spot on
              the 45-degree angle sponge as in
              exposure 4. Angle the x-ray beam
              isometrically to 22.5 degrees (one half of
              the angle formed between the coin and
              the film). Maintain SID by reducing the
              tabletop-tube distance to 90 cm, and
              center to the coin.

RESULTS

Visually observe the images on a view box. If
distortion effects are not obvious, use a ruler to measure
the objects and images along the axis at which the beam
or coin was angled.

EXERCISES

1 Visually compare exposures 1 and 2. Does angling the
  x-ray beam distort the true shape of a spherical
  object?

2 Note the width of the spherical image, the axis
  crosswise to the direction the beam was angled.
  Compare exposure 2 to exposure 1. You can super-
  impose the images with a bright light for visual
  comparison or use a ruler and measure the width. For
  magnification to occur, both the length and the width
  of the image should be increased from exposure 1.
  Did angulation of the beam cause magnification of the
  image when distances were maintained?

3 Compare the coin image on exposure 4 to that on
  exposure 3. Is distortion caused when the object is
  angled in relation to the film and the beam is kept
  perpendicular to the object? If so, what specific type
  of distortion occurs?

4 Compare the coin image on exposure 5 to that on
  exposure 3. Is distortion caused when the object is
  angled in relation to the film and the beam is kept
  perpendicular to the film? If so, what specific type of
  distortion occurs?

5 Compare the coin image on exposure 6 to that on
  exposure 3. Is distortion caused when the object is
  angled in relation to the film and the beam is angled
  isometrically between the object and the film?

EXPERIMENT **20**

Anode Heel Effect

OBJECT

To demonstrate the variation of x-ray intensity in a plane perpendicular to the central axis of the useful beam.

DISCUSSION

The radiation intensity across the useful x-ray beam is higher on the cathode side than on the anode side. Along a line perpendicular to the anode-cathode axis, the radiation intensity is constant. The x rays produced from a depth in the tube target must traverse a greater thickness of target material on the anode side than on the cathode side. Because of this self-absorption of photons within the "heel" of the anode, the resulting distribution of the x-ray intensity is known as the **heel effect.**

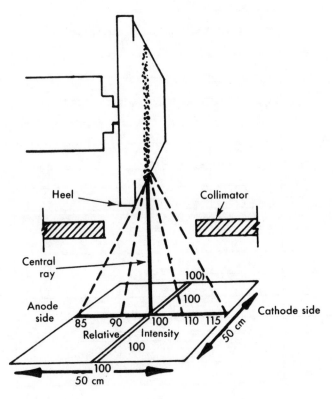

MATERIALS REQUIRED

Radiographic x-ray unit
Ionization chamber
50 cm × 50 cm grid marked in 5 cm intervals

PROCEDURE

1. Tape the 50 cm × 50 cm grid to the tabletop so that the central axis of the useful x-ray beam intersects the center of the grid.
2. Position the x-ray tube target 80 cm above the tabletop.
3. The x-ray machine may be used as it is normally filtered. Record the amount of total filtration if known. Adjust the tube potential to 70 kVp, and select an appropriate mAs that will produce a response of the ionization chamber that is at least half scale. The kVp, mA, and exposure time will remain constant throughout the experiment.
4. Position the detector on the central ray, and, using the data sheet provided, record the response. Three measurements are necessary.
5. Reposition the detector at 5 cm intervals along the four major radii from the central axis (two along the anode-cathode axis and two perpendicular to that axis).
6. Calculate the average intensity (mR) at each location.
7. Calculate the percentage of the central ray intensity at each location as follows:

Central ray intensity (%) =
$$\frac{\text{Intensity at grid location (mR)}}{\text{Intensity at central ray (mR)}} \times 100$$

RESULTS

On the linear graph paper provided, plot the percentage of the central ray intensity vs. the position of the x-ray beam along the anode-cathode axis and vs. the position of the x-ray beam along the axis perpendicular to the anode-cathode axis.

EXERCISES

1 If a 10 in × 12 in film were centered on a grid with the 12-in (30 cm) dimension along the anode-cathode axis, what percentage of the central ray exposure would exist along the four sides of the film?

2 Discuss the effect, if any, that changing from the small focal spot station to the large focal spot station would have on the magnitude of the heel effect.

3 Discuss the effect, if any, that changing the target angle would have on the magnitude of the heel effect.

4 In each of the following examinations, how should the anode-cathode axis of the x-ray tube be oriented with respect to the patient—or does it not matter?

a. extremity   _____
b. chest   _____
c. skull   _____
d. pelvis   _____
e. mammogram   _____

DATA SHEET
Laboratory experiment 20

Constant factors
70 kVp mA_____
Exposure time(s)_____
75 cm source-to-detector distance
Filtration_____mm Al

Grid position	Exposure (mR)			Average exposure (mR)	Percent of central ray
	First	Second	Third		
Central ray					100
2					
3					
4					
5					
6					
7					
8					
9					
10					
11					
12					
13					
14					
15					
16					
17					
18					
19					
20					
21					
22					
23					
24					
25					

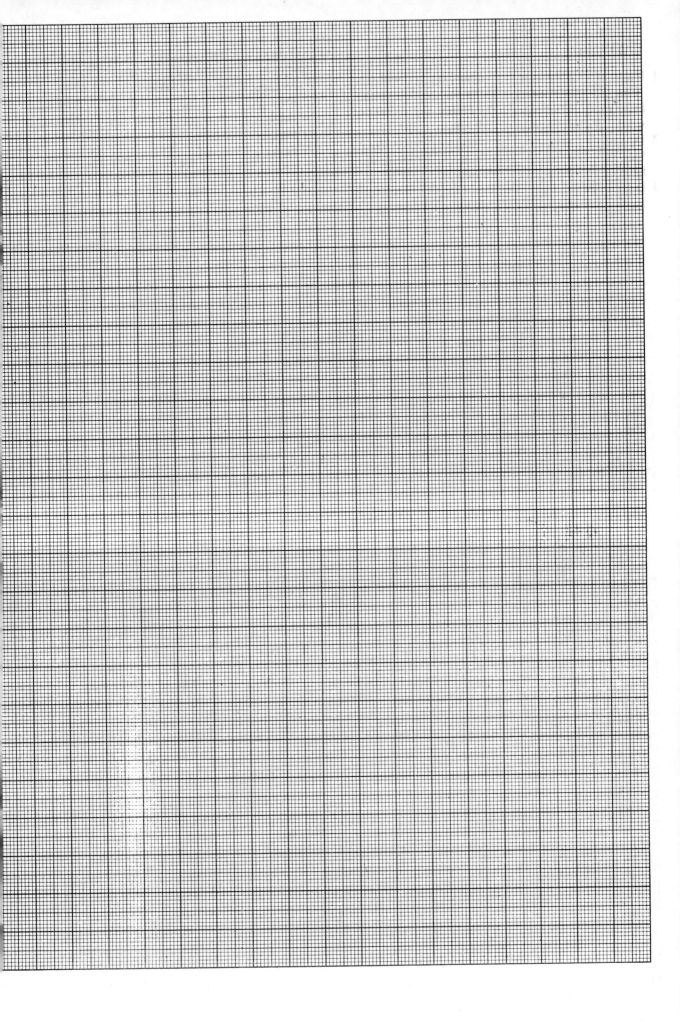

EXPERIMENT 21

Effective Focal Spot Size

OBJECT

To measure the effective focal spot size under differing conditions of x-ray tube current.

DISCUSSION

There are currently three methods for measuring effective focal spot size while the tube is energized. The use of the **pinhole camera** is simplest in concept but somewhat difficult to use. When x rays from the focal spot are incident on an aperture, or pinhole, which is much smaller than the focal spot and positioned midway between the target and the image receptor, the resulting image will have the same size and shape as the effective focal spot. If the pinhole is located at any other position between target and film, magnification or minification will occur. Positioning of the pinhole is critical. It must lie on the central ray of the x-ray beam, midway between the target and image receptor and in a plane parallel with the image receptor yet perpendicular to the central axis.

$$EFS = AFS \times \sin \theta$$

where

$$EFS = \text{Effective focal spot size}$$
$$AFS = \text{Actual focal spot size}$$
$$\theta = \text{Target angle}$$

The use of a **star test pattern** is much easier, but the theoretic basis for its use is more complicated and unnecessary to the success of this experiment. The star test pattern must be centered on the central ray of the x-ray beam and perpendicular to it. With this device, however, precise positioning is less necessary. The effective focal spot size (**EFS**) is calculated from

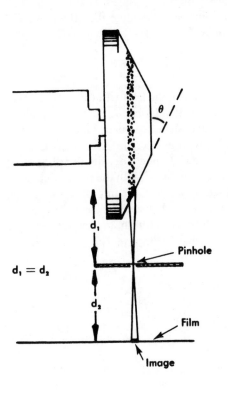

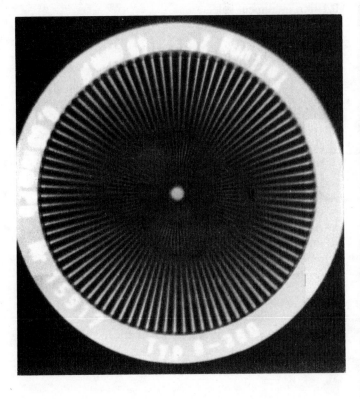

measurements made from the star test pattern image as follows:

$$EFS = \frac{N}{57.3} \times \frac{D}{(m-1)}$$

where

EFS = Effective focal spot size in millimeters

  N = Star pattern angle in degrees (usually 1 or 2 degrees and indicated on the pattern)

  D = Blur diameter measured in millimeters from the image

  $m = \dfrac{\text{Image size}}{\text{Object size}}$ (magnification factor)

The blur diameter should be measured across the image along the anode-cathode axis and its perpendicular axis. The results may demonstrate that the EFS is not square.

The third method employs a **slit camera**. The slit camera is used in much the same way as the pinhole camera, and when used correctly it is the most accurate of the three. The slit camera is used by manufacturers in their laboratories and by medical physicists in the clinic. Because of the time and precision required for its use, it is not included as a part of this experiment.

MATERIALS REQUIRED

Dual-focus radiographic x-ray unit
Pinhole camera with approximate 0.03 mm opening
Tape measure
360-degree star test pattern
Magnifying glass
0.1 mm increment rule

PROCEDURE
Pinhole Camera

1. Select 50 kVp and an mA station for which both large and small focal spot sizes are available. Usually the 100 mA station is suitable. Begin with the small focal spot station.
2. Position the pinhole camera midway between the target and image receptor, and cone down the useful beam to about 5 cm × 5 cm on the film, centered on the pinhole. The source-to-image receptor distance (SID) should be about 75 cm.
3. Adjust the pinhole alignment until an acceptable image is obtained. At least 1000 mAs may be required, and therefore multiple exposures may be necessary.

TABLE E21–1

	mm × mm		
	Small spot, low mA	Large spot, low mA	Large spot, high mA
Pinhole camera			
Star test pattern			

4. Change to the large focal spot station and repeat step 3.
5. Using the large focal spot, increase the mA to the highest possible value while maintaining a constant mAs and repeat step 3.

Star Test Pattern

1. Replace the pinhole camera with the star test pattern. It is acceptable to tape the test pattern to the light-localizing collimator.
2. Repeat steps 3, 4, and 5 of the pinhole camera procedure. A much lower mAs will be required. Try 50 mAs as a starter.

RESULTS

With the magnifying glass and scale ruled to the nearest 0.1 mm, measure the length and width of each of the three focal spot images obtained with the pinhole camera. Measure the perpendicular blur diameters from the three star test pattern exposures. Use the attached data sheet as a guide and calculate the effective focal spot size. Complete Table E21-1, which shows results.

EXERCISES

1 When mA is increased, the EFS will often increase in size. This effect is called *blooming*. Using the pinhole data and the star data, calculate the percentage increase in EFS with an increase in mA.
2 Describe the shape and optical density distribution of each of the images obtained with the pinhole camera.
3 If the actual focal spot of a 13-degree target angle tube is 4.8 mm × 1.0 mm, what will be the EFS?
4 If the EFS is 0.6 mm × 0.6 mm and the target angle is 10.5 degrees, what is the actual focal spot size?

PINHOLE CAMERA

d = _____cm. The distance on the pinhole plate separating the large localizing holes, which is usually 1.27 cm.

d' = _____cm. The distance on the image separating the localizing holes.

Small focal spot (low mA)
   Focal spot image length _____mm
   Focal spot image width_____mm
Large focal spot (low mA)
   Focal spot image length_____mm
   Focal spot image width_____mm
Large focal spot (high mA)
   Focal spot image length_____mm
   Focal spot image width_____mm

Effective focal point size (mm) =

$$\text{Image size} \left(\frac{d}{d' - d} \right)$$

STAR TEST PATTERN

N = _____degrees, the star test pattern angle.
Object size = _____, the diameter of the star test pattern.
Image size = _____, the diameter of the image of the star test pattern.
m = _____.

Small focal spot (low mA)
   Blur diameter _____ mm × _____ mm
Large focal spot (low mA)
   Blur diameter _____ mm × _____ mm
Large focal spot (high mA)
   Blur diameter _____ mm × _____ mm

Effective focal spot size (mm) =

$$\frac{N}{57.3} \times \frac{\text{Blur diameter}}{(m - 1)}$$

EXPERIMENT 22

Repeat Analysis

OBJECT

To demonstrate how to conduct a repeat analysis.

DISCUSSION

Repeat analysis can be conducted either for an individual radiographer or for an entire radiology department. Studies have shown that when an imaging department initiates a quality control program, including repeat analysis, sensitometric processor monitoring, and the use of technique charts, the exposures repeated because of improper optical density (OD) can be cut by one third to one half. This saves money for the department, reduces unnecessary patient dose, and should be taken seriously by every radiographer.

By analyzing and categorizing repeated exposures, the department can identify specific areas of need for continuing education. The individual radiologic technologist can recognize areas for improvement as well as personal strong points. The more detailed the analysis, the more useful it will be.

MATERIALS NEEDED

A box, drawer, or file in which to store throwaway films for each individual or group under study

PROCEDURE

1. For a period of 2 to 4 weeks, as directed by your instructor, place all of your throwaway films in a separate box, drawer, or file with your name on it so no one will inadvertently misplace it.
2. During this time you must also keep fairly accurate records of the total number of views taken. For accuracy, it is best to use the following record A, which you must mark after every procedure, summing the number of views taken (not films used). However, if you do not have time to do this, a fair estimate can be made by using record B, which must

be filled out at the end of each working day to the best of your memory. The totals would be estimated at the end of the study period by multiplying the number of views taken for that procedure. Choose record A or record B, and fill in the required information.
3. At the end of the study period, fill in the data under the following section and complete the exercises.

Record A for Repeat Analysis

After each procedure performed, fill in the number of views (*not* films) taken in the appropriate category below. NOTE: "Torso" includes chest film, abdomen films, and intravenous pyelograms (IVPs). "Extremity" includes pelvic and shoulder girdle films. "Fluoroscopic" includes upper gastrointestinal films, barium enemas, and air contrast barium enemas.

Record B for Repeat Analysis

At the end of each working day, fill in the number of each type of procedure performed that day. At the end of the study period, fill in the routine number of views taken for each type of procedure. Multiply the number of views by the number of each procedure done to obtain a total.

RESULTS

Refer to the record, and record here the total number of views taken:_____

Record the number of views taken in each of the following:

Torso	_____
Head	_____
Spines	_____
Extremities (and girdles)	_____
Fluoroscopic procedures	_____
Other	_____

Record the total number of repeat exposures made (Include films from the throwaway file.):

Type of procedure					
Torso	Head	Spine	Extremity	Fluoroscopic	Other

Totals for period: Grand total

No. of views for period (add all columns): _____

Now carefully examine each film in the throwaway file, and determine the primary cause for its being repeated. Sort the films into the following groups. When this is done, count and record the number of films in each group:

Reason for repeat	Number of repeats
Density too dark	_____
Density too light	_____
Not flashed or not properly marked	_____
Artifacts on patient, film, or table	_____
Motion	_____
Blank film or processing artifacts	_____
Positioning, alignment, and collimation	_____

From the positioning category only, sort and total the following:

Torso	_____
Head	_____
Spines	_____
Extremities	_____
Fluoroscopic procedures	_____
Other	_____

EXERCISES

1 Refer to the "Results" section, and determine the overall repeat rate as follows. Divide the total number of repeats taken for the entire period by the total number of views taken. Multiply the result by 100. Record here:

Overall repeat rate: _____ %

2 Compute the percent of all repeats caused by each of the following problems, as follows. Divide the number of repeats taken for this reason by the total number of repeats taken for the entire period. Multiply this result by 100. Record here for each category:

Density too dark	_____
Density too light	_____
Not flashed or not properly marked	_____
Artifacts on patient, film, or table	_____
Motion	_____
Blank film or processing artifacts	_____
Positioning, alignment, and collimation	_____

3 What type of problem caused the most repeat exposures? What type of problem caused the second-most repeats?

4 What type of problem caused the least repeats?

5 Refer to the "Results" section, and compute the repeat rate for each of the following types of procedures, as follows. Divide the number of repeats taken for each procedure by the total number of views taken for each procedure. Multiply this result by 100. Record here:

Torso	_____ %
Head	_____ %
Spines	_____ %
Extremities (and girdles)	_____ %
Fluoroscopic procedures	_____ %
Other	_____ %

6 Which general type of procedures has the highest repeat rate? What could be done to improve this area?

Day of month or of study period

Procedure	Routine number of views	1	2	3	4	5	6	7	8	9	10	11	12	13	14	15	16	17	18	19	20	21	22	23	24	25	26	27	28	29	30	31	Total procedures	Total views taken
Torso																																		
Chest																																		
Abdomen																																		
IVP																																		
Head																																		
Skull																																		
Sinus/facies																																		
Mandible																																		
Orbits																																		
Other																																		
Spines																																		
Cervical																																		
Thoracic																																		
Lumbar																																		
Sacrum/C																																		
Extremities																																		
Hand/finger																																		
Wrist																																		
Forearm																																		
Elbow																																		
Humerus																																		
Shoulder																																		
Clavicle/scapula																																		
Foot/toe																																		

Procedure	Routine number of views	\ multicolumn Day of month or of study period																														Total procedures	Total views taken
		1	2	3	4	5	6	7	8	9	10	11	12	13	14	15	16	17	18	19	20	21	22	23	24	25	26	27	28	29	30	31		
Ankle																																			
Leg																																			
Knee																																			
Femur																																			
Hip																																			
Pelvis																																			
Fluoroscopic																																			
Upper gastrointestinal																																			
Air contrast barium enema																																			
Barium enema																																			
Other																																			

Grand total no. of views for period: _____

| EXPERIMENT **23** |

Tomography

OBJECT

To demonstrate the effect of different motions and angles on the tomographic image.

DISCUSSION

Frequently obtaining an acceptable radiograph is difficult because of the superimposition of overlying anatomic structures. For example, examination of the bronchi is difficult with a conventional radiograph because of the adjacent sternal and vertebral bony structures. A tomographic motion will blur the image of the overlying sternum and underlying spine while maintaining detail of structures in the plane of focus—the plane containing the pivot or fulcrum.

During tomography, the x-ray tube and image receptor are separated by a fixed distance and move in synchrony about the pivot or focal point. A variety of motions are available: linear, circular, elliptic, hypocycloidal, and trispiral. For most motions a range of tomographic angles is permitted. Complex motions produce more blurring of objects outside the plane of focus than simple motions. This has the effect of increasing the contrast of objects in the plane of focus.

Similarly, an increase in tomographic angle will increase the blurring of objects outside the plane of focus. Additionally, an increase in tomographic angle will reduce the thickness of the in-focus layer.

MATERIALS REQUIRED

Tomographic phantom
Multidirectional tomograph
Film marking pencil
Lead diaphragm with pinhole
200-speed cassette, 10 in × 12 in (25 cm × 30 cm)
View box

NOTE: This experiment has been designed for use with the 3M Tomographic Phantom. Other phantoms are available, but they may not be compatible with all parts of this laboratory experiment.

PROCEDURE
Part I: Pinhole Tracing

Place a lead diaphragm containing the pinhole on the examination table and position it 17 cm above the plane of focus. Shield a large area around the pinhole with lead masks or apron. With the collimators fully open, make a separate exposure on 10 in × 12 in (25 cm × 30 cm) film, using each of the possible movements of the tomograph (try 65 kVp, 120 mAs). The pinhole tracings that you obtain can be used to evaluate the following tomographic characteristics.

1. **Geometric form of the motion.** Any gross deviations from the intended motion will be observed.
2. **Mechanical stability.** Unwanted motion in the x-ray tube housing or the image receptor assembly will result in a wavy tracing, or "wobble."
3. **Completeness of exposure.** Open sections in the image tracing indicate incomplete exposure, whereas overlapped sections indicate unnecessary double exposure.
4. **Uniformity of intensity.** Undesirable changes in radiation intensity during exposure will appear on the tracing as variations in optical density (OD).

Observations on each of these characteristics are to be made on the data sheet.

Part II: Thickness of Cut

The section thickness can be measured and compared with that stated by the manufacturer.

Center the tomographic phantom on the table, set the focal plane at the level of the scale (~ 4.0 cm above the table), and make an exposure (try 120 mAs at 50 kVp). Do this procedure for each motion, using a constant tomographic angle. The phantom should be positioned perpendicular to the direction of the tube movement for the linear motion. Examine the image of the inclined wires next to the scale. One wire measures in millimeter increments, whereas the other measures in centimeter increments.

Place the film on a view box, and use a film marking pencil to mark lightly where each end of the wire comes into focus. Lay a piece of paper next to the wire image and mark the in-focus length of wire. Use the paper as a guide and lay it next to the image of the scale. Read the thickness of cut, using the appropriate scale, and record these values on the data sheet.

Compute the percent error as follows:

$$\% \text{ Error} = \frac{\text{Difference between indicated and measured thickness}}{\text{Indicated thickness}}$$

Observe the quality of the image of the bone lesion.

Part III: Effect of Tomographic Angle

Center the tomographic phantom on the table and adjust the focal plane to the level of the scale. Make an exposure of the tomographic phantom (try 120 mAs at 50 kVp), using tomographic angles of 10, 20, and 30 degrees in the linear or any of the multidirectional modes. Remember to place the tomographic phantom perpendicular to the tube movement when the linear motion is used. Compare the blur images of the circle and star patterns. The patterns nearest the scale are in the plane of focus, and their image should be sharp. The patterns farthest from the scale are 5 mm above the plane of focus. Their image should demonstrate the effect of blurring of objects out of the plane of focus.

Using the technique in Part II, measure the thickness of cut. Observe the quality of the image of the bone lesion. Record your observations and values on the data sheet.

RESULTS

Complete the data sheet below.

EXERCISES

1 Briefly discuss the clinical application of each motion you studied and the reason it was selected for that examination.

DATA SHEET
Laboratory experiment 23

PART I: PINHOLE TRACING

Type of motion	Integrity of motion	Mechanical stability	Completeness of exposure	Intensity uniformity
Linear				
Circular				
Elliptic				
Trispiral				
Hypocycloidal				

PART II: THICKNESS OF CUT   Tomographic angle _____

Type of motion	Indicated section thickness	Measured section thickness	% error	Quality of image of bone lesion
Linear				
Circular				
Elliptic				
Trispiral				
Hypocycloidal				

PART III: EFFECT OF TOMOGRAPHIC ANGLE   Type of motion _____

Tomographic angle	Angle thickness	Width of blur	Quality of image of bone lesion
10 degrees			
20 degrees			
30 degrees			

EXPERIMENT 24

Radiographic Quality Control Survey

OBJECT

To evaluate the operation of a radiographic unit for deficiencies in image quality and radiation safety.

DISCUSSION

In the United States, two organizations are directly concerned with the safe design and operation of medical x-ray apparatus: the National Council on Radiation Protection and Measurement (NCRP) and the Center for Devices and Radiological Health (CDRH), an arm of the U.S. Food and Drug Administration (FDA). The NCRP is an advisory group and has no authority to enforce compliance with its recommendations. The CDRH does have the authority to set standards and enforce them. In addition to the CDRH, many state governments in general subscribe to NCRP recommendations.

The tests included in this experiment are adopted from CDRH and NCRP documents and are designed as relatively simple evaluations that the radiologic technologist can perform to maintain good image quality and to control the radiation exposure of patients and radiology personnel.

MATERIALS REQUIRED

Single-phase radiographic unit with variable-aperture light-localizing collimator
Tape measure
Paper clips
Spinning top
Portable ionization chamber survey meter
Aluminum filters
Aluminum step wedge
200-speed cassette

PROCEDURE

The format of this experiment is slightly different from previous experiments. A statement will be made regarding proper operation of a specific component of the radiographic equipment. This is followed by instructions on how to determine whether the given operation is consistent with acceptable radiation control characteristics.

1. Coincidence of the x-ray beam and light field.
   The error of coincidence must not exceed 2% of the source-to-image receptor distance (SID) on any side of the field.
   Place a cassette at 100 cm SID, outline the light field with paper clips, and make an exposure. Measure the deviation in both directions, and determine if the degree of coincidence is acceptable.

2. Accuracy of the distance indicator.
   The SID indicator should be correct to within 2% of the indicated distance.
   Locate the position of the target of the x-ray tube. It is marked on many tube housings. If it is not, the target position may be estimated by the procedure demonstrated in experiment 1. With a tape measure, determine the actual distance from the target to the image receptor when the indicator shows 100 cm. Repeat this measurement at the maximum and minimum travel of the tube.

3. Exposure switch location.
   The exposure switch should be so located that it cannot be conveniently operated outside a shielded area.
   Examine the exposure switch to see if the cord is too long or if the console-mounted button is in such a position that it allows a technologist to make an exposure while part of her or his body is outside the shielded area. If the cord is too long, it should be shortened or permanently affixed to the console. If the console is too close to the edge of the protective barrier, warning tape should be placed on the floor.

4. Exposure timer accuracy.
   Single-phase exposure timers should be accurate to the time indicated.
   The timer on single-phase equipment can be checked with a conventional spinning top. Place the spinning

top on a cassette at any convenient SID, and expose it while it is spinning. It should be exposed for 1/60, 1/30, 1/20, and 1/10 second. Compare the number of dashes observed with the number expected.

5. Indication of "beam-on."

The control panel should include a device (usually a milliammeter) to give positive indication of the production of x rays whenever the x-ray tube is energized.

Check for a positive indication of beam-on by deflection of the needle of the mA meter during an exposure. Newer equipment provides a separate lamp and an audible signal as well.

6. Exposure linearity.

The radiation exposure obtained by operation of adjacent mA stations at constant exposure time should not vary more than 10% when expressed as mR/mAs.

If a direct-reading ionization chamber is used, the results are directly obtainable; exposure time should remain constant while mA is increased. Otherwise, the simultaneous exposure of a spinning top and penetrometer will suffice. There should be no readily detectable difference in the penetrometer image when exposed to adjacent mA stations at constant mAs. Try 80 kVp at 100 ms as follows:

$$100 \text{ mA} = 10 \text{ mAs}$$
$$200 \text{ mA} = 20 \text{ mAs}$$
$$400 \text{ mA} = 40 \text{ mAs}$$
$$800 \text{ mA} = 60 \text{ mAs}$$

7. Reproducibility.

The radiation intensity obtained during sequential exposures at a fixed technique should exhibit a coefficient of variation (c) of not more than 0.05 where

$$c = \frac{\sqrt{\frac{\Sigma(X_i - \overline{X})^2}{n-1}}}{\overline{X}} \leq 0.05$$

This requirement essentially states that the variation in output intensity of a constant technique shall not exceed 5%. To test this, 10 successive exposures are made and the radiation intensity recorded for each. From these measurements the coefficient of variation is calculated.

8. X-ray quality.

The following total filtration is required:

Operating kVp	Minimum total filtration (inherent plus added)	Minimum acceptable HVL
Below 50 kVp	0.05 mm Al	0.6 mm Al at 50 kVp
50 to 70 kVp	1.5 mm Al	1.3 mm Al at 60 kVp
Above 70 kVp	2.5 mm Al	2.2 mm Al at 70 kVp

If the added filtration is not directly measurable, determine the half-value layer at 70 kVp as demonstrated in experiment 10. If the unit is ever operated above 70 kVp, 2.5 mm Al or an HVL of 2.2 mm Al must exist.

RESULTS

1. Coincidence of the x-ray beam and light field.
   SID = _____
   2% SID = _____
   Misalignment
   Width: _____ + _____ = _____
   ≤2% SID? ☐Yes ☐No
   Length: _____ + _____ = _____
   ≤2% SID? ☐Yes ☐No
   Is this acceptable? ☐Yes ☐No

2. SID indication.
   Selected SID = _____
   2% Selected SID = _____
   Measured SID = _____
   Difference = _____
   ≤2% Selected SID? ☐Yes ☐No

3. Is the exposure switch adequately located?
   ☐Yes ☐No

4. Exposure timer accuracy.

Time(s)	Expected dashes	Observed dashes	Acceptable?
1/10			
1/20			
1/30			
1/60			

5. Positive indication of beam-on.
   Visible: ☐Yes ☐No
   Audible: ☐Yes ☐No

6. Exposure linearity.   70 kVp

No.	mA	Time (s)	mAs	Exposure (mR) 1st	2nd	3rd	Average exposure (mR)	mR/mAs
1	100							
2	200							
3	300							

Is $(\text{mR/mAs}_1 - \text{mR/mAs}_1) < 0.1 \ (\text{mR/mAs}_1 + \text{mR/mAs}_2)$? ☐Yes ☐No
_____ − _____ < 0.1 (_____ + _____)
Is $(\text{mR/mAs}_2 - \text{mR/mAs}_3) < 0.1 \ (\text{mR/mAs}_2 + \text{mR/mAs}_3)$? ☐Yes ☐No
_____ − _____ < 0.1 (_____ + _____)
Is this acceptable? ☐Yes ☐No

7.

Exposure number (n)	Xi (mR)	$X_i - \overline{X}$	$(X_i - \overline{X})^2$
1			
2			
3			
4			
5			
6			
7			
8			
9			
10			

$$\text{Total } X_I = \underline{\hspace{2cm}}$$

$$\overline{X} = \frac{\text{Total } X_i}{10} = \underline{\hspace{2cm}}$$

$$\text{Total } (X_i - \overline{X})^2 = \underline{\hspace{2cm}}$$

$$\frac{\text{Total } (X_i - \overline{X})^2}{9} = \underline{\hspace{2cm}}$$

$$\sqrt{\frac{\text{Total } (X_i - \overline{X})^2}{9}} = \underline{\hspace{2cm}}$$

$$\frac{\sqrt{\dfrac{\text{Total } (X_i - \overline{X})^2}{9}}}{\overline{X}} = \underline{\hspace{2cm}} = c$$

$$c \leq 0.05 \quad \square\,\text{Yes} \quad \square\,\text{No}$$

8. Beam quality.

70 kVp   _____ mA
40 in (100 cm) SID   _____ s
Normal filtration   _____ mm Al

Added filtration (mm Al)	Exposure (mR)			Average exposure (mR)	mR/mAs
	1st	2nd	3rd		
0					
0.5					
1.0					
2.0					
3.0					
4.0					
5.0					

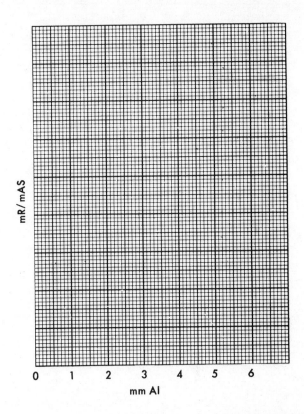

Plot the resulting mR/mAs as a function of mm Al on the graph above and estimate the half-value layer.
HVL = _____ mm Al
HVL ≥ 2.2 mm Al?   □ Yes   □ No

EXERCISES

1 A 25 cm × 40 cm (10 in × 16 in) light field is set at an SID of 100 cm (40 in). The x-ray beam has exactly the same dimensions, but it misses superimposition by 1 cm on all sides. Is this acceptable? What is the limit of acceptability in this instance?

2 The SID indicator shows 91 cm, but actual measurement shows 89 cm. Is this acceptable? What is the range of accpetability for this situation?

3 A portable unit (single-phase, half-wave rectified) is operated with the exposure timer at 1/30 second. How many dashes from the image of the spinning top would be expected?

4 The following exposure data are obtained from a conventional radiographic unit operated at 70 kVp:

50 mA, 0.5 s, 210 mR (5.4×10^{-5} C/kg)
100 mA, 0.5 s, 390 mR (1.0×10^{-4} C/kg)
200 mA, 0.5 s, 704 mR (1.8×10^{-4} C/kg)

Are these acceptable?

EXPERIMENT 25

Fluoroscopic Quality Control Survey

OBJECT

To evaluate the design and operation of a fluoroscope for deficiencies in image quality and radiation safety.

DISCUSSION

As with the previous experiment, this experiment consists of a series of measurements and observations, each designed to test compliance with a specific radiation control recommendation of the NCRP or the CDRH. The procedure section contains statements of requirements followed by directions for measuring compliance with those requirements.

MATERIALS REQUIRED

Image-intensified fluoroscope
Aluminum block patient phantom
Lead attenuation block
Ionization chamber
Portable ionization chamber survey meter
Tape measure
Aluminum filters

PROCEDURE

Caution must be exercised during this experiment to ensure that the image intensifier is not damaged because of exposure to an unattenuated primary beam. Always position the aluminum block patient phantom, the lead attenuator, or both in the useful beam during exposure.
1. Protective curtain and Bucky slot cover.
   Shielding devices of at least 0.25 mm Pb equivalent must be available to intercept scatter radiation that would otherwise reach the technologist and radiologist standing to the side of the table.
   This is a visual inspection. See that a protective curtain of adequate design is affixed to the intensifier tower and that it drapes all the way to the tabletop regardless of source-to-image receptor distance

(SID). When the Bucky is moved to the end of the table, a cover for the space between the tabletop and the side panel, the Bucky slot cover, should automatically move into place.
2. Exposure switch and timer.
   A dead-man type of switch is required for energizing the fluoroscopic x-ray tube. A 5-min preset timer is also required, and an audible alarm should sound at the end of 5 min. The sound should continue until the timer has been reset.
   Check all exposure switches to be sure that a continuous pressure by the operator is required during the entire exposure. Set approximately 15 s on the timer, and observe whether the audible alarm functions properly when the time expires.
3. X-ray tube target position.
   The source-to-tabletop distance should be at least 15 inches (38 cm).
   Place a flat, regularly shaped metal object on the tabletop, and take a spot film of it. Measure the tabletop-to-image receptor distance, and calculate the

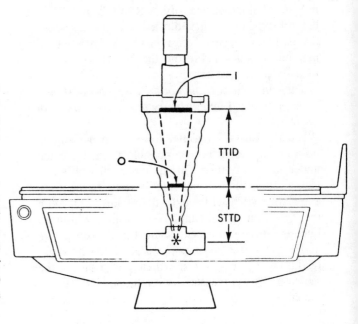

distance of the x-ray tube target to the tabletop as follows:

$$SOD = (SID)\frac{O}{I}$$

where

$$SOD = \text{Source-to-tabletop distance}$$
$$SID = \text{Source-image receptor distance}$$
$$O = \text{Object size}$$
$$I = \text{Image size}$$

4. Beam quality.

   The total filtration, including the tabletop, should be at least 2.5 mm Al equivalent.

   Position the ionization chamber approximately 8 inches (20 cm) above the tabletop, and sequentially insert graduated thicknesses of aluminum filtration between the ionization chamber and the tabletop. When the fluoroscope is operated at 80 kVp, if the estimated half-value layer (HVL) is 2.4 mm Al or greater, total filtration is sufficient. If it is only possible to operate in the automatic exposure mode, the total thickness of aluminum filtration must remain constant. Begin with the total thickness of aluminum filtration positioned in the x-ray beam above the ionization chamber. Each aluminum filter positioned between the ionization chamber and the tabletop should come from the stack above.

5. Beam quantity.

   When operated at 80 kVp, the tabletop exposure rate should not exceed 3.2 R/mA-min (0.83 mC/kg-mA min), and under no conditions of operation should the output intensity exceed 10 R/min (2.6 mC/kg-min).

   Adjust the fluoroscopic tube potential and, with the ionization chamber on the tabletop, record the tube mA and the output intensity in R/m (C/kg-m). It is helpful if the mA is first adjusted to an integer value, that is, 1, 2, or 3. Next adjust the kVp and mA to their maximum values and record the R/m (C/kg-m).

6. Primary protective barrier.

   The entire cross section of the useful beam should be intercepted by a primary protective barrier at all SIDs.

   When the image intensifier tower is in the parked position, it should not be possible to energize the undertable x-ray tube. On equipment that fails this test, a simple microswitch interlocked with the x-ray exposure switch will satisfy the requirement. With the tower at maximum SID and in position to intercept the wide open beam, the exposure rate above the tower must not exceed 2 mR/hr (0.52 μC/kg-hr) for every R/m (0.26 μC/kg-m) at the tabletop. This is measured with the portable survey meter.

7. Primary beam limitation.

   When the adjustable collimators are fully open, the primary beam should be restricted to the diameter of the input phosphor.

   Open the collimators wide and elevate the tower so that the input phosphor is 15 inches (38 cm) from the tabletop. With the x-ray tube energized, an unexposed border should be visible on four sides of the image field. In newer equipment, as the elevation of the tower is changed, the collimators should automatically compensate to continue the unexposed borders on the viewing system.

RESULTS

1. Protective curtain and Bucky slot cover.
   Is an adequate protective tower curtain present?
   ☐ Yes ☐ No
   Is there a tightly fitting Bucky slot cover?
   ☐ Yes ☐ No

2. Exposure switch and timer.
   Is a dead-man type of exposure switch in use?
   ☐ Yes ☐ No
   Is there a properly functioning 5-min reset timer?
   ☐ Yes ☐ No
   Is the signal Audible? ☐ Yes ☐ No
   Visual? ☐ Yes ☐ No
   Does the timer terminate the exposure?
   ☐ Yes ☐ No
   For how long?_____

3. X-ray tube target position.
   Object size (O)_____ Image size (I)_____
   Tabletop-to-image receptor distance (TTID)
   _____

   $$STTD = \frac{(TTID)\ O/I}{(1 - O/I)}$$

   Source-to-tabletop distance (STTD)_____
   ≤38 cm? ☐ Yes ☐ No

4. Beam quality.

80 kVp
Normal filtration_____ mA

Added filtration (mm Al)	Exposure rate (R/min)
0	
0.5	
1.0	
2.0	
3.0	
4.0	
5.0	

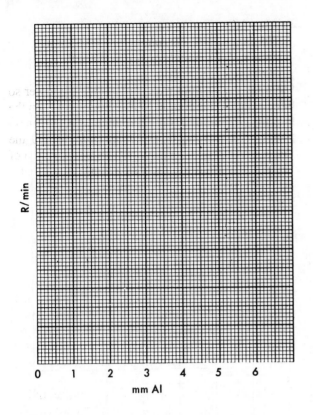

R/min

mm Al

Plot the resulting R/min as a function of mm Al on the graph and estimate the half-value layer.

HVL = _____ mm Al

HVL ≥ 2.4 mm Al?   ☐ Yes ☐ No

5. Beam quantity.
   Tube current _____ mA
   Tabletop exposure rate _____ R/min
   Output intensity _____ R/mA-min ≤ 3.2 R/mA
   Maximum output intensity _____ R/m
      Obtained at _____ kVp and _____ mA
         <10 R/min?   ☐ Yes ☐ No

6. Primary protective barrier.

Is the intensifier tower assembly properly connected and interlocked with the x-ray tube?

☐ Yes ☐ No

Table output intensity _____ R/min
Exposure rate above and around the intensifier tower _____ mR/hr

_____ (mR/hr) ÷ _____ (R/min) = _____

$$\frac{mR/hr}{R/min} \leq \frac{2mR/hr}{R/min}?$$

☐ Yes ☐ No

7. Primary beam limitation.
   Do the primary beam collimators function properly?   ☐ Yes ☐ No

EXERCISES

1 Calculate the quantity of R/mA-min for each of the following conditions of operation:
   a. 70 kVp, 1.5 mA, 3.2 R for 2 min
   b. 95 kVp, 4.2 mA, 4.1 R for 30 s
   c. 115 kVp, 2.7 mA, 6.8 R for 5 min

2 A silver dollar measures 3.8 cm in diameter. Its image on a spot film measures 9.1 cm, and the object and image planes are separated by 30 cm. What is the x-ray tube target-to-tabletop distance, and is it sufficient?

3 The following beam quality data were obtained at 80 kVp and 5 mA, and the detector was positioned 20 cm above the tabletop. The x-ray target-to-tabletop distance was 40 cm (16 inches).

Added filtration (mm Al)	0	0.5	1	2	3	4	5
R/min		5.3	4.5	3.9	3.1	2.5	1.9	1.5

Is the total filtration adequate? Is the tabletop exposure rate acceptable? Use the graph paper provided to assist in the solution.

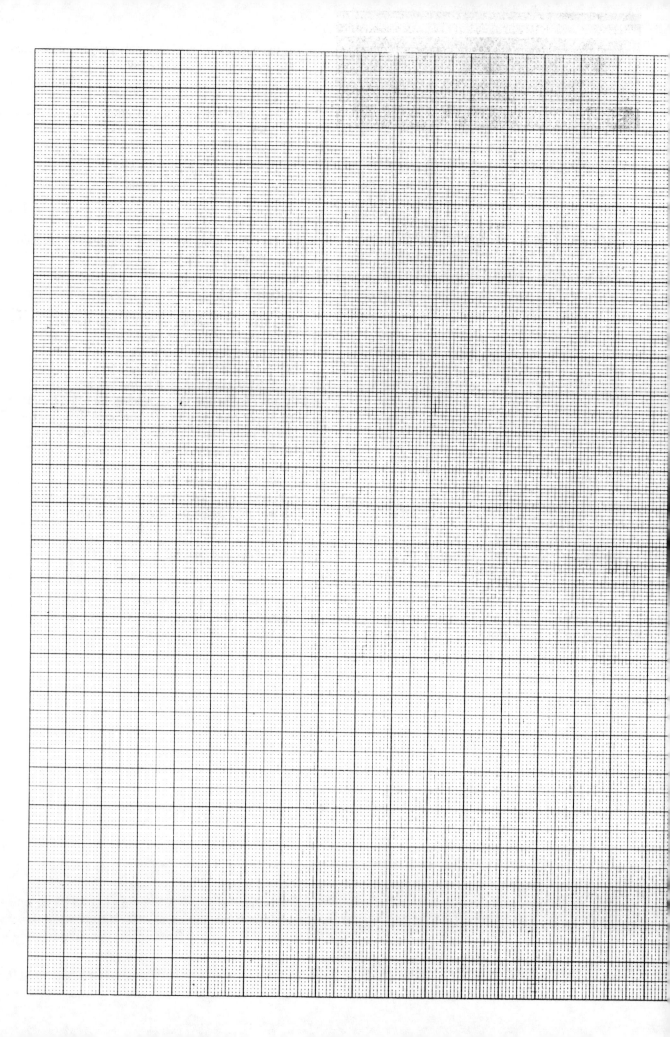

MATH TUTOR

CONTRIBUTED BY QUINN B. CARROLL

Name _____

Date _____

Working with Decimal Timers

CALCULATING TOTAL mAs VALUES

······················

One of the first things you will learn in any radiographic imaging course is the relationship between milliamperage (mA) and exposure time (s) in producing a total mAs. The total mAs value is very important, because it directly relates to how dark the radiograph will turn out. The exposure time cannot be considered alone, nor can the mA, in controlling the *total* density of the resulting image.

A key point to remember is that mA is a *rate*. It tells us how many x rays are emitted from the x-ray tube per second, or how "fast" they are coming out.

The speedometer in your car measures a *rate* as well. It does not tell you what the end result of your trip will be, however. To determine when you will arrive in, for example, Dallas, you must also known how long you will be driving at that rate. That is, you must multiply the miles per hour (the rate) by the number of hours (the time) to find the total miles you will travel. It makes no difference whether you go 50 mph for 2 hours or 25 mph for 4 hours—the end result will be the same distance covered.

Likewise, whether the x-ray tube emits 1 million x rays per second for 1 second, or 0.5 million x rays per second for 2 seconds, the resulting total exposure to the film will be the same. As a radiologic technologist, your first concern is to produce adequate density on the film for a visible image. This depends on how "fast" the x rays are being emitted *and* how long the tube is left on. It depends on the mA multiplied by the time, or the *total mAs.*

Since many combinations of mA and time can be used

to achieve the same total mAs, radiologic technologists must become skilled at computing these numbers, so they can adapt to different equipment and different situations. Some would argue that mAs conversion charts are often available on the wall in the control booth—all you need to do is look it up; but such charts are almost never found on mobile (portable) machines or in surgery, and often they do not match the equipment in the department.

Suppose you normally use 400 mA and 1/80 second for an ankle radiograph in the department and you are called to do a portable ankle radiograph using a mobile unit with a maximum of 300 mA available. It is a timesaving and repeat-avoiding skill to be able to quickly, mentally convert the total mAs value as 5 mAs, to be obtained at 300 mA, yielding a needed time of 1/60 second.

Such mental math should be second nature to every radiologic technologist. It is not as hard as you might think; it just requires practice. The drills that follow are designed to provide the practice needed to develop that skill.

This section first focuses on total mAs conversions using decimals (since most modern equipment uses decimal timers), followed by several drills on conversions using fractional times. Next, conversion of fractions to decimals and vice versa are reviewed. This is helpful because radiologic technologists often must adjust from equipment using decimal timers to equipment with fractional timers, and back.

On x-ray machines the most used mA stations are in multiples of 100. On the exposure timers the most used decimal times consist of two digits after the decimal, that is, they are "hundredths" (e.g., 0.25, 0.05). This provides an easy starting point for practicing decimal conversions: all you must do to figure the total mAs is to get into the habit of moving the decimal point on the exposure time two places to the right in your mind's eye; then ignore the two zeros on the mA station while multiplying. You are simply cancelling the hundreds with hundredths.

For example, find the total mAs for the following:

200 mA at 0.05 s

Moving the time decimal two places to the right, you have 5. Ignoring the two zeros on the mA, you have 2. This is simply 2×5, or 10 mAs.

Think of 300 mA at 0.080 seconds (ignore the last zero) as simply 3×8, or 24 mAs; and 100 mA at 0.025 seconds is 1×2.5, or 2.5 mAs. Examine these three examples carefully before going on.

If three digits follow the decimal, as in 0.008 seconds, you will use the same method but will still be dealing with a decimal in multiplying. For example, 200 mA at 0.008 seconds should be thought of as 2×0.8, for a total of 1.6 mAs. There are relatively few time settings on x-ray machines in the thousandths like this.

If there is only one digit behind the decimal point, such as 0.4 seconds, again move the decimal two places over. This time it will add a zero to your time number, so you will consider 0.4 as 40. Hence, 200 mA at 0.4 seconds will be thought of as 2×40, for a total of 80 mAs. Think of 100 mA at 0.2 seconds as 1×20; and 500 at 0.8 is 5×80, or 400 mAs.

If there are two nonzero numbers after the decimal, you will simply ignore the decimal. That is, 0.16 will be thought of as 16. Three positive numbers after the decimal keep the decimal in the problem: 300 mA at 0.125 is thought of as 3×12.5. Multiply 3×12 first for 36; then add 3 halves for a total of 37.5 mAs.

On most x-ray machines a repeating pattern is available in the time settings. Note for example the following times from one common brand of equipment, in order: .002 s, .003, .004, .005, .007, .01, .015, .02, .025, .03, .035, .05, .07, .1, .15, .2, .25, .3, .35, .5, .7, 1, 2, and 4. One pattern you will see is that between a 5 and a 1 there is always a 7. Table MT-1 simply reorganizes these numbers so you can see the repetition.

Consider the recurring sevens on this machine: .007, .07, and .7. Once you become familiar with mAs values at, say, the .07 time, you can easily do figuring with the other two "seven" times by simply moving the decimal point in your answer:

As previously discussed, you should be thinking of 200 mA at 0.07 seconds as 2×7, for 14 mAs total.

Think of 200 mA at 0.007 also as 2×7, only with a decimal added in the answer: 1.4 mAs.

Think of 200 mA at 0.7 seconds as 2×7 with a zero added, or 2×70, for 140 mAs.

The act of writing down something helps you to remember it, even if you never refer again to your note. An excellent exercise for memorizing mAs values on a

particular machine is to jot down the available times in just the format shown in Table MT-1. Write at the top the mA station you use most, perhaps 200 or 300 mA, and then write to the side of each time setting the total mAs produced at that mA station. When you are through, look at the pattern of mAs values. Note the repeating patterns.

Do the following part of this exercise on your own, calculating total mAs values mentally. If you get stuck on one, review the instructions above for help. Do not check your answers after each question; do the whole exercise first, figuring the problems in your head and then writing the answer down. When completed, check your answers and correct those you missed.

To benefit from this drill, *do not figure your calculations on paper—do them mentally,* and then write your answer in. *Do not* look at the answers after trying each question; try the entire exercise, writing your answers down, and then check all your answers with the key in Appendix B.

TABLE MT–1 Decimal exposure times available on typical x-ray machine

		.01	.1	1
		.015	.15	
.002		.02	.2	2
		.025	.25	
.003		.03	.3	
		.035	.35	
.004				4
.005		.05	.5	
.007		.07	.7	

	mA	×	Time(s)	=	mAs
1	100	@	0.05	=	5
2	100	@	0.064	=	64
3	100	@	0.019	=	1.9
4	100	@	0.125	=	12.5
5	100	@	0.8	=	80
6	200	@	0.02	=	4
7	200	@	0.05	=	10
8	200	@	0.064	=	12.8
9	200	@	0.15	=	30
10	200	@	0.015	=	3
11	200	@	0.125	=	25
12	200	@	0.3	=	60
13	200	@	0.4	=	80
14	200	@	0.008	=	1.6
15	200	@	0.003	=	
16	200	@	0.035	=	7
17	300	@	0.03	=	9
18	300	@	0.07	=	21
19	300	@	0.7	=	210
20	600	@	0.05	=	30
21	600	@	0.25	=	150

	mA	×	Time(s)	=	mAs
22	600	@	0.8	=	480
23	600	@	0.006	=	3.6
24	600	@	0.008	=	4.8
25	300	@	0.1	=	30
26	300	@	0.3	=	90
27	300	@	0.04	=	12
28	300	@	0.015	=	4.5
29	300	@	0.25	=	75
30	300	@	0.025	=	7.5
31	300	@	0.15	=	45
32	300	@	0.006	=	1.8
33	300	@	0.004	=	1.2
34	400	@	0.01	=	4
35	400	@	0.04	=	16
36	400	@	0.07	=	28
37	400	@	0.16	=	64

	mA	×	Time(s)	=	mAs
38	400	@	0.016	=	64
39	400	@	0.33	=	132
40	400	@	0.8	=	320
41	400	@	0.7	=	280
42	400	@	0.007	=	2.8
43	500	@	0.08	=	40
44	500	@	0.03	=	15
45	500	@	0.2	=	100
46	500	@	0.7	=	350
47	500	@	0.007	=	3.5
48	500	@	0.125	=	62.5

Be sure to review those problems you answered incorrectly, going back to the instructions just given. When you have reviewed all of these, *go to Part I of Worksheet 7.* (If you have done Worksheet 7 before, try it again to see if your score improves.)

EXERCISE	2

Working with Fractional Timers

THE 100 mA STATION

....

Exposure timers reading in fractions are somewhat more difficult than decimals to work mentally, yet they also tend to follow patterned sequences, and with just a few memorized pairs of numbers you can do most of them.

For this unit we will practice drills for each mA station separately. At each mA station, certain pairs of numbers always go together. For example, at the 100 mA station, fives and twos always go together:

100 mA at 1/2 s = 50 mAs

100 mA at 1/5 s = 20 mAs

100 mA at 1/50 s = 2 mAs

100 mA at 1/20 s = 5 mAs

and so on. Zeros may be added or decimal points moved, but a time fraction using a 5 will always result in a total mAs involving a 2 and vice versa.

At the 100 mA station, the following pairs of numbers always go together—commit them to memory before you go on. The best way to memorize them is to get a study partner to drill you as if it were an oral test.

3 and 33
4 and 25
5 and 2
6 and 16
7 and 15
8 and 12

Note that these numbers are rounded up *or* down to make it easier to memorize them. For example, 100 mA

at 1/6 second is actually 16.67 mAs and would normally round up to 17. However, it is easier to remember 16, because the mind associates the sixes in 1/6 and 16 together. The results are close enough for any radiographic technique. Likewise, 1/8 of 100 is actually 12.5, and 1/12 of 100 is actually 8.33. In these units on fractions, all answers will be rounded out. The goal is for you to *mentally* derive a good estimated technique, not an exact answer.

Memorizing the pairs of numbers will not tell you where to put any decimal points—you will have to learn that by practice.

It is important to solve these problems mentally, not on paper. After you have completed this entire exercise, check your answers and review those you missed.

	mA	×	Time(s)	=	mAs
1	100	@	1/2	=	
2	100	@	1/20	=	
3	100	@	1/50	=	
4	100	@	1/5	=	
5	100	@	1/8	=	
6	100	@	1/80	=	
7	100	@	1/12	=	
8	100	@	1/120	=	
9	100	@	1/7	=	
10	100	@	1/15	=	
11	100	@	1/40	=	
12	100	@	1/3	=	
13	100	@	1/30	=	
14	100	@	1/6	=	
15	100	@	1/60	=	
16	100	@	2/3	=	

Name _____

Date _____

Working with Fractional Timers

THE 200 mA AND 50 mA STATIONS

·····················

Having memorized the number pairs for the 100 mA station, you can figure the total mAs for most time settings at the 200 mA station simply by doubling the answer you would get at 100 mA. For example, once it becomes second nature to you that 100 mA at 1/60 second is 1.7 mAs, whenever you see 200 mA at 1/60 second you can simply double 1.7 in your mind for a total of 3.4 mAs.

In a similar fashion you can cope with the 50 mA station: simply cut the answer you would get at the 100 mA station in half. If 100 mA at 1/30 second is 3.3 mAs, 50 mA at 1/30 second will be approximately 1.6 or 1.7 mAs.

Practice these conversions for typical fractions in this exercise. Carefully correct and review your answers with Appendix B after completing the entire exercise.

	mA	×	Time(s)	=	mAs
1	200	@	1/8	=	
2	50	@	1/20	=	

	mA	×	Time(s)	=	mAs
3	200	@	1/5	=	
4	200	@	1/50	=	
5	50	@	1/8	=	
6	200	@	1/80	=	
7	200	@	1/12	=	
8	200	@	1/120	=	
9	50	@	1/12	=	
10	50	@	1/120	=	
11	50	@	1/7	=	
12	200	@	1/15	=	
13	200	@	1/40	=	
14	50	@	1/3	=	
15	50	@	1/30	=	
16	200	@	1/3	=	
17	200	@	1/30	=	
18	200	@	1/6	=	
19	200	@	1/60	=	
20	200	@	2/3	=	
21	50	@	1/6	=	
22	50	@	1/60	=	
23	50	@	1/80	=	
24	200	@	1/7	=	

EXERCISE   **4**

Working with Fractional Timers

THE 300 mA STATION
....

The 300 mA station is an odd number and produces its own unique number pairs when a fractional timer is used. For example, at the 300 mA station, fives and sixes always go together: 1/5 second yields 60 mAs total, whereas 1/6 second produces 50 mAs. The following pairs of numbers always go together when using 300 mA. Commit these to memory, drilling with a study partner if you can:

           5 and 6
           15 and 20
           12 and 25

Other combinations can be made, but these three pairs are very common. For other times, such as 1/8 second or 1/7 second, it is easier to simply use the paired number you memorized for the 100 mA station and then triple that number. Here are some examples:

300 mA at 1/7 s   Remember that at the 100 mA sta-
                       tion, sevens always pair with fif-
                       teens. One seventh of 100 is about
                       15. So think of this as:

= 3 sets of 15
= approx. 45 mAs

300 mA at 1/8 s   Remember that at the 100 mA sta-
                       tion, eights always pair with
                       twelves. So think of this as:

= 3 sets of 12
= approx. 36 mAs

With these tips and with the previous exercises completed, you should be able to figure most mAs values for the 300 mA station in your head.

Proceed to solve the following problems mentally and write only your answer down. Then check and review your answers using the answers in Appendix B.

	mA	×	Time(s)	=	mAs
1	300	@	1/5	=	
2	300	@	1/6	=	
3	300	@	1/50	=	
4	300	@	1/60	=	
5	300	@	1/20	=	
6	300	@	1/2	=	
7	300	@	1/15	=	
8	300	@	1/12	=	
9	300	@	1/120	=	
10	300	@	1/25	=	
11	300	@	1/4	=	
12	300	@	1/40	=	
13	300	@	1/8	=	
14	300	@	1/80	=	
15	300	@	1/7	=	
16	300	@	1/30	=	

EXERCISE 5

Working with Fractional Timers

THE 400, 500, AND 600 mA STATIONS
....

Number pairs can also be made for these higher (400, 500, and 600) mA stations, but once you become comfortable with fractions at those stations up to 300 mA, it would be unnecessary. For the 600 mA station, the total mAs values learned at the 300 mA station can simply be doubled. The same thing can be done with the 400 mA station, doubling the results from the 200 mA station.

Further, any of these can be solved by going back to the number pairs you memorized for the 100 mA station. Whenever you get stuck, use this approach of solving for the 100 mA station and then multiplying the result by the first digit of the mA. As an example, when you see:

500 mA at 1/20 s   You may recognize right away that the answer is 25 mAs. Or, you may mentally remove a zero from both the mA and the time, yielding

= 50 at 1/2 s
= 25 mAs

But *if you are not comfortable* with these other approaches, *go back to the 100 mA number pairs* you memorized. Remembering that 2 and 5 always go together and that 1/20 of 100 is 5, think of this problem as:

500 mA at 1/20 s
  = 5 *sets* of 5
  = 25 mAs

Proceed to the following questions, and then check and review your answers from the key in Appendix B.

	mA	×	Time(s)	=	mAs
1	400	@	1/20	=	
2	500	@	1/20	=	
3	600	@	1/20	=	
4	400	@	1/5	=	
5	600	@	1/5	=	
6	400	@	1/50	=	
7	600	@	1/50	=	
8	500	@	1/4	=	
9	600	@	1/4	=	
10	500	@	1/40	=	
11	600	@	1/40	=	
12	600	@	1/30	=	
13	400	@	1/30	=	
14	400	@	1/60	=	
15	400	@	1/7	=	
16	400	@	1/8	=	
17	400	@	1/80	=	
18	500	@	1/8	=	
19	600	@	1/12	=	
20	600	@	1/120	=	
21	500	@	1/12	=	
22	400	@	1/120	=	
23	400	@	1/15	=	
24	500	@	1/15	=	
25	400	@	1/25	=	
26	500	@	1/25	=	
27	600	@	1/25	=	
28	400	@	1/3	=	

EXERCISE   6

Working with Fractional Timers

COMPLEX FRACTIONS
....

If you have completed all of the previous sections, you are ready to move on to fractional times that involve numerators other than "1" on the top, such as 2/5 or 7/20. These are not as hard as they might seem at a glance. You must do them in two steps, dividing the bottom (denominator) into the mA station first and then thinking of the top number as "sets."

For example, to solve:

200 mA at 2/5 s

first, ignore the top (numerator) in the fraction, considering it as a "1"; in other words, find 1/5 of 200. When you have this number, multiply it by the top of the fraction, thinking in "sets," as follows:

1/5 of 200 = 40

2 sets of 40 = 80 mAs

Think of 200 mA at 7/20 second as 7 sets of 10, and think of 300 mA at 3/15 second as 3 sets of 20. Using this approach, solve all of the following problems mentally, and then check and review your answers.

	mA	×	Time(s)	=	mAs
1	100	@	2/5	=	
2	100	@	2/15	=	
3	100	@	3/15	=	
4	100	@	3/20	=	
5	100	@	7/20	=	
6	200	@	3/4	=	
7	200	@	2/5	=	
8	200	@	3/5	=	
9	200	@	4/5	=	

	mA	×	Time(s)	=	mAs
10	200	@	3/10	=	
11	200	@	7/10	=	
12	200	@	2/15	=	
13	200	@	3/15	=	
14	200	@	3/20	=	
15	200	@	7/20	=	
16	400	@	2/5	=	
17	400	@	3/5	=	
18	400	@	4/5	=	
19	400	@	3/10	=	
20	400	@	7/10	=	
21	300	@	2/3	=	
22	300	@	2/5	=	
23	300	@	3/5	=	
24	300	@	4/5	=	
25	300	@	3/10	=	
26	300	@	7/10	=	
27	300	@	2/15	=	
28	300	@	3/15	=	
29	300	@	3/20	=	
30	400	@	3/20	=	
31	400	@	7/20	=	
32	500	@	2/5	=	
33	500	@	3/10	=	
34	500	=	7/10	=	
35	500	@	3/20	=	
36	600	@	2/5	=	
37	600	@	3/5	=	
38	600	@	3/10	=	
39	600	@	3/20	=	
40	600	@	3/15	=	

After you have completed *and reviewed* Exercises 2 to 6, you are ready to *go to Part II of Worksheet 7.* All kinds of fractions and mA stations are mixed in this exercise for you to find the total mAs produced.

EXERCISE 7

Timers: Converting Fractions into Decimals and Vice Versa

CONVERTING FRACTIONS INTO DECIMALS
....

A radiologic technologist who is used to working with decimal timers should be able to quickly adapt to an x-ray machine employing a fractional timer. The reverse is also true, and both types of machines are commonly found. It turns out that the mathematics for doing this is very similar to the mathematics used for mAs conversions.

For example, to convert the fraction 1/6 into a decimal number, 6 is simply divided into 1.00 for an answer of 0.16. Note how similar this operation is to taking 1/6 second at 100 mA to obtain 16 mAs. The only difference is the placement of the decimal point.

Further, you should recall from "Working with Fractional Timers" that certain number pairs always go together; one of these pairs was 6 and 16. In converting fractions to decimals and back, these number pairs always apply: 1/6 = 0.16, 1/16 = 0.6. (Although the sixteens are actually 16.6666, we are rounding down rather than up because it results in an easy memory device, associating the sixes.) Once again, the list of number pairs that always go together is as follows:

3 and 33
4 and 25
5 and 2
6 and 16
7 and 15
8 and 12

Committing these number pairs to memory will be of great help in solving technique problems in your head.

To change a fraction into a decimal, simply divide the numerator (top) by the denominator (bottom), but first place a decimal point to the right of the numerator and add as many zeros as needed to complete the division. For example, to find the decimal equivalent for 3/20:

$\dfrac{3.0}{20}$ Temporarily remove the decimal:

$\dfrac{30}{20}$ Remove the extra zeros:

$\dfrac{3}{2} = 1.5$ Now, "replacing" the decimal moves it one place to the left in the answer:

$\dfrac{3.0}{20} = 0.15$

If you are comfortable with the mA station exercises in "Working with Decimal Timers" and "Working with Fractional Timers," you will find it even easier to pretend that the numerator is an mA station, in multiples of 100. To illustrate:

$\dfrac{3.0}{20}$ Think of the numerator (3.0) as the 300 mA station:

$\dfrac{300}{20}$ Recall from "Working with Fractional Timers" that at 300 mA, the number pair 15 and 20 always go together:

$\dfrac{300}{20} = 15$ Now, since you added two zeros to the numerator above, you must move the decimal two places to the left in your answer:

$\dfrac{3.00}{20} = 0.15$

In this exercise, convert each fraction listed into its decimal equivalent. Rely as much as you can on the skills developed in "Working with Decimal Timers" and "Working with Fractional Timers." For unusual fractions or where these skills do not apply, simply divide the numerator by the denominator. Do the entire exercise, and then review your answers using the key in Appendix B. (When you complete this exercise, go

337

on to Exercise 8 and finish it. Then, when you have completed this entire section, go to Part III of Worksheet 7.)

	Fraction		Decimal
1	3/4	=	
2	2/3	=	
3	1/4	=	
4	1/5	=	
5	1/6	=	
6	1/7	=	
7	1/8	=	
8	1/12	=	
9	1/15	=	
10	1/20	=	
11	1/25	=	
12	1/30	=	
13	1/40	=	
14	1/50	=	

	Fraction		Decimal
15	1/60	=	
16	1/80	=	
17	1/100	=	
18	1/120	=	
19	7/10	=	
20	2/15	=	
21	3/20	=	
22	2/5	=	
23	3/5	=	
24	4/5	=	
25	1/3	=	
26	3/15	=	
27	7/20	=	
28	1/150	=	
29	3/8	=	
30	5/16	=	

Timers: Converting Fractions into Decimals and Vice Versa

Name _____

Date _____

CONVERTING DECIMALS INTO FRACTIONS
....

To convert a decimal number into a fraction requires three steps. First, find the numerator (top of the fraction) by simply writing out all of the nonzero figures to the right of the decimal point. Then, to find the denominator (bottom of the fraction), write 1 for the decimal point and a zero for each decimal place after it. For example, find the fractional equivalent for 0.0125:

0.0125   For the numerator, write out nonzero figures to the right of the decimal point: 125 is the numerator.
For the denominator, write a 1 in place of the decimal point. There are four figures or decimal places to the right of the decimal point (0.0125), so you will write four zeros after the 1: 10,000 is the denominator. The fraction is:

$$\frac{125}{10,000}$$

Finally, reduce the fraction if possible to its lowest common denominator. In the preceding example, 125 and 10,000 do not have a lower common denominator, and the fraction cannot be reduced. Following is an example of a decimal number that can be reduced after converting it into a fraction:

0.6   For the numerator, write the nonzero figures to the right of the decimal point: 6 is the numerator.
For the denominator, write a 1 for the decimal point and a zero for each place after it: 10 is the denominator. The fraction is:

$\frac{6}{10}$ Six and ten share a common denominator: they are both divisible by 2. Reduce the fraction by dividing both numbers by 2:

$\frac{6/2}{10/2}$

$\frac{3}{5}$ This fraction cannot be further reduced, and it is the answer.

In this exercise, convert the decimal numbers listed into equivalent fractions. Some of these problems are easily solved by computing them, whereas *others are better solved by simply recognizing the number pairs listed in Exercise 2.* Do the entire exercise; then check and review your answers using the key in Appendix B. When you are through with this entire section, *go to Part III of Worksheet 7.*

	Decimal		Fraction
1	0.05	=	
2	0.0333	=	
3	0.2	=	
4	0.75	=	
5	0.025	=	
6	0.6667	=	
7	0.143	=	
8	0.002	=	
9	0.08	=	
10	0.167	=	
11	0.125	=	
12	0.6	=	
13	0.0625	=	
14	0.00833	=	

EXERCISE   9

Finding mA and Time Combinations for a Desired mAs

_____

WARM-UP CALCULATIONS
....

_____

Common mathematics problems each radiologic technologist faces in daily practice include (1) having a desired total mAs in mind and trying to mentally determine an mA-time combination that will yield that total, (2) mentally applying the 15% rule for kVp to adjust techniques, and (3) mentally applying the inverse square law for distance changes.

The following exercises will help you to develop the ability to do all three of these types of problems in your head. If you have trouble following the instructions on any of these, you may wish to review Part One and Worksheets 6 and 7. When you have completed Exercises 9, 10, and 11, *go to Worksheet 68,* and see how well you can do on it.

Probably the most common mathematics problem a radiologic technologist faces every day is that of having a desired total mAs in mind and trying to mentally determine an mA-time combination that will yield that total.

This is exactly the reverse of the exercises in Part One, yet if you have completed those previous exercises, you will see how they help you in this one. The same number pairs are used. The only difference is that now you must decide what mA station your desired total mAs will divide into easily. With a little practice the correct time fraction will then come to mind.

One unique thing about fractions (which you will not find in working with decimals) is that some of the answers can only be found in "complex fractions" as we

have defined them. To solve these, you must again learn to think in "sets," such as using two sets of 20 mAs to obtain 40 mAs.

For example, how would you obtain 80 mAs using the 200 mA station? Since 80 does not divide *evenly* into 200, no usable fraction with a "1" on top as the numerator can be found (that is, to simply divide it out, you will get 2.5 as the denominator, resulting in a fraction of 1/2.5; this is a complex fraction that will not be found on the timer knob). However, if you learn to recognize that 80 is 2 sets of 40, you can find a usable time:

First, divide 40 mAs into 200 mA = 5.
5 is the denominator of your fraction.
In other words, the fraction used to obtain 40 mAs is 1/5.
Now, simply go back and take *2 sets* of 1/5 by changing the numerator to 2.
The answer is 2/5 second.
80 mAs = 200 mA at 2/5 second
(80 mAs = 2 sets of 40 mAs)

This exercise will "warm you up" to finding these sets of numbers. For each total mAs listed, express it as so many sets of a smaller number that will easily divide into one of the typical mA stations. There are *one or two* answers to each problem but no more, because, for that smaller number, you must choose a number that does not require further reduction. For example:

120 mAs can be expressed as _____ sets of _____.
If you use 6 sets of 20, this ratio can then be reduced to 3 sets (of 40). It is not a good answer.
One good answer is *3 sets of 40,* since this number of sets cannot be further reduced.
Another good answer is *2 sets of 60,* since, again, this

number of sets cannot be further reduced. (One set of 120 is absurd, because there is no 120 mA station available.)

Note that sets of 40 will be evenly divisible into the 200 mA station, whereas sets of 60 will be divisible into the 300 mA station.

It sounds complicated at first, but try the following part of this exercise and you will find it is not as hard as you might have expected:

1 80 mAs can be expressed as _____ sets of _____.
2 45 mAs can be expressed as _____ sets of _____.
3 66 mAs can be expressed as _____ sets of _____.
4 75 mAs can be expressed as _____ sets of _____.
5 180 mAs can be expressed as _____ sets of _____.
6 120 mAs can be expressed as _____ sets of _____.
            or as _____ sets of _____.

7 160 mAs can be expressed as _____ sets of _____.
            or as _____ sets of _____.
8 240 mAs can be expressed as _____ sets of _____.
            or as _____ sets of _____.
9 90 mAs can be expressed as _____ sets of _____.
10 320 mAs can be expressed as _____ sets of _____.
    Check your answers in Appendix B.

In Exercises 10 and 11 the total mAs desired is given along with the mA station to be used. You must mentally decide which time to use. Use only those times that are available on most x-ray machines. In Exercise 10 your times must be expressed as fractions. In Exercise 11 use decimals. Do the exercises mentally, and then check your answers.

EXERCISE 10

Finding mA and Time Combinations for a Desired mAs

CALCULATIONS USING FRACTIONS

....

	Total mAs	= mA	× seconds
1	4 mAs	= 100 mA	× _____
2	2.5 mAs	= 100 mA	× _____
3	66 mAs	= 100 mA	× _____
4	7 mAs	= 100 mA	× _____
5	17 mAs	= 100 mA	× _____
6	8 mAs	= 100 mA	× _____
7	3.3 mAs	= 100 mA	× _____
8	1.7 mAs	= 100 mA	× _____
9	1.25 mAs	= 100 mA	× _____
10	0.8 mAs	= 100 mA	× _____
11	40 mAs	= 100 mA	× _____
12	5 mAs	= 150 mA	× _____
13	2.5 mAs	= 50 mA	× _____
14	1.25 mAs	= 50 mA	× _____
15	25 mAs	= 200 mA	× _____
16	40 mAs	= 200 mA	× _____
17	120 mAs	= 200 mA	× _____
18	5 mAs	= 200 mA	× _____
19	2.5 mAs	= 200 mA	× _____
20	14 mAs	= 200 mA	× _____
21	50 mAs	= 300 mA	× _____
22	6 mAs	= 300 mA	× _____
23	20 mAs	= 300 mA	× _____
24	2.5 mAs	= 300 mA	× _____
25	45 mAs	= 300 mA	× _____
26	180 mAs	= 300 mA	× _____
27	240 mAs	= 300 mA	× _____
28	75 mAs	= 300 mA	× _____
29	80 mAs	= 400 mA	× _____
30	240 mAs	= 400 mA	× _____

Name _____

Date _____

Finding mA and Time Combinations for a Desired mAs

CALCULATIONS USING DECIMALS

	Total mAs	= mA	× seconds
1	4 mAs	= 100 mA	× _____
2	2.5 mAs	= 100 mA	× _____
3	66 mAs	= 100 mA	× _____
4	7 mAs	= 100 mA	× _____
5	16 mAs	= 100 mA	× _____
6	8 mAs	= 100 mA	× _____
7	3.3 mAs	= 100 mA	× _____
8	1.7 mAs	= 100 mA	× _____
9	40 mAs	= 100 mA	× _____
10	2.5 mAs	= 50 mA	× _____
11	1.25 mAs	= 50 mA	× _____
12	25 mAs	= 200 mA	× _____
13	40 mAs	= 200 mA	× _____
14	120 mAs	= 200 mA	× _____
15	5 mAs	= 200 mA	× _____
16	2.5 mAs	= 200 mA	× _____
17	14 mAs	= 200 mA	× _____
18	50 mAs	= 300 mA	× _____
19	6 mAs	= 300 mA	× _____
20	21 mAs	= 300 mA	× _____
21	180 mAs	= 300 mA	× _____
22	75 mAs	= 300 mA	× _____
23	80 mAs	= 400 mA	× _____
24	240 mAs	= 400 mA	× _____

After checking and reviewing Exercises 10 and 11 thoroughly, *Go to Worksheet 68.*

Name _____

Date _____

Technique Adjustments

APPLYING THE 15% RULE FOR kVp
....
APPLYING THE RULE IN STEPS
....
APPLYING THE RULE IN PORTIONS
....

Radiologic technologists must often adjust techniques using the 15% rule for kVp in order to increase penetration or change the contrast on the radiograph while maintaining overall density. The ability to make these adjustments mentally should be second nature to the radiologic technologist. It is not very difficult to develop this ability, but it does require practice and repetition. The following drills, in conjunction with Worksheet 68, will help you develop this ability.

The rule states that a 15% adjustment in kVp will change the resulting image density by a *factor of 2*. A 15% increase will double the film density, and a 15% reduction will cut the image density to one half the original. This is an approximation, but it works very well and is the only practical rule of thumb for predicting the effects of kVp on the ultimate darkness of the radiograph.

To find 15% of the original kVp mentally, think of the operation as taking 10% first and then adding half as much again. For example, to find 15% of 80 kVp:

$80 \times 10\% = 8$	Take 10% of the kVp.
$8/2 = 4$	Figure one half of 8.
$8 + 4 = 12$	Add these two numbers.
$80 \times 15\% = 12$	

Fifteen percent of 60 kVp would be $6 + 3 = 9$. Fifteen percent of 120 would be $12 + 6 = 18$.

This number is added to the original kVp to double film density, and it is subtracted to obtain one half of the original density. In the above example using 80 kVp, what new total kVp would compensate for cutting the mAs to one half? The answer is 92 kVp $(80 + 12)$. What would the new kVp be if, because of overpenetration, a radiograph turned out twice too dark and you wished to cut the density in half? The answer is 68 kVp.

You should also become comfortable with applying the 15% rule in steps and in portions.

A common misconception is that an adjustment of 10 kVp changes density by a factor of 2. This stems from the fact that 15% of 70 is 10.5, and 70 may be considered an "average" kVp for radiographic procedures. However, a 10 kVp change in the range of 40 kVp will almost double the density *twice*, whereas a 10 kVp change in the range of 100 kVp is only two thirds of the change needed to double or halve the density. For accuracy it is important to use the 15% rule as prescribed rather than the "10 kVp rule."

Sometimes the desired adjustment in image density is much greater than a doubling or halving. Suppose you need to repeat an extremely light radiograph caused by underpenetration, and the density needs to be increased fourfold. Always translate the desired changes into terms of doublings (factors of two), and you can apply the rule.

To produce a radiograph four times darker, think of this change as two doublings. To obtain two doublings, you will need to increase 15% kVp *in two steps*. (It is not as accurate to simply make a 30% change, and the greater the change, the less accurate this approach is.) For example, if the original radiograph was exposed using 80 kVp:

$80 \times 15\% = 12$	Step 1: increase by 15% of the original kVp.
$80 + 12 = 92$	This increase achieves the first doubling.
$92 \times 15\% = 14$	Step 2: increase by 15% of the *adjusted kVp, not the original kVp.*
$92 + 14 = 106$	This increase achieves the second doubling.

A fourfold increase in image density will result from 106 kVp. It would also compensate for a reduction of mAs to one fourth of the original.

Only rarely is kVp adjusted by more than 1 set of 15%, especially for reductions, which might result in an underpenetrated radiograph regardless of increases in mAs. It is to be emphasized that mAs, *not* kVp, is the primary density control for radiographs, and that kVp is only changed to adjust for penetration, scatter radiation levels, image contrast, or gray scale. Nonetheless, when such adjustments are made, the mAs must often be compensated to maintain density, and the 15% rule comes into play.

One practical example of a kVp adjustment using two steps of 15% is found in deriving a barium technique (upper GI or solid column barium enema) from a routine abdomen technique. If the technique for an AP projection of the abdomen were 30 mAs and 80 kVp, the following calculations would allow adequate penetration of the same abdomen when the gastrointestinal tract is filled with barium:

30 mAs @ 80 kVp	Routine AP abdomen
15 mAs @ 92 kVp	First step increase of 15% (12 kVp), accompanied by one half the mAs to maintain density
7.5 mAs @ 106 kVp	Second step increase (14 kVp) is 15% of 92, with another halving of the mAs

For a solid column barium procedure (not air contrast) approximately 7 mAs at about 110 kVp would provide good penetration through the barium while keeping overall image density at an optimum level. (For an air contrast technique, simply reduce 10 to 15 kVp with the mAs still at about 7.)

The image density on a radiograph must be changed by at least one third or about 30% for the human eye to detect any difference. In practice, efforts to ever increase overall radiographic technique by less than 50% or to decrease it by less than 30% are wasted. Changes such as these can be made using the 15% rule in portions.

Suppose you wish to reduce the density but decide that cutting it in half would be too much. You must reduce overall technique by at least one third to make any visible difference. Taking one third of 15%, we can derive a kVp change of about 5%. The kVp must be reduced by a minimum of 5% to lighten up the image. To find 5% of the original kVp, think of it as one half of 10%. For this problem, if the original kVp was 120 kVp, the solution would be as follows:

$120 \times 10\% = 12$	Figure 10% of the kVp.
$12 \times 1/2 = 6$	Take one half of that amount.
$120 - 6 = 114$	Subtract this number from the original kVp.

The kVp must be reduced at least to 114 to visibly lighten up the density in this case.

Although a 2 kVp adjustment may visibly change image density in the 40 kVp range, the same adjustment will not make a visible difference in higher ranges. The change must be at least 5%.

Consider an increase in density of 50% or 1.5 times the original. You will recall the recommendation to think of technique changes in terms of doublings or halvings. In this context, such a 50% increase should be thought of as *halfway to doubling*. (Similarly, a 25% reduction in overall technique would be thought of as halfway to cutting it in half.) Since a 15% increase in kVp will double the density, one half of 15% should bring the density halfway to a doubling. In other words, to increase the density 50%, increase the kVp by one half of 15%.

For example, suppose a radiograph taken at 80 kVp comes out a bit light. Doubling the density would be too much. You decide to increase density by about one half, or 50%:

$80 \times 15\% = 12$	Find 15% of the kVp.
$12 \times 1/2 = 6$	Find one half that amount.
$80 + 6 = 86$	Add this number to the original kVp.

For a radiograph 50% darker, increase kVp to 86.

Complete this exercise using the 15% rule. Some problems will require you to apply the rule in sequential steps, some in portions of one third or one half of 15%. Finish the entire exercise; then check and review your answers using the key in Appendix B. When you have thoroughly reviewed this section, *go to Worksheet 68*.

1 What is 5% of 120? 6
2 What is 5% of 90? 4.5
3 What is 5% of 80? 4
4 What is 5% of 50? 2.5
5 What is 5% of 60? 3
6 What is 15% of 70? 10.5
7 What is 15% of 40? 6
8 What is 15% of 60? 9
9 What is 15% of 110? 16.5
10 What is *one half* of 15% of 40? 3
11 What is *one half* of 15% of 70? 5
12 What is *one half* of 15% of 80? 6
13 What is *one half* of 15% of 50? 3.75
14 What is *one half* of 15% of 90? 6.75
15 What is *one half* of 15% of 120? 9
16 Starting at 120 kVp, what new kVp would result in a density one half as dark as the original? 102 kVp
17 Starting at 40 kVp, what new kVp would result in a density twice as dark as the original? 46 kVp
18 Starting at 60 kVp, what new kVp would result in a density 50% darker than the original (halfway to double the original)? 64.5 kVp
19 Starting at 80 kVp, what new kVp would result in a density about 75% (halfway to one half) of the original? 74 kVp

346

EXERCISE 13

Technique Adjustments

ADJUSTING FOR DISTANCE CHANGES

THE INVERSE SQUARE LAW

THE SQUARE LAW

RULES OF THUMB FOR DISTANCE CHANGES

As described in the textbook, radiologic technologists should be completely familiar with the inverse square law. It describes the relationship between radiation quantity or intensity in the x-ray beam and the distance from the x-ray tube. Because the x-ray beam "fans out" over larger areas with increasing distance, the concentration of x rays decreases at a rate inversely proportional to the square of the distance. The formula is as follows:

$$\frac{I_1}{I_2} = \frac{(D_2)^2}{(D_1)^2}$$

where I_1 is the original quantity or concentration of x rays, I_2 is the new radiation quantity after the distance change, and D_1 and D_2 are the old and new distances (SIDs), respectively.

The inverse square law can be used to predict radiation exposure to the patient, operator, or film. Because the density produced on the film is generally directly proportional or "reciprocal," to the exposure, the inverse square law can be used to predict image density changes when distance is altered. Some of the questions in this exercise apply this formula.

However, this section also focuses on two derivations from the inverse square that are extremely helpful in daily practice: the "square law" and rules of thumb for distance changes.

Whereas the inverse square law is used to predict image density, the *square law* is used to compensate technique so that density is maintained when distance changes. The formula for the square law is as follows:

$$\frac{mAs_1}{mAs_2} = \frac{(D_1)^2}{(D_2)^2}$$

where mAs_1 is the original mAs used at D_1, the original SID, and mAs_2 is the new mAs needed to maintain equal density if the SID is changed to D_2.

When the original mAs is not given or known, place a 1 in the formula for "mAs_1" and solve for mAs_2. The resulting number will be the *factor* by which mAs should be changed. A 2.0 would indicate that the original mAs, whatever it was, should be doubled. A result of 0.5 would indicate that it should be cut in half, and so forth.

As an example, suppose the distance (SID) is increased from the usual 40 inches to 60 inches. The technique chart is written for 40 inches. What change would need to be made in the overall technique taken from the chart to maintain adequate image density at 60 inches?

$\dfrac{1}{mAs_2} = \dfrac{40^2}{60^2}$	Since the actual mAs is not given, place a 1 for "mAs_1". D_1 is 40 inches, and D_2 is 60 inches.
$\dfrac{1}{mAs_2} = \dfrac{1600}{3600}$	Square the distances.
$1600(mAs_2) = 3600$	Cross multiply.
$mAs_2 = \dfrac{3600}{1600}$	Isolate mAs_2 by dividing both sides of the equation by 1600.
$mAs_2 = 2.25$	This is the *factor* by which mAs should be changed.

The 40-inch technique should be increased 2.25 times to maintain density at 60 inches SID.

The solutions to square law problems are always the inverse of those for solving inverse square law problems. For example, if a distance change would result in twice as dark a film by the inverse square law, then the technique that would be required to maintain the original density at the new distance would be one half the mAs. If the density change can be predicted, simply invert this change to find the technique adjustment.

Although the inverse square law is important to understand, in practice radiologic technologists rarely

New distance (in)	Technique change computed by square law	Rule of thumb technique change
30	0.56	½
40	1.0 (standard)	1
60	2.25	2×
72	3.24	3×
80	4.0	4×
96	5.76	6×

use a calculator or pencil to apply it accurately. Rather, when doing a mobile procedure at 60 inches SID, for example, they will likely make a mental estimate of the increase in technique required when compared to the usual 40-inch SID. This section provides some simple rules of thumb that, if committed to memory, will greatly improve your accuracy in making this kind of technique adjustment.

A handful of distances (30, 40, 60, 72, and 96 inches) applies to more than 95% of radiographic procedures. By taking the most commonly used 40 inches as a standard and comparing the others to it, rules of thumb are easily derived and learned.

It helps to think of distance changes in factors of two, that is, doublings and halvings. For example, the square law formula shows that if SID is increased from 40 inches to 80 inches (a doubling), the technique must be increased by four times to maintain density. However, by thinking of this quadrupling of the technique as *two doublings,* rules of thumb can be formulated for other distance changes:

For example, think of increasing the SID from 40 inches to 60 inches as going *halfway to doubling* the SID. That is, 60 inches is halfway from 40 to 80. Since 80 inches would require two doublings of technique, 60 inches will require one half of that increase, or one doubling. For a 60-inch projection, double the mAs used at 40 inches.

In a similar manner, 30 inches can be considered as halfway to cutting 40 inches in half. A 20-inch distance would require one fourth of the overall technique, or two halvings. Thus 30 inches requires only one halving of the 40-inch technique.

Table MT-2 summarizes these rules of thumb for the most used distances. A column listing the actual solution based on the square law formula is provided as well so that you can see how close these rules of thumb are for accuracy. If you keep in mind that density must be changed by at least 30% to see a visible difference, the rules of thumb are clearly accurate enough for practical use.

By far the most useful of these rules of thumb will be those for 60 inches and 72 inches because these distances are frequently used both in mobile procedures and in the radiology department. For mobile procedures the rules of thumb can be taken one step further to derive a technique for 50 inches SID.

If you consider 50 as halfway to 60, the technique would be increased halfway to a doubling, or increased 50%. By the square law formula, the needed increase is 1.57 times the original. The rule of thumb rounds it to 1.5 times. *Radiologic technologists assigned to mobile units should remember that compared to the usual 40-inch technique, a 50-inch SID requires a 50% increase in overall technique (preferably using mAs), a 60-inch distance requires a doubling, and a 72-inch distance requires a tripling.*

Since chest radiography is commonly performed with the 72-inch SID, it is well to emphasize that the 72-inch distance requires three times the 40-inch technique and that a 40-inch distance requires one third of the 72-inch technique. This relationship is frequently encountered in performing upright or decubitus abdomen radiographs along with chest radiographs. *Remember that the relationship between a 40-inch SID and a 72-inch SID is a factor of 3.*

These rules of thumb can also be used to solve for density problems, if you remember to invert them (make fractions out of them). For example, if the distance is increased from 40 inches to 72 inches, and the technique is *not* compensated for this change, how dark will the radiograph be? Simply invert the factor for 72 inches from Table MT-2. The answer is that the new radiograph will have one third the density of the original. A radiograph taken at 60 inches without compensating technique would be one half as dense, and so on.

Complete this exercise as directed. The first 13 questions should be done mentally, using rules of thumb. Note that those starting at 60 inches or 30 inches can also be solved in your head if you analyze the distance changes as doubling, halving, halfway to doubling, or halfway to halving. Questions 14 to 25 employ the square law to find a new mAs that will compensate for the change in distance.

After completing the entire exercise, carefully check and review your answers using the key in Appendix B. Then *go to Worksheet 68.*

Use the technique rules of thumb to solve these problems:

	From:	To maintain density:
1	25 mAs	75 mAs
	40-in SID	72-in SID
2	15 mAs	30 mAs
	40-in SID	60-in SID
3	7.5 mAs	30 mAs

	From:	To maintain density:
	40-in SID	80-in SID
4	6 mAs	_____mAs
	40-in SID	96-in SID
5	60 mAs	_____mAs
	40-in TFD	20-in TFD
6	2.5 mAs	_____mAs
	30-in TFD	60-in TFD
7	30 mAs	_____mAs
	40-in TFD	30-in TFD
8	12.5 mAs	_____mAs
	30-in TFD	45-in TFD
9	30 mAs	120 mAs
	80 kVp	_____kVp
	40-in TFD	60-in TFD

Use the density rules of thumb to solve these problems:

	From:	To:
10	40-in TFD	20-in TFD
	Density = 1	Density = ___ 1/4
11	60-in TFD	45-in TFD
	Density = 1	Density = _____
12	40-in TFD	80-in TFD
	Density = 1	Density = _____
13	30-in TFD	45-in TFD
	Density = 1	Density = _____

Use the square law to solve these problems:

	From:	To maintain density:
14	10 mAs	_____mAs
	40-in TFD	100-in TFD

	From:	To maintain density:
15	5 mAs	_____mAs
	60-in TFD	50-in TFD
16	2.5 mAs	_____mAs
	72-in TFD	40-in TFD
17	2.5 mAs	_____mAs
	60-in TFD	20-in TFD
18	2.5 mAs	2.5 mAs
	80 kVp	_____kVp
	60-in TFD	42.5-in TFD
19	180 mAs	20 mAs
	36-in TFD	_____TFD
20	45 mAs	5 mAs
	90-in TFD	_____TFD
21	30 mAs	120 mAs
	20-in TFD	_____TFD
22	5 mAs	45 mAs
	20-in TFD	_____TFD
23	12 mAs	_____mAs
	96-in TFD	30-in TFD
24	25 mAs	_____mAs
	96-in TFD	40-in TFD
25	40 mAs	_____mAs
	80-in TFD	36-in TFD

Use the inverse square law to solve these problems:

	From:	To:
26	40-in TFD	72-in TFD
	Density = 1	Density = _____
27	60-in TFD	72-in TFD
	Density = 1	Density = _____
28	50-in TFD	36-in TFD
	Density = 1	Density = _____
29	72-in TFD	96-in TFD
	Density = 1	Density = _____

APPENDICES

APPENDICES

WORKSHEET ANSWERS

CONCEPTS OF RADIATION
Worksheet 1 Answers:

1 d	6 b	11 c	16 a
2 d	7 a	12 b	17 d
3 c	8 a	13 c	18 c
4 b	9 b	14 d	19 b
5 b	10 a	15 c	

Worksheet 2 Answers:

1 b	7 b	13 d	19 b	25 e
2 c	8 a	14 b	20 c	26 b
3 c	9 b	15 a	21 d	27 f
4 d	10 a	16 b	22 d	
5 c	11 a	17 e	23 c	
6 d	12 c	18 a	24 a	

Worksheet 3 Answers:

1 a	6 c	11 b	16 d
2 b	7 d	12 d	17 a
3 d	8 b	13 a	18 b
4 c	9 d	14 b	19 b
5 c	10 a	15 b	20 a

Worksheet 4 Answers:

1 c	6 d	11 b	16 c	21 1.3 nC
2 c	7 d	12 b	17 d	22 7 MHz
3 d	8 a	13 c	18 d	23 400 pA
4 c	9 a	14 b	19 d	24 1 mg
5 c	10 a	15 a	20 a	25 457 kV

26 25.4 mC/kg	30 3 keV/μm	34 .000001 L, 10^{-6} L
27 5 Gy	31 1.2 A, 1.2×10^0 A	35 0.007 R, 7×10^{-3} R
28 80 ms	32 0.1 m, 10^{-1} m	36 10^{-7}
29 1.5 mSv	33 10 kg, 10^1 kg	

Worksheet 5 Answers:

1 c	9 d	17 d	25 a
2 b	10 d	18 c	26 joule
3 b	11 a	19 c	27 gray
4 a	12 b	20 b	28 becquerel
5 d	13 d	21 d	29 sievert
6 c	14 d	22 c	30 coulomb/
7 d	15 a	23 b	kilogram
8 c	16 a	24 e	

FUNDAMENTALS OF PHYSICS
Worksheet 6 Answers: (continued on next page)

1 737	8 10	15 −1 13/20
2 319,090	9 1358.9	16 1/8
3 1452.68	10 114.5913	17 5/8
4 352.08	11 3/4	18 18 61/128
5 66.705	12 11/16	19 1 ½
6 37,652	13 1 25/32	20 2
7 269.094	14 3/16	21 189.0

22 5.21	**34** 375 mAs	**46** 1.6×10^{-3}
23 90	**35** 200 mAs	**47** 1.26×10^{7}
24 5.58	**36** 35 mAs	**48** 2.49×10^{-1}
25 2.35	**37** 7	**49** 10^{20}
26 a = 9.7	**38** 444 mR	**50** 10^{9}
27 b = −126	**39** 14.3 mR	**51** 10^{-16}
28 c = 1 7/8	**40** 2.74192×10^{3}	**52** 3×10^{8}
29 x = 53.5	**41** 9.174843×10^{6}	**53** 20:1
30 x = −7/24	**42** 7.713×10^{3}	**54** 2.18×10^{-22} g
31 1:4	**43** 5.58×10^{2}	**55** 2×10^{5} : 1
32 6 mR	**44** 8.9482×10^{2}	
33 224 mAs	**45** 3.7617×10^{4}	

Worksheet 7 Answers:

(NOTE: Where two answers are given, the first is the rounded answer using number pairs as described in the "Math Tutor Section," and the second one is the computed answer for comparison.)

Part I—Decimal/Fraction Conversions

1 0.2	**15** 0.35
2 0.05	**16** 1/20
3 0.13 (0.125)	**17** ⅓
4 0.017 (0.0167)	**18** 1/80
5 0.07 (0.067)	**19** 1/50
6 0.025	**20** 2/5
7 0.008 (0.0083)	**21** 1/60
8 0.67 (0.666)	**22** 1/40
9 0.033	**23** 1/7
10 0.4	**24** 3/4
11 0.15	**25** 1/12
12 0.13 (0.133)	**26** 1/15
13 0.7	**27** 4/5
14 0.6	**28** 1/120

Part II—Decimal Times

29 7 mAs	**39** 24 mAs	**49** 100 (99) mAs	**59** 35 mAs
30 1.3 mAs	**40** 40 mAs	**50** 10 (9.9) mAs	**60** 20 mAs
31 3.3 mAs	**41** 120 mAs	**51** 4.5 mAs	**61** 200 mAs
32 25 mAs	**42** 1 mAs	**52** 0.6 mAs	**62** 2 mAs
33 0.9 mAs	**43** 3 mAs	**53** 32 mAs	**63** 2.5 mAs
34 8 mAs	**44** 24 mAs	**54** 12 mAs	**64** 300 mAs
35 14 mAs	**45** 15 mAs	**55** 14 mAs	**65** 12 mAs
36 5 mAs	**46** 150 mAs	**56** 80 mAs	**66** 90 mAs
37 7 mAs	**47** 60 mAs	**57** 140 mAs	**67** 1.8 mAs
38 70 mAs	**48** 48 mAs	**58** 0.8 mAs	**68** 75 mAs

Part III—Fractional Times (continued on next page)

69 13 (12.5) mAs	**79** 13 (13.3) mAs	**89** 7 (6.7) mAs
70 0.8 (0.83) mAs	**80** 5 mAs	**90** 42 (41.5) mAs
71 7 (6.7) mAs	**81** 7 (6.7) mAs	**91** 33 (33.3) mAs
72 2.5 mAs	**82** 33 (33.4) mAs	**92** 25 mAs
73 17 (16.7) mAs	**83** 60 mAs	**93** 15 mAs
74 2.5 mAs	**84** 5 mAs	**94** 20 mAs
75 0.4 mAs	**85** 20 mAs	**95** 5 mAs
76 0.6 mAs	**86** 2.5 mAs	**96** 24 mAs
77 2.5 mAs	**87** 20 mAs	**97** 120 mAs
78 17 (16.7) mAs	**88** 5 mAs	**98** 13 (13.3) mAs

99 35 mAs	103 40 mAs	106 60 mAs
100 160 mAs	104 90 mAs	107 75 mAs
101 60 mAs	105 240 mAs	108 90 mAs
102 240 mAs		

Worksheet 8 Answers:

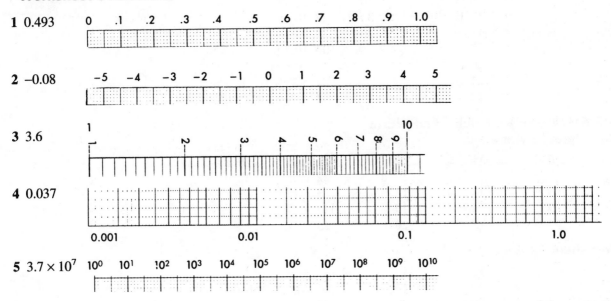

1 0.493

2 −0.08

3 3.6

4 0.037

5 3.7×10^7

6-8 Individual graphs

9 b	13 b
10 c	14 c
11 b	15 b
12 a	16 a

Worksheet 9 Answers:

1 c	6 c	11 b	16 s^{-2}
2 c	7 a	12 d	17 ampere
3 d	8 b	13 c	18 mAs
4 c	9 a	14 d	19 10^5
5 a	10 b	15 a	20 10^7

Worksheet 10 Answers:

1 d	12 c	21 80 N maximum, 40 N minimum
2 d	13 c	22 158 N
3 b	14 c	23 170.6 N
4 a	15 b	24 19.6 m/s, 58.8 m/s
5 b	16 6 ft/s, 1, 6.8 km/hr	25 450 kg
6 c	17 80 km/hr	26 1 lb = 4.41 N
7 d	18 300 km/hr^2	27 12 m/s^2
8 a	19 19.6 N	28 7.9×10^2 m/s^2
9 c	20 3.26 N	29 5.62 m/s^2
10 b		
11 a		

Worksheet 11 Answers:

1 a, d	**12** d	**23** 240 J
2 a, b, d, e, f	**13** b	**24** 40 W
3 e, f	**14** c	**25** 0.05 hp
4 d, f	**15** b	**26** 2800 J
5 d, e, f	**16** d	**27** 28 W
6 a	**17** b	**28** 10^4 J
7 b	**18** e	**29** 0.67 hp
8 c	**19** a	**30** 16.7 m/s
9 b	**20** d	**31** 10 m/s
10 d	**21** c	**32** 5.23×10^5 J
11 b	**22** a	**33** 1.47×10^7 J; 170 W

THE ATOM—WORKSHEET ANSWERS
Worksheet 12 Answers:

1 c	**6** c	**11** c	**16** c	**21** a	**26** c
2 d	**7** c	**12** d	**17** d	**22** c	**27** d
3 a	**8** c	**13** b	**18** b	**23** a	
4 b	**9** c	**14** c	**19** b	**24** a	
5 b	**10** d	**15** d	**20** b	**25** b	

Worksheet 13 Answers:

1 b	**6** d	**11** c	**16** c	**21** a
2 c	**7** c	**12** b	**17** a	**22** Al, S, Sr, Hg
3 d	**8** b	**13** b	**18** b	**23** 74
4 c	**9** c	**14** a	**19** c	**24** 10, 8
5 a	**10** d	**15** b	**20** c	**25** a. 53, b. 53, c. 76, d. 129

26

	Charge		Mass		
	Relative	C	Relative	amu	kg
Neutron	0	0	1838	1	1.675×10^{-27}
Proton	+1	$+1.6 \times 10^{-19}$	1836	1	1.673×10^{-27}
Electron	−1	-1.6×10^{-19}	1	0	9.109×10^{-31}

Worksheet 14 Answers:

1 b	**6** a	**11** b	**16** c	**21** d	**26** a
2 i	**7** e	**12** c	**17** d	**22** a	**27** b
3 g	**8** j	**13** d	**18** d	**23** b	**28** c
4 f	**9** h	**14** d	**19** d	**24** d	**29** a
5 d	**10** c	**15** b	**20** b	**25** c	

30 Isomer	S	S	S
Isotone	D	D	S
Isobar	D	S	D
Isotope	S	D	D

Worksheet 15 Answers:

1 d	**7** a	**13** c
2 d	**8** d	**14** b
3 b	**9** b	**15** a
4 a	**10** c	**16** a. 0.2 Ci
5 b	**11** b	b. 7.4×10^9
6 c	**12** a	c. 12.5 mCi

d. 8 PM the previous night

17 a. 5000 µCi
b. 20 days
c. 12
d. 13 half-lives or 65 days

18 3.13 mCi
19 6.2 mCi, 2.3 mCi
20 32 days

Worksheet 16 Answers:

1 d	6 d	11 d	16 d	21 d
2 d	7 b	12 c	17 a	22 a
3 c	8 a	13 c	18 c	23 c
4 b	9 c	14 b	19 d	
5 b	10 c	15 d	20 c	

ELECTROMAGNETIC RADIATION

Worksheet 17 Answers:

1 c	6 d	11 a	16 a	21 5 cycles
2 d	7 c	12 d	17 c	22 0.4 s
3 c	8 b	13 b	18 a	23 5 cm
4 d	9 a	14 b	19 d	24 125 cm
5 d	10 d	15 b	20 c	

Worksheet 18 Answers:

1 d	6 b	11 b	16 b	21 b
2 a	7 b	12 d	17 a	22 d
3 d	8 c	13 d	18 b	23 c
4 d	9 b	14 a	19 c	24 d
5 d	10 c	15 a	20 d	25 b

Worksheet 19 Answers:

1 d	6 a	11 c	16 b	21 a
2 a	7 c	12 c	17 d	22 d
3 a	8 b	13 d	18 b	23 a
4 b	9 a	14 c	19 c	24 d
5 d	10 a	15 c	20 b	25 c

Worksheet 20 Answers:

1 a	6 c	11 d	16 c
2 c	7 b	12 c	17 d
3 a	8 d	13 c	18 b
4 d	9 a	14 d	19 c
5 d	10 c	15 a	20 b

Worksheet 21 Answers:

1 d	6 d	11 b	16 c	21 d
2 a	7 a	12 a	17 a	22 d
3 d	8 c	13 c	18 b	23 a
4 c	9 c	14 c	19 d	24 b
5 b	10 a	15 b	20 c	25 c

Worksheet 22 Answers:

1 d	6 b	11 b
2 c	7 b	12 b
3 d	8 d	13 c
4 a	9 b	14 c
5 d	10 c	15 b

ELECTRICITY AND MAGNETISM
Worksheet 23 Answers:

1 c	6 a	11 a	16 d	21 c
2 b	7 d	12 d	17 c	22 b
3 a	8 c	13 c	18 b	23 b
4 d	9 d	14 a	19 b	24 c
5 d	10 d	15 b	20 b	25 a

Worksheet 24 Answers:

1 d	7 b	13 a	19 a	25 c
2 a	8 c	14 a	20 d	26 b
3 c	9 d	15 c	21 c	27 b
4 c	10 c	16 d	22 d	28 56 Ω
5 b	11 c	17 b	23 a	29 78.6 V
6 c	12 b	18 e	24 e	30 3.93 A

Worksheet 25 Answers:

1 c	6 d	11 a	16 a	21 a
2 c	7 d	12 c	17 c	22 a
3 c	8 a	13 d	18 d	23 d
4 d	9 a	14 c	19 c	24 b
5 a	10 b	15 b	20 b	25 c

Worksheet 26 Answers:

1 d	6 a	11 c	16 c	21 a
2 d	7 c	12 d	17 a	22 b
3 c	8 a	13 d	18 d	23 c
4 a	9 c	14 b	19 b	24 c
5 d	10 b	15 c	20 b	25 d

ELECTROMAGNETISM
Worksheet 27 Answers:

1 c	6 a	11 c	16 c	21 d
2 c	7 c	12 b	17 c	22 a
3 b	8 c	13 d	18 b	23 b
4 a	9 d	14 c	19 d	24 b
5 c	10 c	15 a	20 d	25 d

Worksheet 28 Answers:

1 d	6 c	11 b	16 a
2 b	7 b	12 d	17 c
3 d	8 d	13 b	18 a
4 b	9 b	14 c	19 b
5 a	10 a	15 c	20 d

Worksheet 29 Answers:

1 d	6 b	11 b	16 a	21 c
2 b	7 c	12 c	17 c	22 c
3 c	8 c	13 b	18 d	23 a
4 a	9 c	14 d	19 a	24 b
5 c	10 d	15 a	20 c	25 a

Worksheet 30 Answers:

1 d	6 a	11 b	16 c	21 e
2 d	7 d	12 d	17 d	22 e
3 c	8 a	13 b	18 a	23 c
4 c	9 d	14 c	19 c	24 b
5 b	10 d	15 c	20 c	25 e

THE X-RAY MACHINE
Worksheet 31 Answers:

1 d	6 c	11 a	16 d	21 200 mA
2 d	7 a	12 b	17 c	22 4.6 A
3 c	8 a	13 a	18 a	23 Two times higher
4 c	9 b	14 a	19 b	24 52% increase
5 b	10 c	15 b	20 d	25 approx. 200 mA

Worksheet 32 Answers:

1 c	6 b	11 b	16 c	21 d
2 c	7 b	12 b	17 a	22 d
3 d	8 d	13 d	18 a	23 b
4 c	9 d	14 c	19 c	24 d
5 c	10 a	15 d	20 b	25 a

Worksheet 33 Answers:

1 b	6 d	11 a	16 a	21 c
2 a	7 a	12 c	17 c	22 a
3 c	8 a	13 d	18 a	23 d
4 d	9 c	14 c	19 d	24 b
5 b	10 c	15 c	20 c	25 b

Worksheet 34 Answers:

1 d	6 d	11 a	16 c
2 c	7 c	12 b	17 b
3 a	8 a	13 b	18 c
4 d	9 d	14 a	19 d
5 d	10 d	15 d	20 b

Worksheet 35 Answers:

1 c	6 a	11 d	16 a
2 c	7 b	12 c	17 d
3 b	8 b	13 d	18 d
4 c	9 c	14 b	19 c
5 b	10 a	15 b	20 a

Worksheet 36 Answers:

1 a	6 c	11 a
2 d	7 d	12 c
3 a	8 c	13 b
4 d	9 a	14 d
5 c	10 c	15 2, 1, 4, 3

Worksheet 37 Answers:

1 T	12 S	22 11:7500	23 yes	33 b
2 T	13 S	12:7500	24 300,000 Hu	34 b
3 F	14 S	13:7500	25 8 m	35 d
4 F	15 U	14:7500	26 6.5 m	36 a
5 F	16 S	15:70,000	27 approx. 1.5 m	37 a
6 F	17 S	16:1200	28 c	
7 T	18 U	17:16,800	29 b	
8 F	19 U	18:48,000	30 d	
9 F	20 S	19:180	31 b	
10 F	21 250 mA;	20:7350	32 d	
11 U	100 ms			

X-RAY PRODUCTION
Worksheet 38 Answers:

1 c	6 d	11 a	16 b	21 c
2 a	7 a	12 b	17 d	
3 c	8 c	13 d	18 c	
4 c	9 c	14 a	19 c	
5 d	10 c	15 d	20 c	

Worksheet 39 Answers:

1 b	6 b	11 a	16 d	21 c
2 d	7 d	12 b	17 b	22 d
3 b	8 d	13 a	18 c	23 b
4 c	9 d	14 a	19 d	24 c
5 a	10 a	15 c	20 a	25 a

Worksheet 40 Answers:

1 c	6 c	11 b	16 d
2 a	7 b	12 b	17 b
3 c	8 a	13 c	18 a
4 d	9 d	14 b	19 b
5 d	10 d	15 b	20 b

Worksheet 41 Answers:

1 a	6 d	11 a
2 b	7 b	12 c
3 c	8 b	13 c
4 d	9 a	14 b
5 a	10 d	15 a

Worksheet 42 Answers:

1 c	6 c	11 a
2 c	7 b	12 d
3 d	8 d	13 c
4 d	9 c	14 b
5 c	10 b	15 b

X-RAY EMISSION—WORKSHEET ANSWERS
Worksheet 43 Answers:

1 b	6 b	11 c	16 b
2 a	7 a	12 c	17 a
3 d	8 a	13 a	18 b
4 c	9 c	14 a	19 d
5 c	10 c	15 c	20 b

Worksheet 44 Answers:

1 b	10 c	18 d	26 c
2 d	11 a	19 c	27 d
3 d	12 c	20 d	28 a
4 b	13 c	21 c	
5 b	14 d	22 d	
6 c	15 a	23 b	
7 a	16 c	24 a	
8 c	17 a	25 c	
9 d			

Worksheet 45 Answers:

1 b	6 c	11 a	16 a	21 d
2 c	7 b	12 b	17 c	22 c
3 d	8 d	13 b	18 d	23 c
4 d	9 d	14 b	19 c	24 a
5 c	10 d	15 a	20 b	25 b

X-RAY INTERACTION WITH MATTER
Worksheet 46 Answers:

1 d	6 d	11 a	16 b	21 a
2 a	7 d	12 b	17 d	22 b
3 c	8 b	13 a	18 a	23 b
4 d	9 b	14 c	19 c	24 b
5 a	10 d	15 b	20 d	25 c

Worksheet 47 Answers:

1 c	6 c	11 d	16 c
2 a	7 b	12 a	17 d
3 d	8 b	13 b	18 a
4 c	9 b	14 b	19 d
5 b	10 b	15 c	20 a

Worksheet 48 Answers:

1 b	6 d	11 b	16 c
2 b	7 b	12 d	17 d
3 d	8 b	13 c	18 c
4 b	9 c	14 b	19 a
5 c	10 c	15 a	20 c

RADIOGRAPHIC FILM
Worksheet 49 Answers:

1 a	6 d	11 d	16 c	21 d
2 d	7 b	12 a	17 a	22 c
3 b	8 c	13 d	18 a	23 b
4 b	9 c	14 c	19 c	24 c
5 d	10 b	15 d	20 b	25 c

Worksheet 50 Answers:

1 c	6 c	11 b	16 b	21 d
2 c	7 d	12 a	17 d	22 c
3 d	8 a	13 d	18 b	23 a
4 d	9 d	14 a	19 b	24 b
5 b	10 c	15 b	20 b	25 c

Worksheet 51 Answers:

1 a	6 c	11 d	16 a	21 b
2 c	7 a	12 b	17 a	22 b
3 b	8 c	13 d	18 c	23 d
4 b	9 b	14 c	19 d	24 a
5 c	10 d	15 c	20 c	25 c

PROCESSING THE LATENT IMAGE
Worksheet 52 Answers:

1 b	6 c	11 b	16 d	21 d	26 b
2 c	7 b	12 a	17 a	22 c	27 d
3 b	8 c	13 d	18 c	23 a	28 b
4 c	9 c	14 a	19 d	24 a	29 a
5 c	10 b	15 d	20 b	25 a	30 c

Worksheet 53 Answers:

1 b	6 c	11 a	16 d	21 c
2 b	7 b	12 c	17 a	22 c
3 a	8 b	13 d	18 d	23 c
4 c	9 b	14 c	19 a	24 b
5 d	10 b	15 b	20 b	25 c

Worksheet 54 Answers:

1 b	6 a	11 b	16 b
2 b	7 b	12 a	17 b
3 d	8 b	13 b	18 d
4 c	9 c	14 c	19 b
5 d	10 d	15 d	20 d

INTENSIFYING SCREENS
Worksheet 55 Answers:

1 b	6 b	11 a	16 c	21 a
2 b	7 c	12 a	17 b	22 d
3 c	8 d	13 b	18 a	23 b
4 b	9 a	14 d	19 b	
5 c	10 a	15 b	20 c	

Worksheet 56 Answers:

1 c	6 d	11 a	16 a	21 a
2 d	7 d	12 c	17 c	22 d
3 d	8 a	13 c	18 c	23 c
4 c	9 d	14 c	19 a	
5 b	10 b	15 b	20 c	

BEAM-RESTRICTING DEVICES
Worksheet 57 Answers:

1 c	6 d	11 b	16 d	21 b
2 d	7 b	12 a	17 b	22 d
3 a	8 b	13 c	18 d	23 d
4 c	9 c	14 d	19 d	24 b
5 c	10 a	15 b	20 c	25 a

Worksheet 58 Answers:

1 c	6 a	11 d	16 a	21 d
2 c	7 a	12 c	17 c	22 c
3 b	8 c	13 b	18 c	23 b
4 c	9 c	14 b	19 c	24 a
5 d	10 c	15 d	20 b	25 d

THE GRID
Worksheet 59 Answers:

1 d	6 c	11 a	16 d	21 b
2 c	7 b	12 c	17 c	22 c
3 a	8 c	13 a	18 d	23 a
4 c	9 a	14 a	19 d	24 d
5 d	10 c	15 d	20 b	25 a

Worksheet 60 Answers:

1 d	6 c	11 d	16 b	21 d
2 b	7 d	12 d	17 d	22 b
3 c	8 b	13 a	18 c	23 b
4 b	9 d	14 d	19 c	24 c
5 a	10 c	15 c	20 b	25 b

Worksheet 61 Answers:

1 d	6 d	11 b
2 c	7 b	12 b
3 a	8 b	13 a
4 b	9 d	14 c
5 c	10 c	15 d

RADIOGRAPHIC QUALITY
Worksheet 62 Answers:

1 b	6 b	11 b	16 a
2 b	7 b	12 a	17 b
3 d	8 c	13 c	18 c
4 c	9 a	14 d	19 a
5 d	10 b	15 b	20 a

Worksheet 63 Answers:

1 a	6 c	11 a	16 b	21 c
2 b	7 c	12 c	17 b	22 d
3 b	8 b	13 d	18 d	23 a
4 b	9 c	14 d	19 a	24 d
5 c	10 d	15 c	20 d	25 c

Worksheet 64 Answers:

1 a	6 c	11 a	16 d	21 c
2 a	7 d	12 a	17 a	22 d
3 d	8 b	13 d	18 a	23 c
4 a	9 b	14 b	19 a	24 b
5 a	10 b	15 c	20 d	25 b

Worksheet 65 Answers:

1 a	6 c	11 c	16 d	21 b
2 d	7 c	12 a	17 b	22 c
3 d	8 b	13 c	18 d	23 a
4 d	9 d	14 b	19 d	24 b
5 b	10 d	15 b	20 c	25 a

Worksheet 66 Answers:

1 c	6 a	10 c	14 b	18 b
2 a	7 c	11 b	15 b	19 a
3 d	8 a	12 a	16 a	20 b
4 b	9 c	13 b	17 b	21 c
5 c				

RADIOGRAPHIC EXPOSURE
Worksheet 67 Answers:

1 2	6 12	11 51 kVp	16 69 kVp
2 3.5	7 15	12 92 kVp	17 87 kVp
3 4.5	8 18	13 61 kVp	18 53 kVp
4 5.5	9 4.5	14 56 kVp	19 88 kVp
5 7.5	10 6	15 65 kVp	20 69 kVp

Worksheet 68 Answers:

1 1/40, 0.025	11 1/14, 0.07	21 1/60, 0.0167
2 1/20, 0.05	12 1/12.5, 0.08	22 1/20, 0.05
3 ⅓, 0.33	13 1/15, 0.067	23 2/5, 0.4
4 1/6, 0.15	14 1/40, 0.025	24 3/10, 0.3
5 1/8, 0.125	15 1/8, 0.125	25 3/5, 0.6
6 1/20, 0.05	16 2/5, 0.4	26 1/80, 0.0125
7 1/60, 0.016	17 4/5, 0.8	27 1/62.5, 0.16
8 1/20, 0.05	18 1/50, 0.02	28 3/5, 0.6
9 2/5, 0.4	19 7/100, 0.07	29 1/5, 0.2
10 1/5, 0.2	20 1/5, 0.2	30 3/5, 0.6

Worksheet 69 Answers:

1 17 mAs	11 2	21 20-in SID
2 28 mAs	12 0.25	22 50-in SID
3 32 mAs	13 0.5	23 90-in SID
4 29 mAs	14 0.3	24 14 mAs
5 61 mAs	15 19.4 mAs	25 40-in SID
6 90 mAs	16 3.9 mAs	26 0.64
7 20 mAs	17 0.5 mAs	27 0.36
8 22.5 mAs	18 0.24 mAs	28 5.76
9 81 kVp	19 68 kVp	29 0.14
10 4	20 10-in SID	

Worksheet 70 Answers:

1 b	6 a	11 c	16 c
2 c	7 b	12 c	17 d
3 b	8 c	13 b	18 c
4 c	9 b	14 c	19 d
5 c	10 d	15 c	20 d

RADIOGRAPHIC TECHNIQUE
Worksheet 71 Answers:

1 b
2 a
3 d
4 c
5 b
6 b
7 a—I, b—III, c—II, d—IV
8 a—III, b—II, c—I, d—IV
9 c
10 b

Worksheet 72 Answers:

1 d	6 c, d, a, b	11 d	16 a	21 b
2 b	7 d	12 b	17 b	22 c
3 a	8 b	13 d	18 b	23 a
4 a	9 a	14 d	19 b	24 a
5 c	10 d	15 a	20 c	25 c

Worksheet 73 Answers:

1 c	6 a	11 b	16 b
2 d	7 b	12 b	17 d
3 b	8 b	13 b	18 b
4 c	9 d	14 b	19 c
5 b	10 a	15 d	20 c

OTHER RADIOGRAPHIC PROCEDURES
Worksheet 74 Answers:

1 b	6 a	11 a	16 a	21 c	26 b	31 c
2 c	7 d	12 b	17 c	22 c	27 b	
3 a	8 c	13 d	18 a	23 d	28 b	
4 a	9 b	14 b	19 b	24 a	29 d	
5 b	10 d	15 b	20 b	25 a	30 c	

MAMMOGRAPHY
Worksheet 75 Answers:

1 d	6 d	11 d	16 d
2 b	7 c	12 d	17 b
3 b	8 a	13 a	18 d
4 c	9 b	14 c	19 b
5 c	10 c	15 a	

Worksheet 76 Answers:

1 d	6 c	11 c	16 d	21 d
2 a	7 c	12 a	17 b	22 c
3 b	8 b	13 c	18 b	23 b
4 b	9 a	14 c	19 a	24 c
5 c	10 c	15 c	20 c	25 c

FLUOROSCOPY
Worksheet 77 Answers:

1 c	6 a	11 d	16 b	21 a	26 b
2 a	7 b	12 b	17 d	22 b	27 d
3 b	8 d	13 d	18 a	23 d	28 c
4 d	9 c	14 d	19 c	24 a	29 c
5 c	10 a	15 c	20 b	25 c	30 b, c, a, d

Worksheet 78 Answers:

1 b	6 a	11 c	16 c	21 c, b	26 d
2 a	7 c	12 d	17 a	22 b, e	27 d
3 a	8 b	13 b	18 d	23 a, d	28 b
4 d	9 c	14 d	19 c	24 c	29 e
5 b	10 d	15 b	20 b, d, a, c, e	25 e	30 b

Worksheet 79 Answers:

1 d	6 d	11 a	16 a	21 b	26 b
2 b	7 b	12 d	17 d	22 b	27 d
3 d	8 c	13 a	18 c	23 a	28 a
4 a	9 b	14 b	19 d	24 a	29 c
5 d	10 a	15 b	20 b	25 b	30 e

INTRODUCTION TO COMPUTER SCIENCE
Worksheet 80 Answers:

1 a	6 a	11 d	16 b	21 a
2 b	7 a	12 d	17 c	22 b
3 d	8 c	13 a	18 c	23 b
4 a	9 c	14 b	19 d	24 a
5 b	10 a	15 d	20 d	

Worksheet 81 Answers:

1 c	6 d	11 c	16 c	21 d	26 111000	31 21
2 d	7 c	12 d	17 b	22 b	27 110101	32 51
3 a	8 c	13 c	18 a	23 c	28 10010011	33 73
4 b	9 c	14 c	19 c	24 a	29 11010000111	34 438
5 b	10 a	15 a	20 b	25 110	30 11	

DIGITAL X-RAY IMAGING
Worksheet 82 Answers:

1 b	6 c	11 a	16 c	21 a	26 a
2 d	7 c	12 b	17 c	22 b	27 b
3 b	8 d	13 c	18 c	23 b	28 a
4 b	9 b	14 b	19 c	24 c	29 d
5 d	10 a	15 a	20 c	25 c	30 b

Worksheet 83 Answers:

1 c	6 a	11 d	16 d
2 b	7 a	12 c	17 b
3 b	8 c	13 d	18 c
4 a	9 d	14 a	19 b
5 c	10 b	15 b	20 b

COMPUTED TOMOGRAPHY
Worksheet 84 Answers:

1 c	6 a	11 b	16 d
2 a	7 b	12 a	17 b
3 c	8 c	13 c	18 c
4 c	9 d	14 a	19 c
5 a	10 d	15 a	20 d

Worksheet 85 Answers:

1 d	6 c	11 c
2 c	7 c	12 a
3 c	8 a	13 c
4 b	9 b	14 d
5 b	10 d	15 b

QUALITY CONTROL
Worksheet 86 Answers:

1 b	6 a	11 d	16 b
2 b	7 b	12 a	17 d
3 d	8 c	13 a	18 d
4 c	9 b	14 a	19 d
5 c	10 a	15 b	20 b

Worksheet 87 Answers:

1 b	6 a	11 b
2 c	7 c	12 d
3 c	8 d	13 d
4 b	9 b	14 d
5 d	10 a	15 c

PHYSICAL PRINCIPLES OF MRI
Worksheet 88 Answers:

1 b	6 d	11 c	16 a	21 d
2 c	7 d	12 b	17 d	22 c
3 c	8 a	13 d	18 a	23 d
4 c	9 b	14 b	19 b	24 a
5 c	10 d	15 a	20 d	25 a

Worksheet 89 Answers:

1 c	6 c	11 a	16 b	21 b
2 b	7 a	12 a	17 b	22 b
3 b	8 b	13 d	18 c	23 a
4 d	9 d	14 c	19 d	24 d
5 b	10 d	15 d	20 b	25 c

MR EQUIPMENT AND IMAGES
Worksheet 90 Answers:

1 c	6 d	11 d	16 a	21 b
2 c	7 a	12 d	17 a	22 b
3 b	8 c	13 b	18 d	23 b
4 b	9 d	14 d	19 a	24 d
5 b	10 d	15 b	20 b	25 d

Worksheet 91 Answers:

1 b	6 b	11 c	16 d
2 d	7 d	12 a	17 c
3 d	8 c	13 a	18 b
4 b	9 b	14 d	19 b
5 a	10 d	15 a	20 c

PHYSICAL PRINCIPLES OF DIAGNOSTIC ULTRASOUND
Worksheet 92 Answers:

1 d	6 a	11 a	16 b
2 d	7 c	12 a	17 c
3 a	8 c	13 a	18 b
4 d	9 d	14 c	19 c
5 a	10 b	15 b	20 d

Worksheet 93 Answers:

1 a	6 c	11 c	16 d
2 d	7 c	12 b	17 c
3 d	8 a	13 d	18 a
4 b	9 c	14 c	19 a
5 a	10 d	15 b	20 a

DIAGNOSTIC ULTRASOUND INSTRUMENTATION AND OPERATION
Worksheet 94 Answers:

1 c	6 b	11 c	16 d
2 c	7 b	12 c	17 b
3 c	8 d	13 a	18 a
4 b	9 a	14 c	19 c
5 b	10 a	15 c	20 a

Worksheet 95 Answers:

1 c	6 b	11 c
2 b	7 a	12 d
3 a	8 d	13 a
4 c	9 b	14 d
5 c	10 b	15 b

FUNDAMENTAL PRINCIPLES OF RADIOBIOLOGY
Worksheet 96 Answers:

1 c	6 d	11 d	16 b	21 d	26 c
2 b	7 a	12 c	17 a	22 c	27 a
3 a	8 b	13 c	18 d	23 d	28 d
4 c	9 d	14 a	19 b	24 c	29 c
5 b	10 d	15 a	20 b	25 c	30 b

Worksheet 97 Answers:

1 b	6 d	11 b	16 c
2 c	7 c	12 c	17 b
3 a	8 a	13 c	18 c
4 c	9 d	14 a	19 b
5 a	10 a	15 b	20 b

Worksheet 98 Answers:

1 a	6 b	11 d	16 c
2 d	7 d	12 a	17 d
3 b	8 b	13 d	18 a
4 c	9 d	14 a	19 b
5 d	10 b	15 b	20 d

MOLECULAR AND CELLULAR RADIOBIOLOGY
Worksheet 99 Answers:

1 c	6 d	11 a	16 c	21 b	26 B
2 c	7 d	12 c	17 c	22 b	27 C
3 c	8 d	13 c	18 c	23 b	28 A
4 b	9 c	14 b	19 b	24 a	29 I
5 a	10 b	15 d	20 d	25 c	30 H

Worksheet 100 Answers:

1 b	6 d	11 d	16 c
2 d	7 a	12 b	17 c
3 c	8 c	13 a	18 a
4 d	9 b	14 d	19 a
5 b	10 b	15 c	

EARLY EFFECTS OF RADIATION
Worksheet 101 Answers:

1 c	6 c	11 c	16 d
2 b	7 d	12 c	17 b
3 b	8 a	13 d	18 a
4 b	9 b	14 b	19 c
5 d	10 c	15 d	20 b

Worksheet 102 Answers:

1 b	6 d	11 a	16 d
2 b	7 b	12 d	17 c
3 d	8 d	13 c	18 a
4 d	9 b	14 d	19 b
5 c	10 a	15 d	20 b

LATE EFFECTS OF RADIATION
Worksheet 103 Answers:

1 c	6 d	11 c	16 b
2 d	7 d	12 c	17 d
3 b	8 a	13 c	18 d
4 c	9 b	14 c	19 c
5 d	10 a	15 b	20 b

Worksheet 104 Answers:

1 b	6 a	11 d	16 c
2 c	7 b	12 b	17 d
3 c	8 c	13 b	18 a
4 a	9 c	14 d	19 a
5 b	10 c	15 c	20 b

HEALTH PHYSICS
Worksheet 105 Answers:

1 c	6 c	11 c	16 b	21 b
2 a	7 d	12 c	17 a	22 d
3 c	8 b	13 b	18 b	23 d
4 d	9 d	14 a	19 d	24 b
5 d	10 c	15 a	20 c	25 d

Worksheet 106 Answers:

1 b	6 c	11 b	16 d
2 d	7 a	12 d	17 d
3 a	8 d	13 d	18 c
4 c	9 d	14 d	19 b
5 d	10 a	15 d	

DESIGN OF RADIOLOGIC IMAGING FACILITIES
Worksheet 107 Answers:

1 c	6 d	11 b	16 a
2 a	7 b	12 a	17 c
3 b	8 d	13 c	18 a
4 c	9 b	14 c	19 b
5 a	10 a	15 d	20 a

DESIGNING FOR RADIATION PROTECTION
Worksheet 108 Answers:

1 b	6 b	11 b	16 d
2 b	7 c	12 d	17 b
3 c	8 c	13 c	18 a
4 b	9 d	14 b	19 d
5 a	10 d	15 c	20 b

Worksheet 109 Answers:

1 a	6 a	11 b	16 a
2 c	7 c	12 a	17 a
3 d	8 d	13 d	18 d
4 c	9 d	14 d	19 b
5 d	10 b	15 c	20 c

RADIATION PROTECTION PROCEDURES
Worksheet 110 Answers:

1 d	6 a	11 b	16 b
2 d	7 b	12 b	17 c
3 d	8 b	13 a	18 d
4 d	9 c	14 c	19 c
5 b	10 b	15 c	20 d

Worksheet 111 Answers:

1 b	6 c	11 d	16 c
2 a	7 d	12 c	17 b
3 b	8 a	13 d	18 a
4 d	9 d	14 c	19 c
5 b	10 a	15 d	20 a

MATH TUTOR—EXERCISE ANSWERS

WORKING WITH DECIMAL TIMERS—EXERCISE ANSWERS
Exercise 1 Answers:

1 5 mAs
2 6.4 mAs
3 1.9 mAs
4 12.5 mAs
5 80 mAs
6 4 mAs
7 10 mAs
8 12.8 mAs
9 3 mAs
10 0.3 mAs
11 25 mAs
12 60 mAs
13 80 mAs
14 1.6 mAs
15 0.6 mAs
16 7 mAs

17 9 mAs
18 21 mAs
19 210 mAs
20 30 mAs
21 150 mAs
22 480 mAs
23 3.6 mAs
24 4.8 mAs
25 30 mAs
26 90 mAs
27 12 mAs
28 4.5 mAs
29 75 mAs
30 7.5 mAs
31 45 mAs
32 1.8 mAs

33 1.2 mAs
34 4 mAs
35 16 mAs
36 ~~32 mAs~~ *28 mAs*
37 64 mAs
38 6.4 mAs
39 132 mAs
40 320 mAs
41 280 mAs
42 2.8 mAs
43 40 mAs
44 15 mAs
45 100 mAs
46 350 mAs
47 3.5 mAs
48 62.5 mAs

WORKING WITH FRACTIONAL TIMERS—EXERCISE ANSWERS
Exercise 2 Answers:

1 50 mAs
2 5 mAs
3 2 mAs
4 20 mAs
5 approx. 12 mAs
6 approx. 1.2 mAs
7 approx. 8 mAs
8 approx. 0.8 mAs

9 approx. 15 mAs
10 approx. 7 mAs
11 2.5 mAs
12 approx. 33 mAs
13 approx. 3.3 mAs
14 approx. 16 or 17 mAs
15 approx. 1.6 or 1.7 mAs
16 approx. 66 or 67 mAs

Exercise 3 Answers:

1 approx. 24 or 25 mAs
2 2.5 mAs
3 40 mAs
4 4 mAs
5 approx. 6 mAs
6 approx. 2.4 or 2.5 mAs
7 approx. 16 or 17 mAs
8 approx. 1.6 or 1.7 mAs
9 approx. 4 mAs
10 approx. 0.4 mAs
11 approx. 7 to 8 mAs
12 approx. 14 mAs

13 5 mAs
14 approx. 16 or 17 mAs
15 approx. 1.6 or 1.7 mAs
16 approx. 66 or 67 mAs
17 approx. 6.6 or 6.7 mAs
18 approx. 32 to 34 mAs
19 approx. 3.2 to 3.4 mAs
20 approx. 132 to 134 mAs
21 approx. 8 to 9 mAs
22 approx. 0.8 to 0.9 mAs
23 approx. 0.6 to 0.7 mAs
24 approx. 30 mAs

Exercise 4 Answers:

1 60 mAs
2 50 mAs
3 6 mAs
4 5 mAs
5 15 mAs
6 150 mAs
7 20 mAs
8 25 mAs

9 2.5 mAs
10 12 mAs
11 75 mAs
12 7.5 mAs
13 approx. 36 mAs
14 approx. 3.6 mAs
15 approx. 45 mAs
16 10 mAs

Exercise 5 Answers:

1 20 mAs (4 sets of 5)
2 25 mAs (5 sets of 5)
3 30 mAs (6 sets of 5)
4 80 mAs (4 sets of 20)
5 120 mAs (6 sets of 20)
6 8 mAs (4 sets of 2)
7 12 mAs (6 sets of 2)
8 125 mAs (5 sets of 25)
9 150 mAs (6 sets of 25)
10 12.5 mAs (5 sets of 2.5)
11 15 mAs (6 sets of 2.5)
12 20 mAs (⅓ of 60, or 6 sets of 3.3)
13 approx. 13 mAs (4 sets of 3.3)
14 approx. 6.4 mAs (4 sets of 1.6)

15 approx. 60 mAs (4 sets of 15)
16 approx. 48-50 mAs (4 sets of 12 or 12.5)
17 approx. 4.8-5 mAs (4 sets of 1.25)
18 approx. 60 mAs (5 sets of 12)
19 approx. 48-50 mAs (6 sets of 8)
20 approx. 5 mAs (6 sets of .8)
21 approx. 40 mAs (5 sets of 8)
22 approx. 3.2-3.3 mAs (4 sets of 0.8)
23 approx. 28 mAs (4 sets of 7)
24 approx. 35 mAs (5 sets of 7)
25 approx. 16 mAs (4 sets of 4)
26 approx. 20 mAs (5 sets of 4)
27 approx. 24 mAs (6 sets of 4)
28 approx. 120-132 mAs (4 sets of 33)

Exercise 6 Answers:

1 40 mAs
2 approx. 14 mAs
   (2 sets of 7)
3 approx. 21 mAs
4 15 mAs (3 sets of 5)
5 35 mAs
6 150 mAs
7 80 mAs (2 sets of 40)
8 120 mAs
9 160 mAs
10 60 mAs
11 140 mAs
12 approx. 28-30 mAs
   $(2 \times 7 \times 2)$

13 approx. 42 mAs $(2 \times 7 \times 3)$
14 30 mAs (3 sets of 10)
15 70 mAs
16 160 mAs (2 sets of 80)
17 240 mAs
18 320 mAs
19 120 mAs (3×40)
20 280 mAs
21 200 mAs
22 120 mAs (2×60)
23 180 mAs
24 240 mAs
25 90 mAs
26 210 mAs (7×30)

27 40 mAs (2×20)
28 60 mAs
29 45 mAs (3×15)
30 60 mAs
31 140 mAs
32 200 mAs
33 150 mAs
34 350 mAs (7×50)
35 75 mAs (3×25)
36 240 mAs (2×120)
37 360 mAs
38 180 mAs (3×60)
39 90 mAs (3×30)
40 120 mAs*

TIMERS: CONVERTING FRACTIONS INTO DECIMALS AND VICE VERSA— EXERCISE ANSWERS
Exercise 7 Answers:

1 0.75
2 0.667
3 0.25
4 0.2
5 0.167
6 0.142
7 0.125
8 0.083

9 0.0667
10 0.05
11 0.04
12 0.033
13 0.025
14 0.02
15 0.0167
16 0.0125

17 0.01
18 0.0083
19 0.7
20 0.133
21 0.15
22 0.4
23 0.6
24 0.8

25 0.33
26 0.2
27 0.35
28 0.0067
29 0.375
30 0.3125

Exercise 8 Answers:

1 1/20
2 1/30 (common denominator is 333)
3 1/5
4 3/4
5 1/40
6 2/3
7 1/7 (common denominator is 143)

8 1/500
9 4/5
10 1/6 (common denominator is 167)
11 1/8
12 3/5
13 1/16
14 1/12 (common denominator is 833)

*Note that on question 40 you may simply take double the answer you would get at the 300 mA station. If you have memorized that 15s and 20s go together at the 300 mA station, then a 15th at 600 would be double 20 or 40. Then take 3 sets of 40. Many problems at the 600 mA station can be solved this way, just doubling the answer you would get at 300 mA. Also, many mAs values can be figured at the 400 mA station in a similar manner by doubling numbers you are familiar with using the 200 mA station.

FINDING mA AND TIME COMBINATIONS FOR A DESIRED mAs—EXERCISE ANSWERS
Exercise 9 Answers:

1 2 sets of 40
2 3 sets of 15
3 2 sets of 33
4 3 sets of 25
5 3 sets of 60
6 3 sets of 40 *or* 2 sets of 60
7 2 sets of 80 *or* 4 sets of 40
8 3 sets of 80 *or* 4 sets of 60
9 3 sets of 30
10 4 sets of 80

Exercise 10 Answers:

1 1/50
2 1/40
3 2/3 (2 sets of 33)
4 1/15
5 1/6
6 1/12
7 1/30
8 1/60
9 1/80
10 1/120
11 2/5 (2 sets of 20)
12 1/30
13 1/20
14 1/40
15 1/8
16 1/5
17 3/5 (3 sets of 40)
18 1/40
19 1/40
20 2/15 (2 sets of 7)
21 1/6
22 1/50
23 1/15
24 1/120
25 3/20 (3 sets of 15)
26 3/5 (3 sets of 60)
27 4/5 (4 sets of 60)
28 1/4 (cut in half twice)
29 1/5
30 3/5 (3 sets of 80)

Exercise 11 Answers:

1 0.04
2 0.025
3 0.67
4 0.07
5 0.16
6 0.08
7 0.033
8 0.017
9 0.4
10 0.05
11 0.025
12 0.125
13 0.2
14 0.6
15 0.025
16 0.0125
17 0.7
18 0.17
19 0.02
20 0.07
21 0.6
22 0.25
23 0.2
24 0.6

TECHNIQUE ADJUSTMENTS—EXERCISE ANSWERS
Exercise 12 Answers:

1 6
2 4.5
3 4
4 2.5
5 3
6 10.5
7 6
8 9
9 16.5
10 3
11 approx. 5
12 6
13 approx. 4
14 approx. 7
15 9
16 102 kVp
17 46 kVp
18 64-65 kVp
19 74 kVp

Exercise 13 Answers:

1 approx. 75
2 approx. 30
3 approx. 30
4 approx. 36
5 15
6 10
7 15
8 25
9 68-70
10 four times
11 two times
12 ¼
13 ½
14 62.5
15 3.47
16 0.77
17 0.28
18 70
19 12-in
20 30-in
21 40-in
22 60-in
23 1.17
24 4.34
25 8.1
26 0.31
27 0.69
28 1.93
29 0.56

CROSSWORD PUZZLE ANSWERS

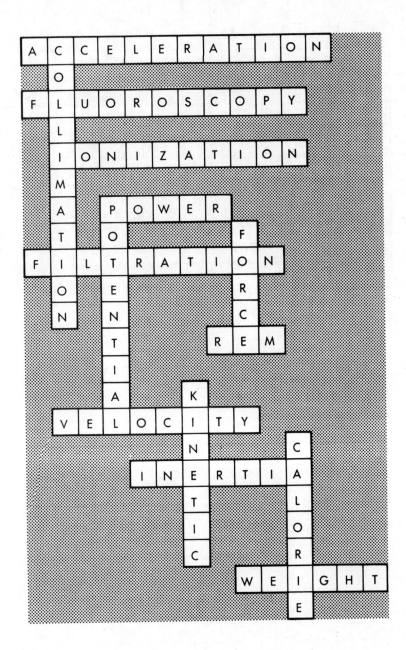

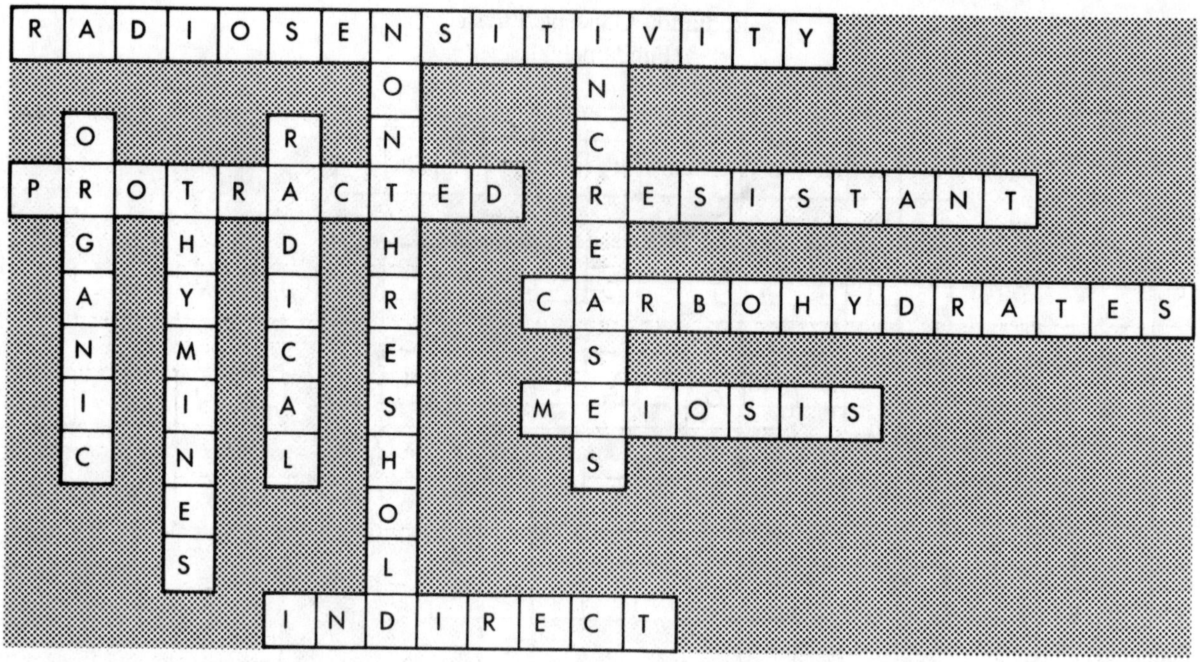

Crossword Puzzle

Across:
- RADIOSENSITIVITY
- PROTRACTED
- RESISTANT
- CARBOHYDRATES
- MEIOSIS
- INDIRECT

Down:
- ORGANIC
- THYMINES
- RADICAL
- ONTHRESHOLD
- INCREASS

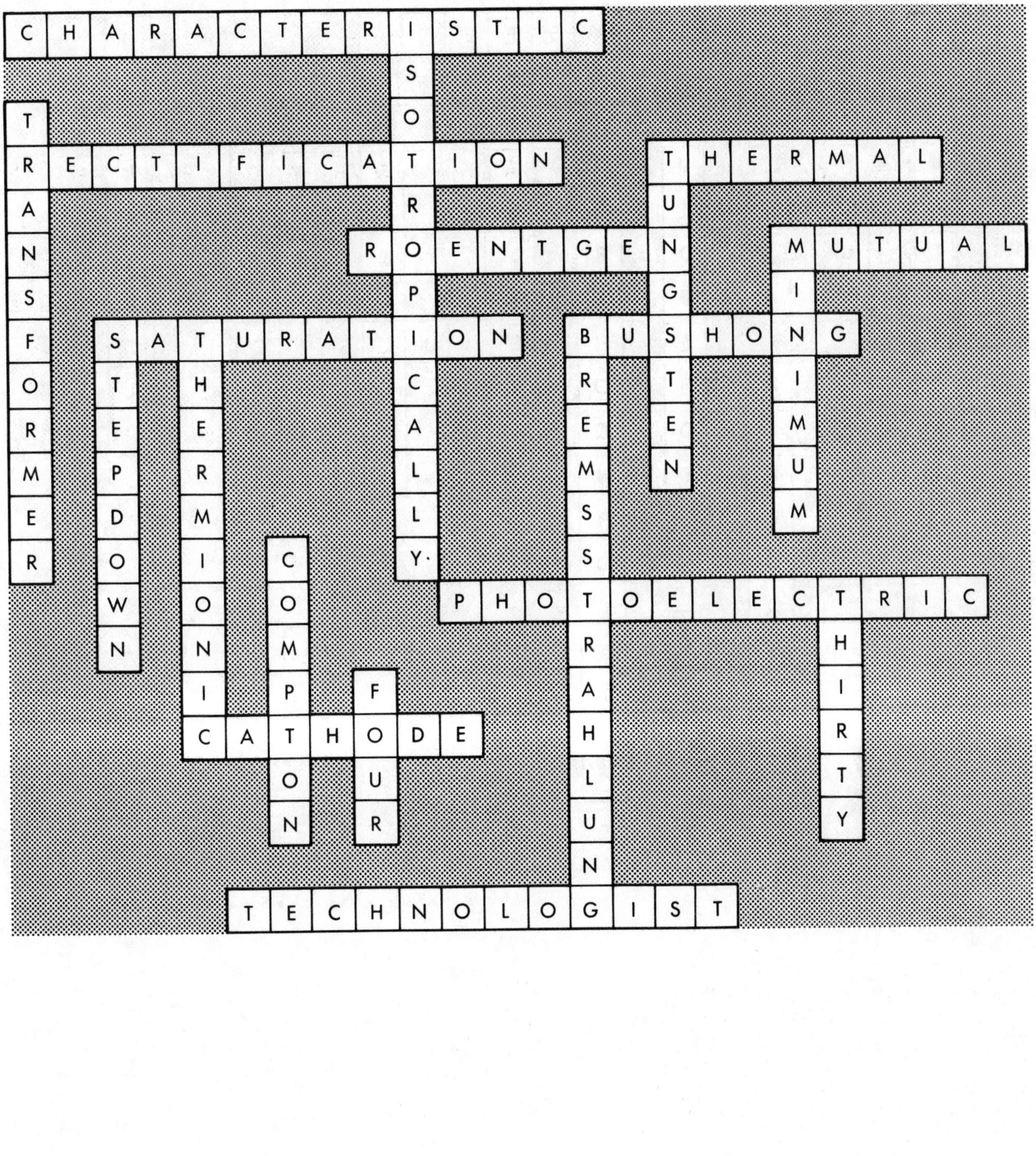
CHARACTERISTIC
ISOTROPICALLY
TRANSFORMER
RECTIFICATION
THERMAL
TUNGSTEN
ROENTGEN
MUTUAL
MINIMUM
SATURATION
BUSHONG
STEPDOWN
THERMIONIC
BREMSSTRAHLUNG
PHOTOELECTRIC
THIRTY
COMPTON
FOUR
CATHODE
TECHNOLOGIST

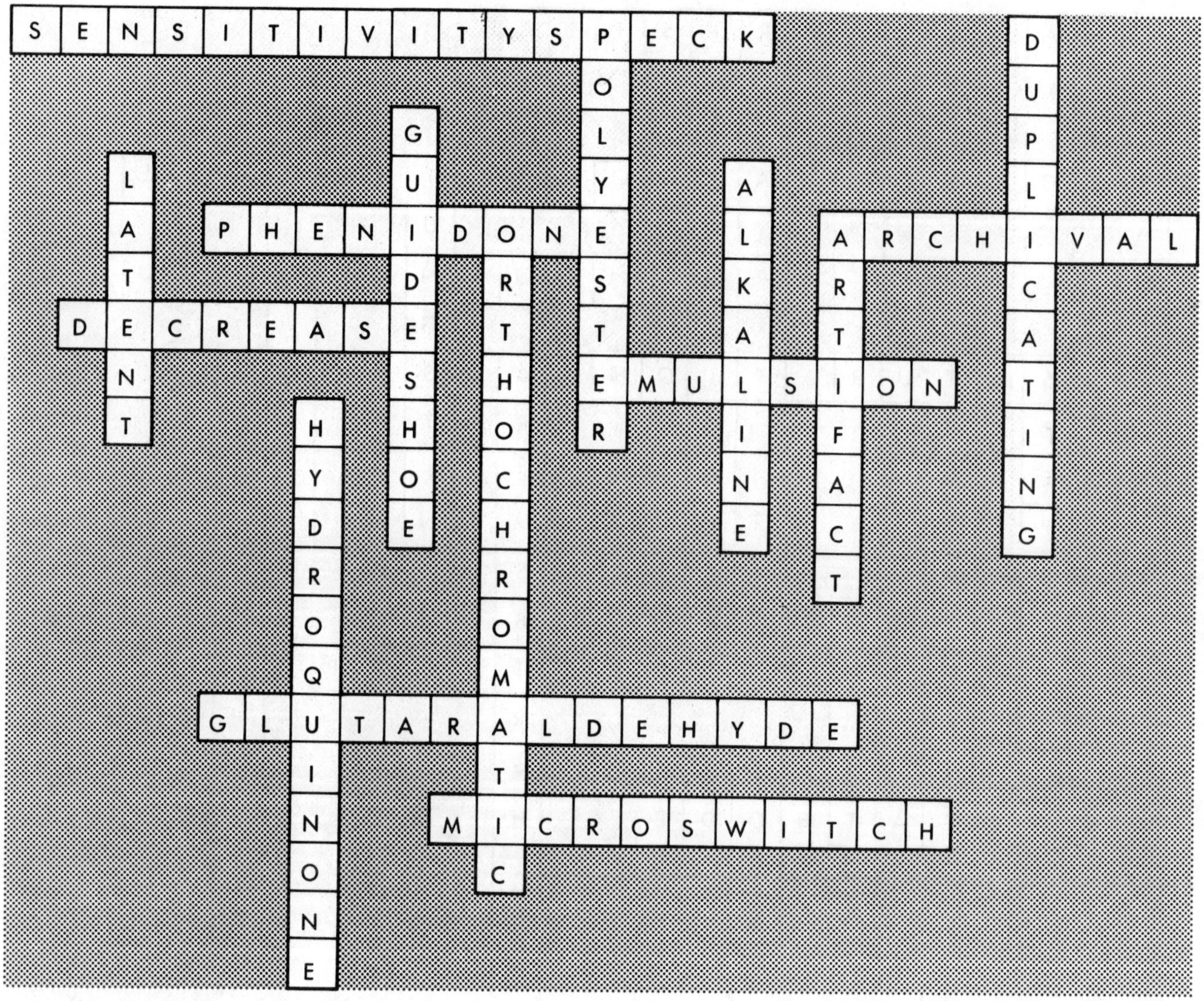

SENSITIVITYSPECK

Across and down entries:

SENSITIVITYSPECK

DUPLICATING

POLYESTER

GUIDESHOE

PHENIDONE

ALKALINE

ARCHIVAL

LATENT

DECREASE

ARTIFACT

EMULSION

HYDROQUINONE

ORTHOCHROMATIC

GLUTARALDEHYDE

MICROSWITCH

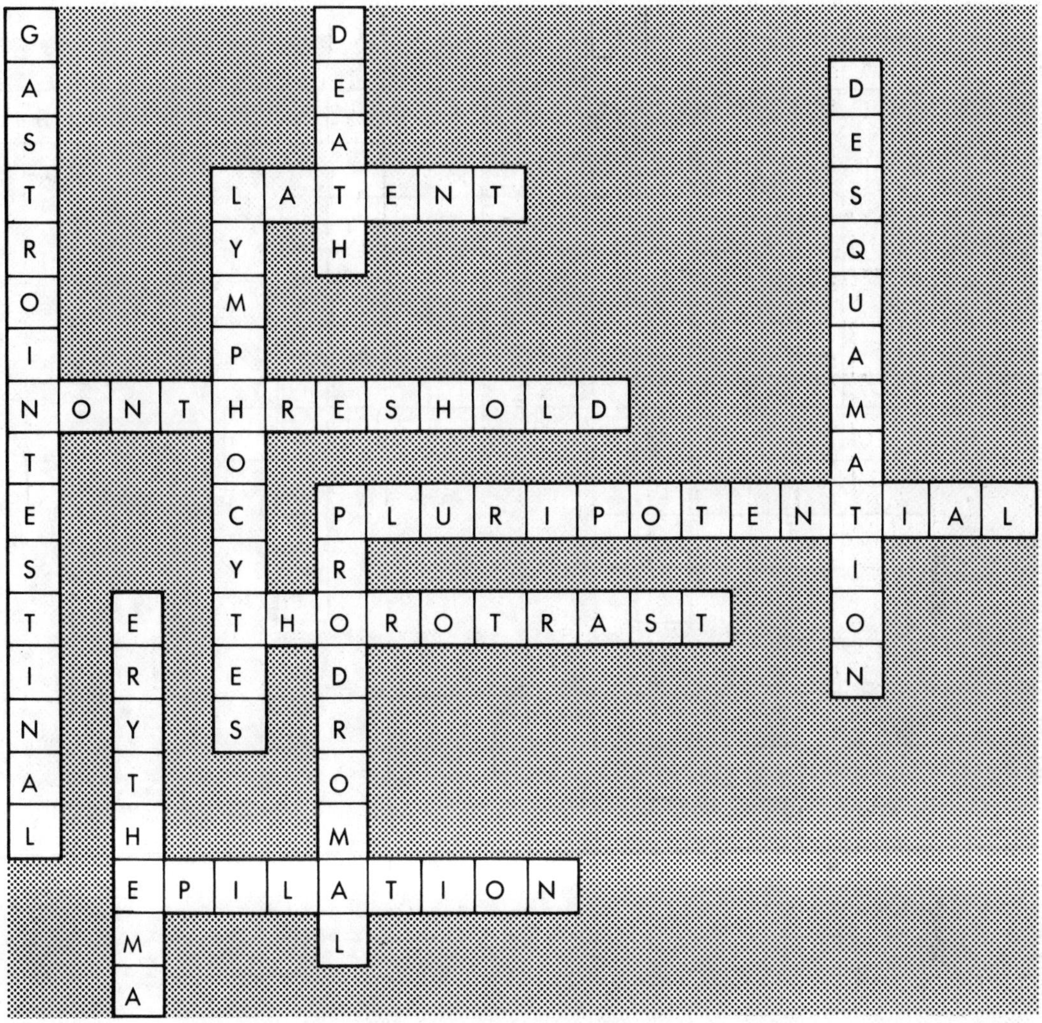
GASTROINTESTINAL
DEATH
DESQUAMATION
LATENT
LYMPHOCYTES
NONTHRESHOLD
PLURIPOTENTIAL
PRODROMAL
THOROTRAST
ERYTHEMA
EPILATION